Heathkit

Educational Systems

Microprocessors

Book 2

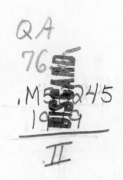

Model EB-6401
HEATH COMPANY
BENTON HARBOR, MICHIGAN 49022
595-2262

Unit 6

THE 6800 MICROPROCESSOR — PART 2

INTRODUCTION

In the previous unit, you were introduced to the architecture and instruction set of the 6800 microprocessor. Much of the MPU's capabilities were discussed; however, three important areas were omitted. These include the microprocessor's stack operation, the use of subroutines, and the interrupt capability. These capabilities are discussed in detail in this unit. You are also introduced to input-output operations.

UNIT OBJECTIVES

When you have completed this unit, you will be able to:

1. Explain the difference between a cascade stack and a memory stack.

2. Write simple programs that can store data in — and retrieve data from — the stack.

3. Write programs that use the stack and indexing to move a list from one place in memory to another.

4. Explain the operations performed by each of the following instructions: PULA, PULB, PSHA, PSHB, DES, INS, LDS, STS, TXS, and TSX.

5. Define stack, subroutine, nested subroutine, interrupt, interrupt vector, and interrupt masking.

6. Write programs that use subroutines and nested subroutines.

7. Explain the operations performed by each of the following instructions: JMP, JSR, BSR, and RTS.

8. Describe how the 6800 MPU performs input and output operations.

9. Draw flowcharts depicting the sequence of events that occur during reset, non-maskable interrupt, interrupt request, software interrupt, return from interrupt, and wait for interrupt.

10. Explain the operation performed by each of the following instructions: WAI, SWI, RTI, SEI, and CLI.

STACK OPERATIONS

In computer jargon, a *stack* is a group of temporary storage locations in which data can be stored and later retrieved. In this regard, a *stack* is somewhat like memory. In fact, many microprocessors use a section of memory as a stack. The difference between a stack and other forms of memory is the method by which the data is accessed or addressed. The discussion will begin by considering a simple stack arrangement used in some microprocessors. Then the more sophisticated stack arrangement used by the 6800 MPU will be discussed.

Cascade Stack

Some microprocessors have a special group of registers (usually 8 or 16) called a *cascade stack*. Each register can hold one 8-bit byte of data. Because these registers are right on the MPU chip, they make excellent temporary storage locations. If we need to free the accumulator for some reason, we can store its contents in the stack. Later, if that piece of data is needed again, we can retrieve the data from the stack. Of course, we could also have freed the accumulator by storing the data in memory. What then is the advantage of the stack?

One advantage of the stack is the method by which it is accessed or addressed. Recall that when a byte is stored in memory, an address is required. That is to store the contents of the accumulator in memory a 2-byte or 3-byte instruction is required. Depending on the addressing mode, the last one or two bytes is the address. Later, if the byte is retrieved, another instruction is required that also has an address.

An advantage of the stack is that data can be stored into it or read from it with single-byte instructions. That is, the instructions used with the stack do not require an address. Therefore, they are single-byte instructions.

Figure 6-1 shows an 8-register stack similar to that found in some microprocessors. This is called a cascade stack because of the method by which data is loaded and retrieved. All data transfers are between the top of the stack and the accumulator. That is, the accumulator communicates only with the top location on the stack. Data is transferred to the stack by a special instruction called PUSH.

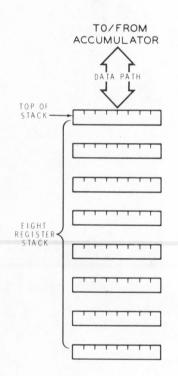

TO/FROM
ACCUMULATOR

DATA PATH

TOP OF
STACK

EIGHT
REGISTER
STACK

Figure 6-1.
A cascade stack.

The PUSH Instruction. Figure 6-2 illustrates how the PUSH instruction places data in the stack. The number 01_{16} is in the accumulator and we wish to temporarily store it. While we could store the number in memory, this would require a 2-byte or a 3-byte instruction. So instead, we use the PUSH instruction to place this number in the stack. Notice that the number is placed in the top location of the stack as shown in Figure 6-2A. The number remains there until we retrieve it or until we push another byte into the stack.

Figure 6-2B shows what happens if, at some time later, we push another byte into the stack. Notice that the accumulator now contains 03_{16}. If the PUSH instruction is executed, the contents of the accumulator are pushed into the top of the stack. To make room for this new number, the original number 01_{16} is pushed deeper into the stack.

Figures 6-2C and 6-2D show two more numbers being pushed into the stack at later points in the program. Notice that new data is always pushed into the top of the stack. To make room for the new data, the old data is pushed deeper into the stack. For this reason, this arrangement is often called a *push-down* or *cascade* stack. The name *cascade stack* comes from the characteristic cascading of data down through the stack as each new byte is pushed in at the top.

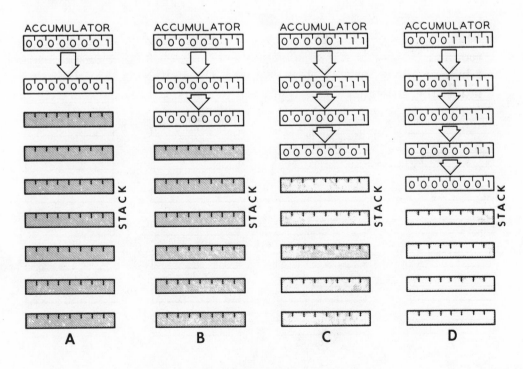

Figure 6-2.
Pushing data into the stack.

The PULL Instruction. The MPU retrieves data from the stack by using the PULL instruction. In some microprocessors, this is referred to as a POP instruction.

Figure 6-3 illustrates how data can be pulled (or popped) from the stack. Figure 6-3A shows the stack as it appeared after the last push operation. Notice that it contains four bytes of data. The last byte of data that was entered is at the top of the stack.

The PULL instruction retrieves the byte that is at the top of the stack. As this byte is removed from the stack, all other bytes move up, filling in the space left by that byte. Figure 6-3B illustrates how OF_{16} is pulled from the stack. Notice that 07_{16} is now at the top of the stack.

Figures 6-3C and 6-3D show how the next two bytes can be pulled from the stack. In each case, the remaining bytes move up in the stack, filling in the register vacated by the removed byte.

If you compare Figures 6-2 and 6-3, you will notice that the data must be pulled from the stack in the reverse order. That is, the last byte pushed into the stack is the first byte that is pulled from the stack. Another name for this arrangement is a last-in/first-out (LIFO) stack.

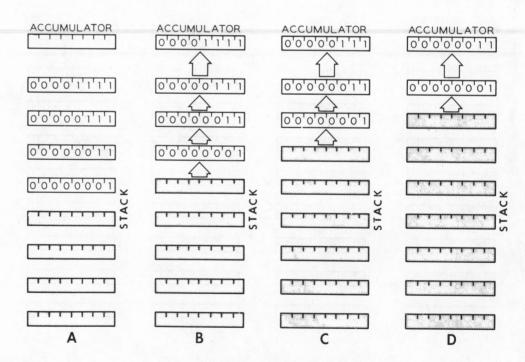

Figure 6-3.
Pulling data from the stack.

Memory Stack

While a cascade stack is valuable, it does have some limitations. For one thing, the number of registers is generally quite limited, with eight being typical. If more than eight pieces of data are pushed into the stack, the "older" bytes are pushed out the bottom and are lost. Also, the readout of the stack is destructive. When a byte is pulled from the stack, it no longer exists in the stack. This is fundamentally different from reading a byte from memory.

Because of these limitations the 6800 MPU does not use a cascade stack. Instead, a section of RAM can be set aside by the programmer to act as a stack. This has several advantages. First, the stack can be any length that the programmer requires. Second, the programmer can set up more than one stack if he likes. Third he can address the data in the stack using any of the instructions that address memory.

Stack Pointer. Recall that the 6800 MPU has a 16-bit register called the stack pointer. In a memory-type stack, the stack pointer defines the memory location that acts as the top of the stack.

The cascade stack considered earlier generally does not require a stack pointer. The top of the stack is determined by hardware. During push and pull operations, the data bytes actually move from one register to another. That is, the top of the stack remains stationary and the data moves up or down in relation to the stack.

In the memory stack, data cannot be easily transferred from one location to the next. Therefore, instead of moving data up and down in relation to the stack, it is much easier to move the top of the stack in relation to the data.

Generally, when the microprocessor-based system is being planned, a section of RAM is reserved for the stack. This should be a section of RAM that is not being used for any other purpose.

Once this is done, the stack can be set up by a program. The top of the stack is established by loading an address into the stack pointer. For example, suppose we wish to establish address $01F9_{16}$ as the top of the stack. The following instruction could be used:

LDS#
01
F9

This loads the address $01F9_{16}$ into the stack pointer and establishes that address as the top of the stack. However, as you will see, the top of the stack moves each time data is pushed into — or pulled from — the stack.

The PUSH Instructions. The 6800 MPU has two push instructions, PSHA and PSHB. These single-byte instructions push the contents of their respective accumulator onto the stack.

Figure 6-4 shows the effects of the PSHA instruction. Before the instruction is executed, the stack pointer contains the address $01F9_{16}$ as a result of a previous LDS instruction. Accumulator A contains a data byte (AA_{16}). If the PSHA instruction is now executed, the contents of accumulator A are pushed into memory location $01F9_{16}$. Then, the stack pointer is automatically decremented to $01F8_{16}$. This automatically moves the top of the stack as shown.

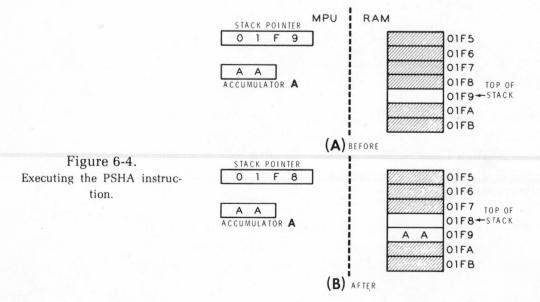

Figure 6-4.
Executing the PSHA instruction.

If you look at your Instruction Set Summary card, you will see that the operation is described as follows:

$$A \rightarrow M_{SP}, SP - 1 \rightarrow SP$$

This means that the contents of the A accumulator are transferred to the memory location specified by the stack pointer. Also, the contents of the stack pointer are replaced by the previous contents of the stack pointer minus one. In other words, after the accumulator-to-stack transfer takes place, the stack pointer is decremented by one.

To reinforce the idea, assume that at some later point in the program, the MPU executes a PSHB instruction. This is illustrated in Figure 6-5. Before PSHB is executed, the B accumulator contains BB_{16} and the stack pointer is still pointing to $01F8_{16}$. When PSHB is executed, the contents of accumulator B are pushed onto the stack and the stack pointer is decremented to $01F7_{16}$.

The PULL Instructions. Data bytes are removed from the stack with the pull instruction. The 6800 MPU has two pull instructions. PULA allows the MPU to pull data from the stack into the A accumulator. PULB performs a similar operation except the data byte goes into accumulator B. In each case, data is pulled from the top of the stack. Thus, the data byte available to the MPU is the last byte that was placed in the stack.

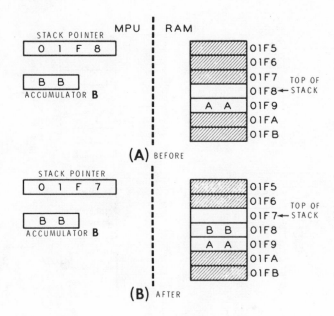

Figure 6-5.
Executing the PSHB instruction.

For example, Figure 6-6A shows the stack as we left it after the last push instruction. Figure 6-6B shows what happens if the PULA instruction is executed. First, the stack pointer is automatically incremented by one to $01F8_{16}$. Then the contents of the memory location designated by the stack pointer are transferred to accumulator A. Thus, BB_{16} goes into accumulator A. Notice that the stack pointer is incremented *before* the byte is pulled from the stack.

To be certain you have the idea, consider what happens if the PULB instruction is now executed. Figure 6-6C shows that the stack pointer is automatically incremented to $01F9_{16}$. The contents of that location are then pulled into accumulator B. This operation is described on your Instruction Set Summary card as:

$$SP + 1 \rightarrow SP, M_{SP} \rightarrow B .$$

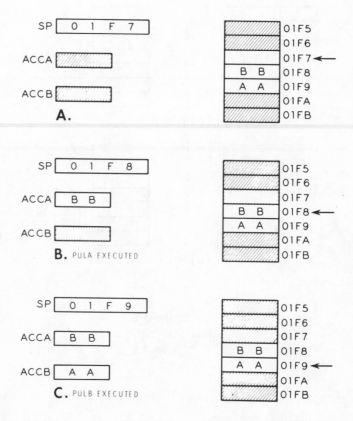

Figure 6-6.
Executing PULL instructions.

Using the Stack. Figure 6-7 summarizes all of the instructions that directly affect stack operations. The push and pull instructions were introduced in this unit while the other instructions were discussed briefly in the previous unit. Find these instructions on your Instruction Set Summary card. The push and pull instructions are listed with the Accumulator and Memory Operations. Those instructions that affect the stack pointer are listed under Index Register and Stack Pointer Operations.

ADDRESSING MODES

STACK AND STACK POINTER OPERATIONS	MNEMONIC	IMMED			DIRECT			INDEX			EXTND			INHER			BOOLEAN/ARITHMETIC OPERATION (All register labels refer to contents)
		OP	~	#	OP	~	#	OP	~	=	OP	~	#	OP	~	#	
Push Data	PSHA													36	4	1	$A \rightarrow M_{SP}, SP - 1 \rightarrow SP$
	PSHB													37	4	1	$B \rightarrow M_{SP}, SP - 1 \rightarrow SP$
Pull Data	PULA													32	4	1	$SP + 1 \rightarrow SP, M_{SP} \rightarrow A$
	PULB													33	4	1	$SP + 1 \rightarrow SP, M_{SP} \rightarrow B$
Decrement Stack Pntr	DES													34	4	1	$SP - 1 \rightarrow SP$
Increment Stack Pntr	INS													31	4	1	$SP + 1 \rightarrow SP$
Load stack Pntr	LDS	8E	3	3	9E	4	2	AE	6	2	BE	5	3				$M \rightarrow SP_H, (M + 1) \rightarrow SP_L$
Store Stack Pntr	STS				9F	5	2	AF	7	2	BF	6	3				$SP_H \rightarrow M, SP_L \rightarrow (M + 1)$
Indx Reg → Stack Pntr	TXS													35	4	1	$X - 1 \rightarrow SP$
Stack Pntr → Indx Reg	TSX													30	4	1	$SP + 1 \rightarrow X$

Figure 6-7.
Stack and stack pointer instructions.

Following are some examples of how the stack can be used. First consider a trivial example. Using only stack operations, swap the contents of accumulators A and B. Assuming the stack pointer has already been set up, the program segment might look like this:

```
PSHA
PSHB
PULA
PULB
```

Assume that accumulator A initially contains AA_{16} and that accumulator B contains BB_{16}. The first instruction pushes AA_{16} onto the stack. Next BB_{16} is pushed onto the stack. The third instruction pulls BB_{16} from the top of the stack and places it in accumulator A. Finally, the last instruction pulls AA_{16} from the stack and places it in accumulator B. As you can see, the contents of the two accumulators are reversed. The following routine accomplishes the same thing with one less instruction:

```
PSHA
TBA
PULB
```

Now look at a more complex example. Assume that you wish to transfer 16_{10} bytes of data from one place in memory to another. As you saw in the previous unit, this type of problem is a good candidate for indexing. However, indexing alone becomes cumbersome if the two lists are over FF_{16} memory locations apart. The reason for this is that the offset address can only extend FF_{16} locations above the address in the index register.

In this example, assume you wish to move the data in memory locations 0010_{16} through $001F_{16}$ to locations $01F0_{16}$ to $01FF_{16}$. While this could be accomplished using indexing alone, the program becomes unnecessarily complicated. Two separate indexes must be maintained; one for loading data from 0010_{16} through $001F_{16}$, the other for storing data in $01F0_{16}$ through $01FF_{16}$. A simpler approach is to use indexing for one operation and the stack capability for the other operation. That is, we could load data from the lower list using indexing and store it in the upper list using the stack capability.

A program that does this is shown in Figure 6-8. The first instruction loads the stack pointer with address $01FF_{16}$. This is the address of the last entry in the new list that will be formed. Recall that the new list is to be written in locations $01F0_{16}$ through $01FF_{16}$. Once location $01FF_{16}$ is established as the top of the stack, we can enter data into the new list simply by pushing data onto the stack. Because the stack pointer is decremented with each push operation, we must push the last entry in the list onto the stack first.

Figure 6-8.
Moving a list of data using both indexing and stack operations.

HEX ADDRESS	HEX CONTENTS	MNEMONICS/ CONTENTS	COMMENTS
0020	8E	LDS#	Load the stack pointer immediately with the
0021	01	01	address of the last entry in the
0022	FF	FF	new list.
0023	CE	LDX#	Load the index register immediately with the
0024	00	00	address of the last entry in the
0025	1F	1F	original list.
0026	A6	LDAA. X	Load accumulator A indexed from
0027	00	00	the original list.
0028	36	PSHA	Push the contents of accumulator A into the new list.
0029	09	DEX	Decrement the index register.
002A	8C	CPX#	Compare the contents of the index register
002B	00	00	with one less than the address of the
002C	0F	0F	first entry in the original list.
002D	26	BNE	If no match occurs, branch back
002E	F7	F7	this far.
002F	3E	WAI	Otherwise, wait.

The second instruction loads the index register with the address of the *last* entry in the original list. This is necessary for the reason pointed out above.

Next, the A accumulator is loaded using indexed addressing. Since the offset address is 00_{16}, the accumulator is loaded with the contents of $001F_{16}$. That is, the last entry in the original list is loaded into accumulator A.

The PSHA instruction then pushes the contents of accumulator A onto the stack. Thus, the last entry in the original list is transferred to location $01FF_{16}$. In the process, the stack pointer is automatically decremented to $01FE_{16}$.

The index register is decremented to $001E_{16}$ by the next instruction. Then, the CPX instruction compares the index register with $000F_{16}$ to see if all entries in the list have been moved. If no match occurs, the MPU branches back and picks up the next entry in the list. The loop is repeated over and over again until the entire list has been moved to its new location.

Other uses of the stack will be revealed later. However, even if the stack did nothing more than has already been explained, it would be a very useful capability to have. But as you will see, the MPU uses the stack in several other ways that makes this capability even more important.

Self-Test Review

1. What is a stack?

2. What is a cascade stack?

3. What is a memory stack?

4. Which type of stack does the 6800 MPU use?

5. What is the name of the instruction that stores data in the stack?

6. What type of instruction is used to retrieve data from the stack?

7. What is the purpose of the stack pointer?

8. The PUSH instruction transfers data from one of the accumulators to _____.

9. The PULB instruction transfers data from the top of the stack to _____.

10. Refer to Figure 6-8. How can we change this program so that the new list is placed in addresses 0220_{16} through 022F?

Answers

1. A stack is a group of registers or a section of memory that is used as a last-in, first-out memory.

2. A cascade stack is a group of hardware registers (usually 16 or less) that is used as a last-in, first-out memory.

3. A memory stack uses a section of RAM as a last-in, first-out memory.

4. A memory stack

5. PUSH

6. PULL

7. The stack pointer indicates the address of the top of the stack.

8. The top of the stack.

9. Accumulator B.

10. By changing the first instruction to: LDS# $022F_{16}$.

SUBROUTINES

A subroutine is a group of instructions that performs some limited but frequently required task. A given subroutine may be used many times during the execution of the main program. In many cases, the easiest way to write a program is to break the overall job down into many simple operations, each of which can be performed by a subroutine.

Because subroutines are used so frequently, most microprocessors have special capabilities that allow them to handle subroutines efficiently. In this section, these capabilities will be examined. The discussion will start with the instructions associated with subroutines.

The 6800 MPU has three instructions that are used to handle subroutines. They are:

> Jump to Subroutine (JSR)
> Branch to Subroutine (BSR)
> Return from Subroutine (RTS)

Each of these will be discussed in this section. One other instruction that has not yet been mentioned will also be discussed. It is the Jump (JMP) instruction. While not used exclusively with subroutines, the JMP instruction makes an excellent introduction to the Jump to Subroutine (JSR) instruction. Therefore, the Jump (JMP) instruction will be discussed first.

Jump (JMP) Instruction

This instruction allows the MPU to jump from one point in a program to another. In this respect, it is somewhat like the Branch Always (BRA) instruction that was discussed earlier. The difference is the method of addressing used. Recall that the BRA instruction used relative addressing. This has the advantage that only a 2-byte instruction is required. Its disadvantage is that the branch must be within the range of -128 bytes to $+127$ bytes of the program count.

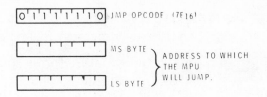

Figure 6-9.
Format of the JMP instruction
using extended addressing.

The JMP instruction can use either the indexed or the extended addressing mode. It does not use relative addressing. When using extended addressing, the format of the JMP instruction is as shown in Figure 6-9. Three bytes are required; the opcode followed by the 2-byte address to which the MPU is to jump. Since a 16-bit address is given, the jump may be to any point in the $65,536_{10}$ byte memory range. This address is loaded into the program counter so that the next opcode is fetched from that address. The previous contents of the program counter are lost. Thus, the MPU starts executing instructions from a new point in memory.

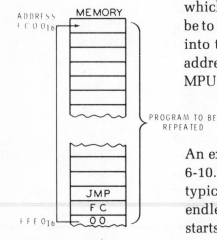

Figure 6-10.
Using the JMP instruction to
repeat a program.

An example of how the JMP instruction can be used is shown in Figure 6-10. Here, a long program is to be repeated over and over again. This is typical of applications such as controllers that repeat the same operations endlessly. The program is contained in the upper 1k bytes of memory. It starts at location $FC00_{16}$ and ends at $FFE0_{16}$. Notice that the last instruction is JMP $FC00_{16}$. This sends the program back to its beginning so that the loop is repeated endlessly.

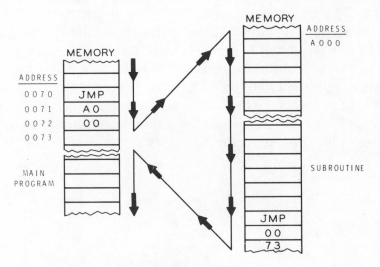

Figure 6-11.
Using the JMP instruction to
call a subroutine.

Another possible use of the JMP instruction is shown in Figure 6-11. Here, the main program is in the lower memory locations shown on the left. The main program requires a subroutine that is up at address A000 (shown on the right). The JMP instruction at address 0070 sends the MPU off to the subroutine as shown. The last instruction in the subroutine is another JMP instruction that sends the MPU back to the main program.

Jumping to a subroutine is often referred to as *calling* a subroutine. While we can call a subroutine using the JMP instruction, this approach has a distinct problem. What happens if the main program wants to call the same subroutine more than once? That is, suppose a situation like that shown in Figure 6-12 is required. Here, the main program (on the left) wishes to call the subroutine (on the right) at two separate points. Jumping to the subroutine is no problem. We can do that as many times as we like, using the instruction JMP A000. The problem is: how do we get back from the subroutine to the main program? The first time through the subroutine, the MPU should return to address 0073. The second time through, the MPU should return to address 0093.

A programmer could get around this problem by changing the last instruction in the subroutine before each call or by constructing a table of return addresses, etc. However, most microprocessors have some instructions that solve this problem for us. The following section will discuss the 6800 MPU's solution to this problem.

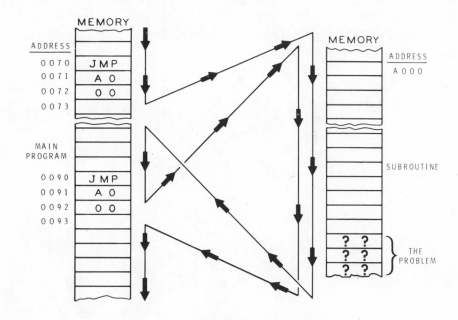

Figure 6-12.
The JMP instruction cannot
handle situations like this one.

JSR and RTS Instructions

If you refer to Figure 6-12 again, you will see that this problem arises because the old program count is not saved when the MPU jumps from one location to the next. However, the 6800 MPU has an instruction that will not only jump to a subroutine, it will also cause the old program count to be stored away. This instruction is called the Jump to Subroutine (JSR) instruction. Its format is exactly the same as the JMP instruction but its execution is different.

Figure 6-13 shows how the earlier problem can be solved using the JSR instruction. Notice that the two JMP instructions in the main program have been replaced by JSR instructions. Notice also that the last instruction in the subroutine is a Return from Subroutine (RTS) instruction. These new instructions ease the problem of calling the subroutine.

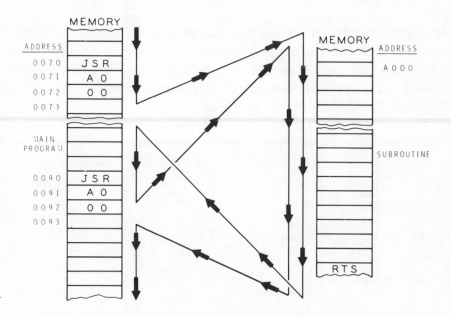

Figure 6-13.
The JSR and RTS instructions can be used to handle this situation.

When the first JSR instruction is executed, the subroutine address $A000_{16}$ is placed in the program counter. However, just prior to this, the program counter was incremented to the address of the next instruction in sequence. That is, the program counter was advanced to 0073_{16} while the contents of address 0072_{16} were being retrieved. This count (0073_{16}) is automatically pushed onto the stack. By saving the old program count, the MPU can tell where to return after the subroutine is finished. As soon as the old program count is tucked away safely in the stack, the subroutine address $A000_{16}$ is placed in the program counter. Thus, the MPU fetches the next instruction from address $A000_{16}$.

Notice that the last instruction in the subroutine is an RTS instruction. When the MPU encounters this single-byte instruction, it will jump back to the point where it left off in the main program. It does this by pulling the old program count (0073_{16}) from the stack and placing it in the program counter. Consequently, the next instruction will be fetched from address 0073_{16}. As you can see, this returns the MPU to the correct point in the main program.

Notice that the programmer does not specify a return address at the end of the subroutine. The return address is automatically pulled from the stack. This allows us to call the subroutine repeatedly from several different points in the main program.

Figure 6-13 shows that the subroutine is called again by the JSR A000 instruction in location 0090_{16}. As this instruction and address are decoded, the program count is incremented to 0093_{16}. This program count is pushed onto the stack. Then $A000_{16}$ is placed in the program counter. Thus, the MPU jumps off to the subroutine. When the subroutine is finished, the RTS instruction causes the old program count to be pulled from the stack into the program counter. This causes the MPU to jump back to address 0093_{16} which contains the next instruction in the main program.

Nested Subroutines

Figure 6-14 shows a situation in which the main program calls subroutine A. In turn, subroutine A calls subroutine B. In this situation, subroutine B is called a *nested* subroutine. That is, a nested subroutine is a program segment that is called by another subroutine. If control is to be eventually returned to the main program, two program counts must be saved. Figure 6-14 shows how the two program counts are saved in the stack.

At the start of the main program, the stack pointer is loaded with the address of the area in memory that has been set aside to act as the stack. If no stack instructions have been executed when the main program arrives at the first JSR instruction, the stack pointer will still be pointing to where it was originally set. The contents of the stack are of no interest until this point.

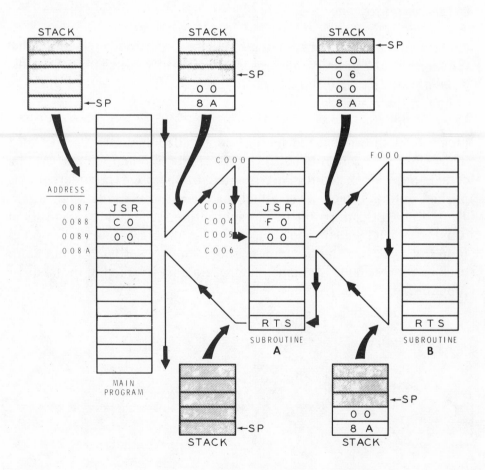

Figure 6-14.
Handling nested subroutines.

When the main program reaches the JSR instruction, the program count is advanced to the address of the next instruction in sequence ($008A_{16}$). When the JSR instruction is executed, this address ($008A_{16}$) is pushed onto the stack as shown. The low order byte goes in first, followed by the high order byte. In the process, the stack pointer is decremented twice. Finally, the new address ($C000_{16}$) is placed in the program counter. This causes the MPU to jump off to subroutine A which starts at $C000_{16}$.

Notice that halfway through subroutine A, subroutine B is called. Consequently, the return address in subroutine A ($C006_{16}$) must be saved. That is, when the program reaches the JSR instruction in subroutine A, the return address ($C006_{16}$) is pushed onto the stack as shown. Notice that there are now two return addresses in the stack. The starting address of subroutine B ($F000_{16}$) is then placed in the program counter and the MPU jumps off to this subroutine.

Subroutine B has no nested subroutines of its own, so the program flow is through the subroutine as shown. The last instruction in subroutine B is the RTS instruction. At this point, the MPU pulls the return address ($C006_{16}$) from the top of the stack and places it in the program counter. This causes the MPU to jump back to the instruction at address $C006_{16}$ in subroutine A.

The remainder of subroutine A is then executed down to the RTS instruction. This instruction causes the MPU to pull the next address ($008A_{16}$) from the stack and place it in the program counter. Notice that this sends the MPU back to the main program.

For simplicity, a single level of subroutine nesting is shown in this example. However, in practice, many levels of nesting may be used. For example, subroutine B could call subroutine C; etc. Any level of nesting can be used as long as enough memory is set aside for the stack. Remember, each return address requires two bytes in the stack.

Branch to Subroutine (BSR) Instruction

Quite often, the subroutine we wish to call is within the -128_{10} to $+127_{10}$ byte range of the relative address. When it is, we can save one byte by using the Branch to Subroutine (BSR) instruction. The execution of BSR is identical to that of JSR except that relative addressing is used. The old program count is saved in the stack before the branch occurs. Thus, the RTS instruction at the end of the subroutine will cause the old program count to be restored.

Summary of Subroutine Instructions

Figure 6-15 shows the four instructions discussed in this section. Notice that the BSR instruction uses relative addressing. The JMP and JSR instructions can use either indexed or extended addressing. The RTS instruction uses inherent addressing since its address is pulled from the top of the stack.

Find these instructions on your Instruction Set Summary card. The operations performed by these instructions are illustrated under "Special Operations" on the back of the card. Also, Appendix A of this course gives a concise description of the operations performed by each of these instructions.

JUMP AND BRANCH OPERATIONS	MNEMONIC	RELATIVE			INDEX			EXTND			INHER		
		OP		#	OP		#	OP		#	OP		#
Branch To Subroutine	BSR	8D	8	2									
Jump	JMP				6E	4	2	7E	3	3			
Jump To Subroutine	JSR				AD	8	2	BD	9	3			
Return From Subroutine	RTS										39	5	1

Figure 6-15.
Subroutine and jump instructions.

Self-Test Review

11. What is a subroutine?

12. What addressing modes can the JMP instruction use?

13. How does the JMP instruction differ from the BRA instruction?

14. How does the execution of the JSR instruction differ from that of the JMP instruction?

15. Why is the program count saved when the JSR or BSR instructions are executed?

16. Where is the program count saved?

17. How is the stack pointer affected by the JSR instruction?

18. Generally, the last instruction in the subroutine will be a _____ instruction.

19. What is a nested subroutine?

20. How is the stack pointer affected by the RTS instruction?

Answers

11. A subroutine is a group of instructions that performs some specific, limited task that is used more than once by the main program.

12. Indexed and extended.

13. Since the BRA instruction uses relative addressing, it can branch only in a -128_{10} to $+127_{10}$ byte range. The JMP instruction uses indexed or extended addressing. Therefore, it can jump to any point in memory.

14. When the JSR instruction is executed, the program count is saved in the stack.

15. The program count is saved so that when the subroutine is finished, the MPU can return to the point it left off.

16. The program count is pushed into the top two locations of the stack.

17. The stack pointer is automatically decremented twice as the program count is pushed onto the stack.

18. Return from Subroutine (RTS).

19. When subroutine A calls subroutine B, subroutine B is said to be nested.

20. The stack pointer is automatically incremented twice as the old program count is pulled from the stack.

INPUT — OUTPUT (I/O) OPERATIONS

A full explanation of input-output (I/O) operations will be given in the next units, but a brief introduction to I/O is necessary at this point. In this section, you will learn what is involved in sending data to — or taking data from — the MPU.

To be useful, a microprocessor system must accept data from the outside world, process it in some way, and present results to the outside world. The input device may be nothing more than a group of switches while the output device can be as simple as a bank of indicator lamps. On the other hand, a single microprocessor might handle several teletypewriters, printers, papertape machines, etc. The point is that the I/O requirements can vary greatly from one application to the next. This section will be concerned with the simplest form of I/O operations.

In the short history of microprocessors, two distinctly different methods have been developed for handling I/O operations. In some microprocessors, I/O operations are handled by I/O instructions. These microprocessors generally have one *input* instruction and one *output* instruction. When the *input* instruction is executed, a byte is transferred from the selected I/O device to a register (usually one of the accumulators) in the MPU. The I/O device is selected by sending out a device selection byte on the address bus. By using an 8-bit byte for device selection, the MPU can specify up to 256_{10} different I/O devices. Of course, no microprocessor system uses that many devices, but the capability is there. The *output* instruction causes a data transfer from the accumulator to the selected I/O device. While this method of handling I/O operations is used in many microprocessors, the 6800 MPU uses a different technique.

The other method for handling I/O operations is to treat all I/O transfers as memory transfers. This is the method used by the 6800 MPU and many other microprocessors. In fact, even those microprocessors that have I/O instructions can ignore those instructions and handle I/O operations as memory transfers.

The 6800 MPU has no I/O instructions. An I/O device is assigned an address and is treated as a memory location. For example, assume that an input keyboard has been assigned an address of 8000_{16}. We can input data into accumulator A by using the instruction:

$$\text{LDAA } 8000_{16}$$

By the same token, an output display may have been assigned the address 9000_{16}. In this case, we can output from accumulator B by using the instruction:

$$STAB\ 9000_{16}.$$

As you can see, the I/O device is treated as a memory location. The system block diagram shown in Figure 6-16 shows how an I/O device is connected to the microcomputer. Notice that both the data bus and the address bus connect to the I/O interface. As you will see in the next unit, the interface can consist of an address decoder, an output or input latch, and buffers or drivers.

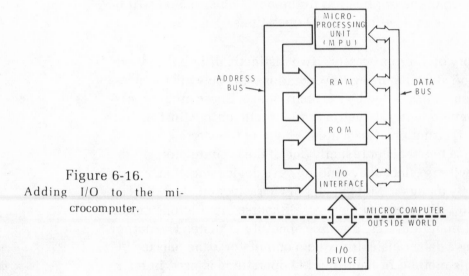

Figure 6-16.
Adding I/O to the microcomputer.

The address decoder monitors the address bus and enables the interface circuitry whenever the proper address is detected. This prevents the I/O interface from interfering when data is being transferred between memory and the MPU.

The I/O interface will generally have an output latch if it is to be used for an output operation. The reason for this is that the data from the MPU will appear on the data lines for only an instant (usually less than one microsecond). By storing the output data in a latch, the I/O device is given a much longer period of time to examine and respond to the data.

Buffers or drivers are also included in the I/O interface. As you will see later, these are frequently necessary when several different circuits are sharing the same bus.

Output Operations

Figure 6-17 shows a simplified output circuit. Here, the output device is a bank of eight light emitting diodes (LEDs). Enough detail is shown to illustrate how an output operation can be performed. The address decoder monitors the address bus, looking for the address 9000_{16}. It also monitors some of the control lines that connect to the MPU. One of those lines is called a read-write line. It goes to its low state when a write (output) operation is initiated by the MPU. The other control lines will be discussed in the next unit.

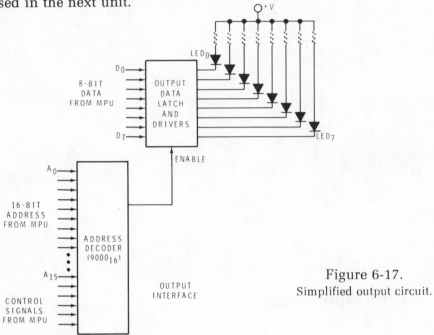

Figure 6-17.
Simplified output circuit.

Notice that the output of the address decoder is used to enable the output data latch and drivers. When these are enabled, the byte on the data lines is stored in the latch. The data bits stored in the latch cause the appropriate LEDs to light up. By outputting appropriate bit patterns, the MPU can cause different binary numbers to be displayed.

Notice that the address decoder (and therefore the display) is given the address 9000_{16}. We can output data to the display in several different ways. For example, we can load the appropriate pattern to be displayed into accumulator A. Then by executing a "store accumulator A" extended instruction, we can transfer the contents of the accumulator to the display. The instruction would be: STAA 9000_{16}. Or, we could output data from accumulator B by using the instruction: STAB 9000_{16}.

In either case, the address 9000_{16} goes out on the address bus for a brief interval of time. The address decoder recognizes this address. At the same time, the control lines indicate that an output operation is called for. In particular, the read-write line goes low. This causes the address decoder to enable the output data latch for an instant. Simultaneously, the 8-bit data byte appears on the data bus. The output latch stores the data byte. The data appears at the input of the latch for less than a microsecond (typically). However, once the data is stored, it appears at the output of the latch until new data is written in. Thus, the output data will be displayed until the next byte of data is outputted by the MPU.

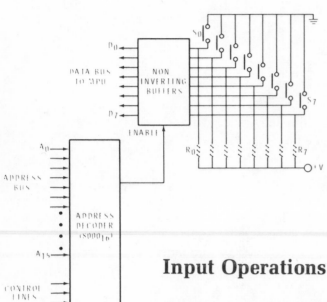

Figure 6-18.
Simplified input circuit.

Input Operations

Figure 6-18 shows a simplified input circuit. Here, the input device is a bank of eight switches. When a switch is open, its respective input line to the buffer is held high by the pull-up resistors. However, when a switch is closed, its respective input line is pulled low because the switch connects it to ground.

In this simple circuit, no latch is required between the switches and the data bus. However, a buffer is used so that the switch bank can be effectively disconnected from the data bus when the switches are not being addressed.

As with the output circuit, an address decoder monitors the address and control lines. Notice that the assigned address is 8000_{16}. To input data from the switch bank to accumulator A, we use the instruction: LDAA 8000_{16}. Or, we could input the data to accumulator B by using the instruction: LDAB 8000_{16}.

In either case, the address 8000_{16} is placed on the address line. The address decoder recognizes this address and enables the buffer. For a brief interval (typically less than one microsecond), the lines of the data bus assume the same state as the lines on the right side of the buffer. If no switch is depressed, all data lines will be high and all 1's (FF_{16}) will be loaded into the accumulator. However, if one of the switches (S_0, for example) is depressed, its respective data line (D_0) will be low. In this case, the number read into the accumulator will be FE_{16}. By examining the byte that is read in, the MPU can determine which switch is depressed.

Input — Output Programming

You now know enough about simple input/output circuits to perform some I/O operations. Refer to Figures 6-17 and 6-18. For the first example, assume that you would like one of the LEDs to light when the corresponding switch is pushed. That is, LED_0 should light when S_0 is pushed; LED_1 should light when S_1 is pushed, etc.

If you refer to Figure 6-17, you will see that an LED is caused to light by placing a 0 in the proper bit in the latch. For example, a 0 in bit 0 will cause LED_0 to be forward biased. Thus, the diode will conduct and emit light. Notice that a 1 at bit 0 will not allow the diode to conduct and emit light. Consequently, a 0 turns the LED on and a 1 turns it off.

Refer to Figure 6-18, and you will find that, when one of the switches is closed, its corresponding line goes to 0. If the switch is not closed, its corresponding line is at 1.

If we load data into one of the accumulators from address 8000_{16} and then store the data at address 9000_{16}, the switches will appear to control the LED's. The program could look like this:

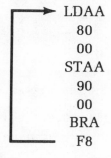

```
    LDAA
     80
     00
    STAA
     90
     00
    BRA
     F8
```

If S_0, and only S_0, is closed when the LDAA 8000 instruction is executed, 11111110_2 will be loaded into accumulator A. The next instruction stores this data byte in the output latch. This causes LED_0, and only LED_0, to light. The BRA instruction holds the MPU in a tight loop. Try a few examples and verify that each time a switch is closed, the corresponding LED will light. If the switches are set to some 8-bit binary number, the LED's will display that 8-bit number.

Now, suppose we change our mind and decide that the LEDs should display the one's complement of the binary number set on the switches. We do not have to touch the hardware. Instead, we just change the program. The new program might look like this:

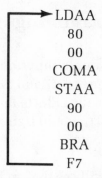

```
  ┌──►LDAA
  │    80
  │    00
  │   COMA
  │   STAA
  │    90
  │    00
  │   BRA
  └──  F7
```

Notice that we have simply inserted the one's complement instruction between the input and output operations.

As another example, suppose we wish to display a number that is four times greater than the number set on the switches. Our program could be changed to this:

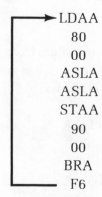

```
  ┌──►LDAA
  │    80
  │    00
  │   ASLA
  │   ASLA
  │   STAA
  │    90
  │    00
  │   BRA
  └──  F6
```

Once again, no hardware change is needed. We simply insert two ASLA instructions between the input and output operations.

Although these examples are very simple, they illustrate the flexibility of this I/O arrangement. Data is pulled from the input device as if it were being pulled from memory. Once in the MPU, the data byte can be modified in any way we like. The data can then be transferred to the output device as if it were being stored in memory. While the data is in the MPU, it can be modified in any number of ways. The input byte can be shifted left or right. It can be added to — or subtracted from — another number. It can be ANDed or ORed with another byte. The possibilities are endless and yet none of these involve a hardware change. All data manipulations can be accomplished by the program.

Program Control of I/O Operations

In the preceding examples, all I/O transfers are controlled by the program and the program alone. The program is in a tight loop that inputs data from the switches, modifies the data (if required), and outputs the data to the displays.

When this arrangement is used, the MPU never knows if the data at the input has changed. It simply reads in the data a number of times each second. By the same token, the MPU outputs the data over and over again. This system works well for simple I/O operations. However, as the I/O requirements become more sophisticated, this technique becomes cumbersome.

The program must be in a loop if it is to repeatedly check for inputs and refresh the output. As the number of data manipulations increase, the loop becomes longer and the MPU must check the inputs less frequently. When several I/O devices are used, it must check each input and refresh each output repeatedly. If the loop becomes too long, the MPU may miss a momentary switch closure. This may be acceptable in some applications but in many others it may be intolerable. Obviously then, a more sophisticated method of handling I/O operations must be available to the microcomputer.

Interrupt Control of I/O Operations

A more effective way of handling I/O operations involves a concept called *interrupts*. Interrupts are a means by which an I/O device can notify the MPU that it is ready to send input data or to accept output data. Generally, when an interrupt occurs, the MPU suspends its current operation and takes care of the interrupt. That is, it might read in or write out a byte of data. After it has taken care of the interrupt, the MPU returns to its original task and takes up where it left off.

An analogy may help you to visualize an interrupt operation. Compare the MPU to the president of a corporation who is writing a report. The interrupt can be compared to a telephone call. The president's main task is the report. However, if the telephone rings (an interrupt), she finishes writing the present word or sentence then answers the phone call. After she has attended to the phone call, she returns to the report and takes up where she left off. In this analogy, the ringing of the telephone notifies the president of the interrupt request.

This analogy shows the difficulty of the program controlled I/O technique discussed earlier. If we remove the interrupt request (the ringing of the phone), we are left with an almost comical situation. The president writes a few words of the report. She then picks up the phone to see if anyone is on the other end. If not, she hangs up the phone, writes a few more words, and checks the phone again. Clearly, this technique wastes an important resource — the president's time.

This simple analogy shows the importance of an interrupt capability. Without it, a great deal of the MPU's time can be wasted doing routine operations. The next section will examine the interrupt capabilities of the 6800 MPU.

Self-Test Review

21. What are the two methods by which microprocessors handle I/O operations?

22. Which method does the 6800 MPU use?

23. Which instruction can be used for transferring data from an I/O device to accumulator A?

24. Which instruction can be used for transferring data from accumulator B to an I/O device.

25. Write a program segment that will: read in data from the switch bank shown in Figure 6-18; double the number; and display the result on the LED bank shown in Figure 6-17.

26. What is meant by program control of an I/O operation?

27. What is meant by interrupt control of an I/O operation?

Answers

21. Some microprocessors have input-output instructions; others treat I/O as memory.

22. The 6800 MPU treats I/O as memory.

23. LDAA

24. STAB

25. One solution is:

> LDAA
> 80
> 00
> ASLA
> STAA
> 90
> 00

26. Using this method, the program regularly reads in or writes out data. All I/O operations are controlled by the program.

27. Using this method, the I/O device itself signals the MPU that it is ready to transmit or receive data. The I/O operations are controlled largely by the I/O device itself.

INTERRUPTS

Interrupts were introduced in the previous section in connection with I/O operations. While I/O operations use part of the interrupt capability of the MPU, interrupts are also used in other ways. The 6800 MPU has four different types of interrupts:

Reset

Non-Maskable Interrupt (NMI)

Interrupt Request (IRQ)

Software Interrupt (SWI)

This section will examine each of these interrupts in detail.

Reset

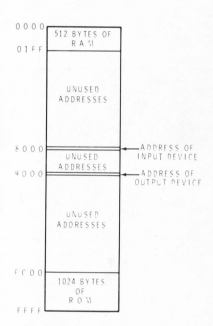

Figure 6-19.
Memory allocations in a typical microcomputer system.

In a typical application, the microcomputer has a control or monitor program in a read-only-memory (ROM). Also, a random access read-write memory (RAM) is used for holding input data, intermediate answers, output data, etc. As we have seen, the 6800 MPU has the capability of addressing up to $65,536_{10}$ memory locations. Most microprocessor applications do not require this much memory. In many applications, the control program requires less than ten percent of the possible locations. The RAM probably uses less than two percent. Generally, the monitor program is placed at the high memory addresses. The RAM is usually given the low memory addresses so that the direct addressing mode can be used. The I/O devices are given intermediate addresses. Thus, the memory addresses may be allocated as shown in Figure 6-19.

Notice that the control or monitor program is placed in a ROM at the very top of memory. In this example, a 1024_{10} byte ROM is used. The addresses of the ROM are $FC00_{16}$ through $FFFF_{16}$. A small RAM is placed at the low end of memory. Addresses 0000_{16} through $01FF_{16}$ are used. Notice that all other addresses are unused except for two. The input device is assigned address 8000_{16}, while the output device is assigned address 9000_{16}.

The monitor program stored in the ROM, controls all the activities of the MPU. At all times, the entire system is being run by this program. In this example, when the microprocessor is initially turned on, it should start executing instructions at address $FC00_{16}$. Also, we should be able to restart the program at this address at any time. In order to accomplish this, the 6800 MPU has a built-in reset capability.

The 6800 MPU has a signal line or control pin that is called $\overline{\text{Reset}}$. This pin or line is connected to a reset switch of some kind. If this line goes low for a prescribed period of time (to be explained later) and then swings high, the MPU will initiate a *reset interrupt sequence*. The main purpose of the reset interrupt sequence is to load the address of the first instruction to be executed into the program counter. This would be easy to accomplish if, in every application, the starting address were the same. However, the starting address differs from one application to the next. Therefore, a convenient means is provided to allow the designer to specify any starting address that he likes.

In any 6800 based microprocessor system, the upper eight bytes of ROM are reserved for *interrupt vectors*. An interrupt vector is simply an address that is loaded into the program counter when an interrupt occurs. Figure 6-20 shows how these eight reserved memory bytes are allocated. Notice that addresses $FFFE_{16}$ and $FFFF_{16}$ contain the reset vector. That is, these two memory locations contain the address of the first instruction that is to be executed when the microcomputer is initially started. In our example, the first instruction in the monitor program is at address $FC00_{16}$. Consequently, this is our reset vector. Location $FFFE_{16}$ must contain the high byte of the address (FC_{16}) and $FFFF_{16}$ must contain the low byte of the address (00_{16}).

Remember locations $FFFE_{16}$ and $FFFF_{16}$ are in the read-only-memory. Therefore, the designer must provide the proper reset vector at the time he is writing the monitor program.

Figure 6-20.
Interrupt vector assignments.

Address

F F F 8	Interrupt Request Vector (high order address)
F F F 9	Interrupt Request Vector (low order address)
F F F A	Software Interrupt Vector (high order address)
F F F B	Software Interrupt Vector (low order address)
F F F C	Non-Maskable-Interrupt Vector (high order address)
F F F D	Non-Maskable-Interrupt Vector (low order address)
F F F E	Reset Vector (high order address)
F F F F	Reset Vector (low order address)

Figure 6-21 shows the sequence of events that occurs when the MPU is reset. First, the interrupt (I) mask bit is set. You will recall that the I flag is one of the condition code registers. As you will see later, if this flag is set, it prevents one of the other interrupts from occurring. Thus, the MPU sets the interrupt mask bit so that the reset sequence will not be interrupted by a request for interrupt by one of the I/O devices.

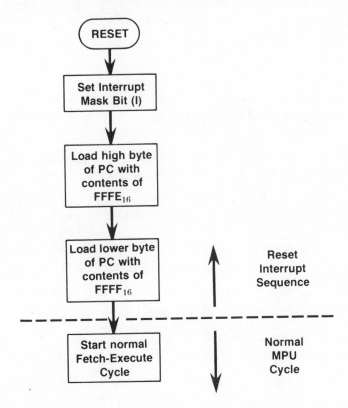

Figure 6-21.
Reset interrupt sequence.

Second, the contents of location $FFFE_{16}$ are loaded into the high byte of the program counter. This is done by sending the address $FFFE_{16}$ out on the address bus. The memory location is read out and its contents are placed on the data bus. The MPU picks up this byte and places it in the upper eight bits of the program counter. In our example, the byte in location $FFFE_{16}$ is FC_{16}.

Next, the contents of location $FFFF_{16}$ are loaded into the lower eight bits of the program counter. This is done by setting the address bus to $FFFF_{16}$. Thus, the contents of the highest memory location are placed on the data bus. In our example, this byte is 00_{16}. At this point, the program counter contains the address of the first instruction which is $FC00_{16}$.

The reset sequence is then terminated by switching the MPU to its normal fetch-execute machine cycle. Thus, the instruction at address $FC00_{16}$ is fetched and executed. From this point on, all MPU activities are controlled by the program.

The microprocessor system will have a reset switch somewhere in the system. This will allow the operator to restart the system if the system locks up or runs away for some reason. In addition, some systems will have an automatic reset feature that will allow the system to reset itself after a power failure. In both cases, the reset capability of the MPU is used.

This reset capability can be considered an interrupt, since the MPU leaves whatever it is doing and jumps off to the start of the monitor program. In most cases, the monitor program would start with a short subroutine that initializes the system. It would do things like set up the stack pointer, initialize displays, etc.

Non-Maskable Interrupts

The 6800 has two other types of hardware interrupts. One of these interrupts is maskable; the other is not. A maskable interrupt is one that the MPU can ignore under certain conditions. Whereas, a non-maskable interrupt cannot be ignored. To illustrate the difference, recall the corporation president analogy.

The president's report writing can be interrupted by the telephone. However, by telling her secretary to hold all calls, she has effectively masked one source of interruptions. In this analogy it is impractical to mask all interrupts. For example, it could be counterproductive to mask the fire alarm.

Somewhat the same situation can exist in a microprocessor controlled system. Some interrupts can be ignored for a few seconds while the MPU is performing a more important task. This type of interrupt can be masked. Others must not be ignored at all. These cannot be masked. Of course, it is up to the designer to decide which interrupts can be masked and which cannot. The 6800 MPU has provisions for handling both types. How the MPU handles the non-maskable type will be discussed first.

The 6800 MPU has a control line called the non-maskable interrupt ($\overline{\text{NMI}}$) line. A high-to-low transition on this line forces the MPU to initiate a *non-maskable interrupt sequence*. The purpose of this sequence is to provide an orderly means by which the MPU can jump off to a service routine that will take care of the interrupt.

This becomes somewhat involved because the MPU must be able to go back to its main program after the interrupt service routine is finished. It must be able to pick up exactly where it left off. Furthermore, all registers must hold exactly the same data and addresses that they held when the interrupt occurred. In other words, when an interrupt occurs, the program count must be saved so that the MPU can later return to this point in the program. Also, the contents of the accumulators, index register, and even the condition code registers must be saved so that the MPU can be restored to the exact condition that existed at the instant the interrupt occurred.

The 6800 MPU accomplishes this by pushing all the pertinent data onto the stack. Then, after the interrupt has been serviced, the MPU returns to its previous status by pulling the data from the stack.

The non-maskable interrupt sequence is shown in Figure 6-22. A non-maskable interrupt is initiated when the $\overline{\text{NMI}}$ line goes from its high state to its low state. The MPU finishes the execution of the current instruction. However, before another instruction is fetched, the MPU pushes the contents of its registers onto the stack. Recall that the stack pointer always points to the top of the stack. For this example, assume that the stack pointer was set by an earlier instruction to address 0068_{16}.

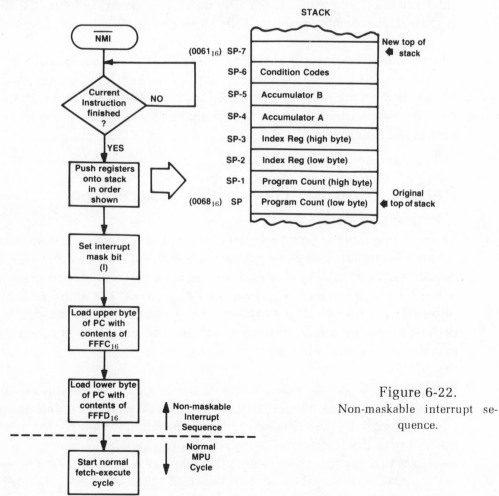

Figure 6-22.
Non-maskable interrupt sequence.

The MPU pushes the lower eight bits of the program counter into memory location 0068_{16}. Then it decrements the stack pointer so that the upper eight bits of the program counter are pushed into address 0067_{16}. Next, the contents of the index register are pushed into addresses 0066_{16} and 0065_{16}. The contents of accumulators A and B and the condition codes are also pushed in as shown. When all this has been done, the stack pointer will have been decremented seven times to 0061_{16}.

Return to the flow chart and notice that the next step is to set the interrupt mask bit. This allows the MPU to ignore any interrupt requests that occur while the non-maskable interrupt is being serviced.

At this point, the MPU is ready to jump to the interrupt service routine. But, what is the address of this routine? Recall the interrupt vector chart that was shown earlier in Figure 6-20. The non-maskable interrupt vector is at addresses $FFFC_{16}$ and $FFFD_{16}$. Thus, the upper byte of the program counter is loaded from $FFFC_{16}$ while the lower byte is loaded from $FFFD_{16}$. This directs the MPU to the first instruction in the non-maskable interrupt service routine. From this point on, the MPU returns to its normal fetch-execute cycle until the service routine is finished.

The sequence of events shown in Figure 6-22 happen automatically when a non-maskable interrupt sequence is initiated. The $\overline{NMI}$ line gives external hardware a method of forcing a jump-to-subroutine to occur. In this case, the subroutine is a short program that performs some action to take care of the interrupt.

Return From Interrupt (RTI) Instruction

The non-maskable interrupt is used when some situation exists that cannot be ignored. You can probably visualize applications that would require such a capability. For example, assume that a microprocessor is being used in a numerically controlled drill press. The non-maskable interrupt could be used in conjunction with limit switches to prevent drilling holes in the work surface. Or, it could be used to shut down the machine if someone's hand got too close.

The purpose of the service routine is to direct the operation of the computer to take care of the interrupt. Typically, it would first determine which external device initiated the interrupt. Then it would determine the nature of the interrupt. Finally, it would take whatever action was necessary to take care of the interrupt. In many cases, the interrupt is of a routine nature and can be easily serviced. In these situations, the MPU should return to the main program and take up where it left off. There is an instruction that allows the MPU to do this. It is called the "Return-From-Interrupt" (RTI) instruction. Look on your Instruction Set Summary card, and you will see that this is a one-byte instruction whose opcode is $3B_{16}$.

Figure 6-23 shows how the RTI instruction is used. The main program is shown on the left, while the interrupt service routine is shown on the right. Assume that the interrupt signal occurs while the LDAB# instruction is being executed. The MPU finishes that one instruction and pushes all pertinent data onto the stack. It then jumps to an address determined by the $\overline{\text{NMI}}$ vector in address FFFC and FFFD. The contents of these two locations determine the starting address of the $\overline{\text{NMI}}$ service routine. Notice that the last instruction in the service routine is the return-from-interrupt instruction. This instruction returns program control to the point in the main program that the MPU left when the interrupt occurred.

This can be done because the previous status of the MPU was preserved in the stack. The RTI instruction causes the accumulators, the index registers, the condition code register, and the program counter to be loaded from the stack. Thus, the same information that went into the stack when the interrupt occurred comes out of the stack when the RTI instruction is executed. This allows the MPU to return to the main program and take up where it left off.

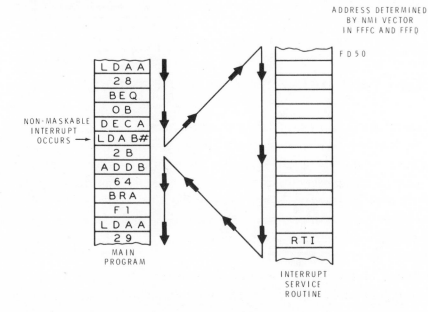

Figure 6-23.
The RTI instruction returns control to the main program after the interrupt has been serviced.

Interrupt Request (IRQ)

The interrupt request is very similar to the non-maskable interrupt. The main difference between the two is that the interrupt request is maskable.

The 6800 MPU has a control line called the interrupt request ($\overline{\text{IRQ}}$) line. When this line is low, an interrupt sequence is requested. However, the MPU may or may not initiate the interrupt sequence depending on the state of the interrupt mask (I) bit in the condition code register. If the I bit is set, the MPU ignores the interrupt request. If the I bit is not set, the MPU initiates the interrupt sequence. This procedure is very similar to the $\overline{\text{NMI}}$ procedure discussed earlier. Figure 6-24 shows the interrupt procedure.

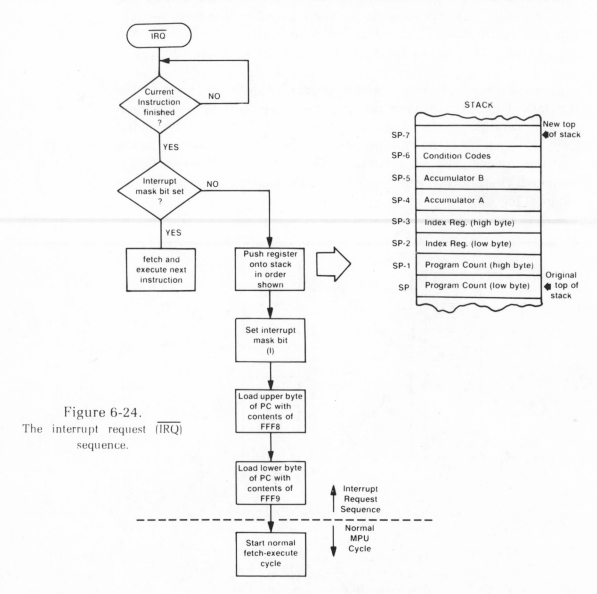

Figure 6-24.
The interrupt request ($\overline{\text{IRQ}}$) sequence.

When the $\overline{\text{IRQ}}$ line is low, the MPU finishes the current instruction. It then checks the interrupt mask bit. If I is set to 1, the MPU ignores the interrupt request and executes the next instruction in sequence. However, if I=0, the MPU pushes the contents of the various registers onto the stack in the order shown.

Next, the interrupt mask bit is set to 1. This prevents the MPU from honoring other interrupt requests until the present interrupt has been serviced.

The address of the $\overline{\text{IRQ}}$ service routine is at addresses $FFF8_{16}$ and $FFF9_{16}$. The program counter is loaded from these addresses. Thus, the next instruction to be executed will be the first instruction in the interrupt request service routine.

Once in the service routine, the MPU goes into its normal fetch-execute cycle. When the interrupt has been serviced, control can be returned to the main program by an RTI instruction.

Interrupt Mask Instructions

The 6800 MPU has two instructions that allow software control of the interrupt mask bit. You have seen that the I bit in the condition code register is set any time an interrupt sequence is initiated. This prevents an $\overline{\text{IRQ}}$ from being honored while a previous $\overline{\text{IRQ}}$ or $\overline{\text{NMI}}$ is being serviced. This is an example of setting the interrupt flag with *hardware*.

In many cases, it is necessary to set the interrupt flag with software. Therefore, the 6800 MPU has an instruction that can do this. It is called the "Set-Interrupt-Mask" (SEI) instruction. If you refer to your Instruction Set Summary card, you will see that this is a one-byte instruction whose opcode is $0F_{16}$. The flag may be set to prevent an interruption on a part of the program that we do not wish to be interrupted. It has the effect of disabling interrupt requests.

Of course, we do not wish to permanently disable the interrupt capability. Therefore, some means must be provided for enabling the interrupt request capability. An instruction called "Clear-Interrupt-Mask" (CLI) is available for this purpose. This is a one-byte instruction whose opcode is $0E_{16}$.

While we can disable or enable the interrupt request line with these instructions, they do not affect the non-maskable interrupt. As the name implies, the $\overline{\text{NMI}}$ line cannot be disabled by the I flag.

Software Interrupt (SWI) Instruction

The 6800 MPU has a software equivalent of an interrupt. It is an instruction called the "Software Interrupt" (SWI). When executed, the instruction causes the MPU to perform an interrupt sequence that is very similar to the hardware interrupt sequences already discussed. As shown on your Instruction Set Summary card, this is a one-byte instruction whose opcode is $3F_{16}$.

Figure 6-25 shows the sequence of events that occurs when this instruction is executed. First the contents of all the pertinent registers are pushed onto the stack in the order shown. Next, the interrupt mask is set so that interrupt requests cannot interfere. Finally, the software interrupt vector is obtained from addresses $FFFA_{16}$ and $FFFB_{16}$. This vector is loaded into the program counter so that the next instruction will be fetched from this address. As with the other interrupts, the MPU will return to the original program when a return-from-interrupt instruction is encountered.

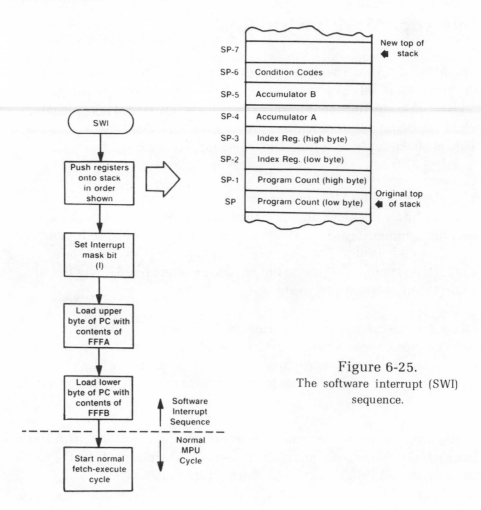

Figure 6-25.
The software interrupt (SWI) sequence.

The software interrupt instruction can be used to simulate hardware interrupts. It is also helpful for inserting pauses in a program. For example, the ET-3400 Microprocessor Trainer uses the software interrupt to perform the single-step function and to implement the breakpoint capability.

Wait for Interrupt (WAI) Instruction

One of the first instructions introduced in this course was the halt instruction (opcode $3E_{16}$). In the previous unit, you learned that this instruction is actually called a Wait-for-Interrupt (WAI). What exactly does this instruction do? It does cause the MPU to halt, but there is more to it than that.

When the WAI instruction is executed, the program counter is incremented by one. Then the contents of the program counter, index register, accumulators, and condition code register are pushed onto the stack. The order is exactly the same as if an interrupt occurs. The MPU then enters a wait state, doing nothing further until, and unless, an interrupt occurs.

The MPU can be forced back into action either by an interrupt request or by a non-maskable interrupt. The $\overline{\text{NMI}}$ sequence is the same as that described earlier except for one important difference. Remember that the contents of the registers have already been pushed onto the stack. Thus, this part of the $\overline{\text{NMI}}$ sequence is omitted. This allows the MPU to respond faster to the interrupt.

The $\overline{\text{IRQ}}$ sequence is also the same as that described earlier except that the registers are not pushed onto the stack again. As always, the $\overline{\text{IRQ}}$ signal is ignored if the interrupt mask bit is set.

Of course, the reset signal can override the wait state. Thus, there are three ways of escaping the wait state.

Self-Test Review

28. List the four types of interrupts available to the MPU.

29. Which interrupt is ignored by the MPU if the interrupt mask bit is set?

30. What is the purpose of the reset interrupt sequence?

31. From what addresses is the reset interrupt vector taken?

32. What is an interrupt vector?

33. List the sequence of events that takes place when a non-maskable interrupt occurs.

34. What is an interrupt service routine?

35. What is usually the last instruction in the interrupt service routine?

36. How does the RTI instruction affect the stack pointer?

37. Which of the interrupts does not cause data to be pushed into the stack?

38. Which instruction can be used to disable the interrupt request capability?

39. List three methods by which the MPU can be released from the wait state following the execution of a WAI instruction.

40. Under what condition will the $\overline{\text{IRQ}}$ and $\overline{\text{NMI}}$ interrupts not cause data to be pushed into the stack?

Answers

28. Reset, non-maskable interrupt, interrupt request, and software interrupt.

29. Interrupt request ($\overline{\text{IRQ}}$).

30. To direct the MPU to the first instruction in the monitor or control program.

31. $FFFE_{16}$ and $FFFF_{16}$.

32. The address of the interrupt service routine.

33. A. The current instruction is executed.
    B. The contents of the pertinent registers are pushed onto the stack.
    C. The interrupt mask bit is set.
    D. The $\overline{\text{NMI}}$ vector from addresses $FFFC_{16}$ and $FFFD_{16}$ is loaded into the program counter.
    E. The instruction at the address specified by the $\overline{\text{NMI}}$ vector is fetched and executed.

34. A routine that takes care of the interrupt and then returns control to the main program.

35. The Return-From-Interrupt (RTI) instruction.

36. The stack pointer is incremented seven times as the previous MPU status is pulled from the stack.

37. Reset.

38. Set Interrupt Mask (SEI).

39. A. By a reset signal.
    B. By a non-maskable interrupt.
    C. By an interrupt request (if I=0).

40. If the MPU is waiting for an interrupt.

Perform Experiments 9 and 10 in the Student Workbook.

Unit 7

INTERFACING — PART 1

INTRODUCTION

As mentioned earlier, there are two things you can do with a micro-processor. You can program it and you can interface it with other circuits. By now you should be able to write simple programs without too much trouble. You will continue to learn new programming techniques as you progress through the course. However, in the remaining portions of the course, the emphasis will shift to interfacing the MPU with other circuits.

Units 7 and 8 will give you enough general information to understand the interfacing experiments providing that you have a general knowledge of digital electronics. That is, these units are written on the assumption that you have training equivalent to that provided in the Heathkit Continuing Education, Individual Learning Program in Digital Electronics.

UNIT OBJECTIVES

When you have completed this unit, you should be able to:

1. Define 3-state logic and explain the need for it.

2. Explain the purpose of each of the control lines on the 6800 MPU.

3. Explain the timing relationships between the clock signals and the information on the address, data, and R/$\overline{W}$ lines.

4. Identify several different arrangements used in static RAMS.

5. Draw the logic diagram of a simple address decoder.

6. Explain the operation of a static RAM storage cell.

7. Show four different methods by which an MPU can drive 7-segment displays.

INTERFACING FUNDAMENTALS

Before going into specific interfacing examples, we must first discuss some fundamental concepts that will be used. First, we will discuss the concept of a bus and the need for 3-state logic. Then we will examine the various control and bus lines of the 6800 MPU. Finally, we will consider the various timing relationships involved in the execution of instructions.

Buses

In computer jargon, a bus is generally defined as a group of conductors over which information is transferred from one place to another. In many cases, the information can originate from any one of several sources and can be transferred to any one of several destinations. Moreover, on some buses, information can be transferred in either of two directions. These are called bi-directional buses. Of course for a given bus, only one transfer of information can occur at a time.

Figure 7-1 shows the data bus arrangement in a typical microcomputer application. Generally in this type of system, all data transfers involve the MPU. Thus, data can be transferred in either direction between RAM and the MPU. However, other data transfers are one way only. Data can be transferred from ROM or the input buffer to the MPU. Also, data can be transferred from the MPU to the output latches.

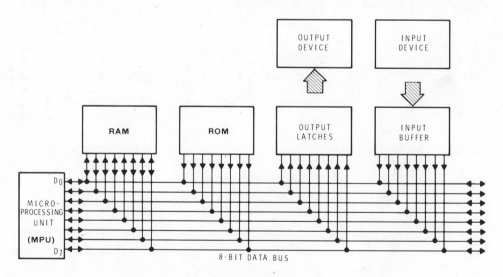

Figure 7-1
Typical Data Bus Arrangement.

In an arrangement like this, two problems arise. First, we must insure that only one data transfer is attempted at any given time. This is done by assigning each destination or source a different address. For example, the RAM, ROM, output latches, and input buffers all have one or more chip enable pins. The proper logic levels on these pins will select or activate the circuit. By assigning each circuit a different address, we insure that only one circuit at a time is enabled.

Figure 7-2 shows the addressing capability added to the block diagram. An address decoder is added for each circuit. The inputs to the address decoders come from the MPU via the address bus. The outputs go to the chip enable lines of the various circuits. Since only one address can appear on the address bus at any given instant, only one of the external circuits will be enabled at a time.

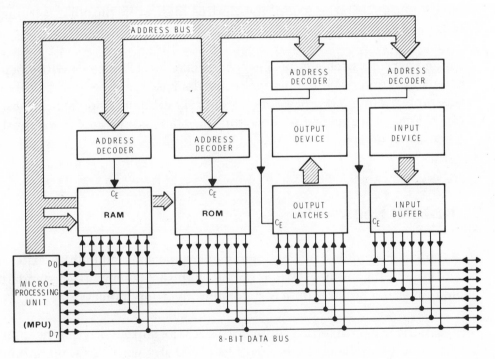

Figure 7-2
Adding the Address Capability.

The memories are assigned many addresses since each byte must have its own address. For example, if a 512_{10}-byte RAM is used, it would probably be assigned addresses 0000_{16} through $01FF_{16}$. When any one of these addresses appear on the address bus, the RAM is selected via its chip enable line. Notice that a portion of the address bus connects directly to the RAM. This selects the individual byte within the RAM.

In the same way, the ROM is assigned a range of addresses. If a 1024_{10} byte ROM is used, it may be assigned addresses $FC00_{16}$ through $FFFF_{16}$. The ROM must be enabled whenever any of these addresses appear on the address bus. The output latch and input buffers are also assigned unique addresses. Thus, the MPU can communicate with any one of the external circuits simply by placing the proper address on the address bus.

The second problem is more fundamental. It arises because of the basic 2-state nature of digital logic circuits. Recall that the output of a standard logic gate will always be either logic 1 (high) or logic 0 (low). The problem is: Which state should the outputs of the circuits that are connected to the data bus assume when they are not selected? Regardless of which state they assume, they interfere with the output of the enabled circuit. For example, if the output of the disabled circuits assume a high state, they interfere with the low output of the enabled circuit. In other words, one circuit tries to pull the bus line high while the other is trying to force it low.

In the past, this problem has been overcome by using gates with open collector outputs. While open collector devices could be used to solve this problem in microprocessors, an entirely different approach is most often used. To understand how this problem is overcome, we must discuss *3-state logic*.

A. STANDARD NON-INVERTING BUFFER.

B. THREE-STATE NON-INVERTING BUFFER.

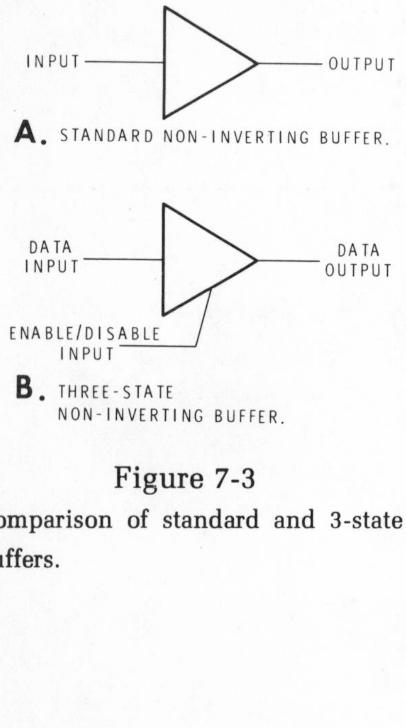

Figure 7-3

Comparison of standard and 3-state buffers.

3-State Logic

As the name implies, 3-state logic devices have a unique third state in addition to the normal 1 and 0 output. Figure 7-3 compares a standard non-inverting buffer with a 3-state, non-inverting buffer.

Recall that a non-inverting buffer increases the current drive of the input signal without changing the logic levels in any way. Thus, the output may be able to drive ten times as many gates as the input. The standard buffer has one input and one output. The output always assumes the same logic level as the input. Because the input must be either 1 or 0, the output must be the same.

By contrast, the 3-state buffer has two inputs. In addition to the normal data input, the buffer has an enable/disable input. This input may be either logic 1 or logic 0 depending upon whether we wish to enable or disable the buffer. The buffer shown in Figure 7-3B is enabled by applying logic 1 to the enable/disable input.

When enabled, the 3-state buffer acts exactly like the standard buffer. The output will assume the same logic level as the data input.

The 3-state buffer is disabled by applying logic 0 to the enable/disable input. When disabled, the output assumes a very high impedance state that is neither logic 1 nor logic 0. While in this high impedance state, the output can be assumed to be disconnected from the rest of the circuit. That is, when the buffer is disabled, its output will not interfere with the circuits to which it is connected.

There are many different types of 3-state devices available. Figure 7-4 shows four different types of 3-state buffers. The buffer shown in Figure 7-4A is the same as that described above. It does not invert and is enabled by logic 1. Notice that the buffer shown in Figure 7-4B has a small circle at the enable/disable input. This means that the buffer is enabled by a logic 0 and disabled by a logic 1.

Figures 7-4C and D show inverting buffers. The first is enabled by a logic 1; the second is enabled by a logic 0.

Generally, four or more 3-state buffers are included in a single integrated circuit. Figure 7-5 shows the 74126 type TTL IC. It contains four 3-state buffers in a single 14-pin dual-in-line package.

Figure 7-6 shows eight 3-state buffers in a single 20-pin package. The four lower buffers are enabled by a logic 0 at pin 1 of the IC. The four upper buffers are enabled by a logic 1 at pin 19. The input buffer shown earlier in Figures 7-1 and 7-2 could use this type of IC. Buffers of this type are often called bus extenders, line drivers, line receivers, etc., depending on how they are used.

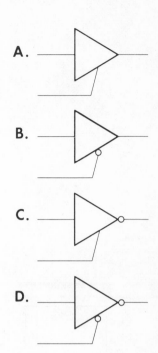

Figure 7-4
Four types of 3-state buffers.

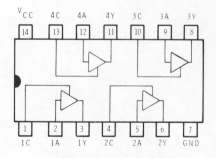

Figure 7-5
The 74126 IC contains four 3-state buffers in a single 14-pin package.

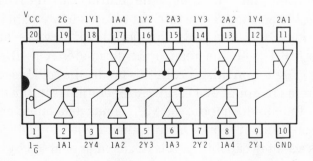

Figure 7-6
The 74LS241 contains eight 3-state non-inverting buffers.

While many different forms of 3-state buffers are available, many microprocessor support circuits do not require separate 3-state buffers. Most RAMS and ROMS have their own 3-state buffers built in. Thus, any time the RAM or ROM is not selected, it automatically goes to its third state. In this state, the outputs are said to be off, disconnected, disabled, floating, or in their high impedance state.

The 6800 MPU Interface Lines

Before you can interface any microprocessor to its support circuits or to the outside world, you must become familiar with its pin assignments, control lines, etc. Figure 7-7 shows the pin assignments of the 6800 MPU. Notice that the MPU is in a single 40-pin dual-in-line package.

Notice that pins 9 through 20 and 22 through 25 make up the *16-bit address bus*. These pins connect to 16 three-state output drivers in the MPU. Each driver is capable of driving one standard TTL load. The TSC line (pin 39) is used to enable or disable the 3-state address bus. When disabled, the address lines act as open circuits. This capability is sometimes used to allow another device to gain control of the address bus. In this way, some external device can address memory. This is referred to as "direct memory access" (DMA).

Pins 26 through 33 are used for the *8-bit data bus*. This is a bi-directional bus that is used to transfer data to and from memory and the input-output circuitry. These are 3-state lines that are enabled and disabled by the DBE line (pin 36).

You are already familiar with four of the control lines: the read/write line, the reset line, the non-maskable interrupt, and the interrupt request line. The *read/write (R/$\overline{W}$) line* tells the peripheral devices and memory whether the MPU is in the read or write mode. A read operation is indicated by a logic 1 on this line. In this mode, the MPU reads data from memory or from an input device. A write operation is indicated by a logic 0 on the R/$\overline{W}$ line. In this mode, the MPU sends data out to memory or an output device. Since it works hand-in-hand with the address bus, the R/$\overline{W}$ line has a 3-state capability. It is disabled or enabled by the TSC line (pin 39).

PIN ASSIGNMENT

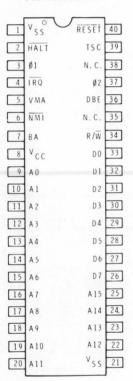

Figure 7-7
The 6800 MPU pin assignments.

The *reset line* (pin 40) was discussed in the previous unit. Recall that it is used to $\overline{\text{reset}}$ and start the MPU when power is initially applied or at anytime that we wish to initialize the system. When this line goes to logic level 1, the MPU starts the reset sequence. Recall that the reset vector is retrieved from addresses FFFE_{16} and FFFF_{16}. This vector is loaded into the program counter so that the first instruction is fetched from that address. This capability is used to direct the MPU to the start of the monitor or control program.

The *non-maskable interrupt* $(\overline{\text{NMI}})$ was mentioned when interrupts were discussed. A high-to-low transition on pin 6 (the $\overline{\text{NMI}}$ line) will initiate the non-maskable interrupt sequence. Recall that this forces the MPU to pick up the $\overline{\text{NMI}}$ vector at addresses FFFC and FFFD. This vector is the address of the $\overline{\text{NMI}}$ service routine.

The *interrupt request* line $(\overline{\text{IRQ}})$ was also discussed earlier. While this is similar to the non-maskable interrupt, there are three fundamental differences. First, the $\overline{\text{IRQ}}$ signal is maskable; it will be ignored if the interrupt mask bit is set. Second, the $\overline{\text{IRQ}}$ sequence picks up the $\overline{\text{IRQ}}$ vector from addresses FFFA_{16} and FFFB_{16}. Third, the $\overline{\text{IRQ}}$ line (pin 4) is level sensitive. That is, a logic 0 on this pin causes the interrupt sequence. Compare this to the $\overline{\text{NMI}}$ line which requires a logic 1-to-0 transition.

This accounts for 28 of the 40 pins. While you are not yet familiar with the remaining 12 pins, five of them are self-explanatory. For example, two of them (pins 35 and 38) are not connected. Also, three of the pins are used for power. Pin 8 is labeled V_{cc}. This is the $+5$ volt supply. Pins 1 and 21 are labeled V_{ss}. These are ground pins. Notice that the 6800 MPU requires a single $+5$-volt supply.

The remaining seven lines require a brief explanation. First, there are two *clock signals* labeled $\emptyset 1$ (pronounced "phi one") and $\emptyset 2$. A 2-phase non-overlapping clock is required. This must be provided to the MPU from some external clock generator. The details of the clock signal will be discussed later. The normal clock frequency is 1 MHz, although higher speed versions of the 6800 MPU are also available.

The *3-state control (TSC) line* (pin 39) was mentioned earlier. This input to the MPU is used in applications in which some external device must periodically take over the address bus. Normally, the MPU has complete control of the address bus and read/write line. However, an external device can effectively disconnect the MPU from the address bus by switching the TSC line to the high state. When TSC goes high, the address bus and read/write line of the MPU go to their off or high impedance state.

This allows the external device direct access to memory without going through the MPU. This is called direct memory access or DMA. In many applications, DMA operations are not required and TSC is permanently connected to ground.

The *data bus enable (DBE) line* (pin 36) is the 3-state control line for the data bus. If this input to the MPU is forced low, the data bus will switch to its off or high impedance state. As you will see later, all data transfers between the MPU and memory take place when the $\phi2$ clock is high. For this reason, the DBE line is often connected to the $\phi2$ clock.

The $\overline{\text{HALT}}$ line (pin 2) provides a hardware method of halting the MPU. If this input is forced low, the MPU will finish its present instruction, then it will halt. When halted, all 3-state lines go to their off state. This effectively disconnects the MPU from the address and data buses. This line is sometimes used to implement single instruction operation. By controlling the $\overline{\text{HALT}}$ line, the MPU can be forced to stop after each instruction is executed. This can be a valuable aid in troubleshooting hardware and debugging programs. In many applications, the halt capability is simply not required. In this case, the $\overline{\text{HALT}}$ line is permanently connected to +5 volts.

The *valid memory address (VMA)* line is an output. It indicates to peripheral devices that the address on the address bus is a valid one. This signal is necessary because occasionally a false address will appear on the address bus. The VMA signal is used to disable peripheral devices when the address is not valid. A logic 1 at pin 5 indicates that the address is valid and that the peripheral devices may respond accordingly. A logic 0 indicates that the address is not valid and that the peripheral devices should ignore the address. As you will see later, the VMA line is used in any decoding scheme.

The final control line that we will consider is the *bus available (BA)* line. This output (pin 7) indicates whether or not the MPU is executing instructions. Recall that the MPU may stop executing instructions for either of two reasons. First, the WAI instruction will cause the MPU to stop until an interrupt is received. Or, the MPU can be stopped by forcing the $\overline{\text{HALT}}$ line low. A logic 0 on the bus available line indicates that the MPU is running. A logic 1 indicates that the MPU has stopped. When the MPU is stopped, all 3-state outputs go to their off state. Thus, the MPU is effectively disconnected from the buses. The BA signal indicates that this condition exists by going to the logic 1 state. During this period the buses are available for other purposes such as DMA operations.

Instruction Timing

Before going further, the timing relationship between the various control and bus signals will be discussed. The discussion will start with the most basic timing relationship: the timing for a single instruction.

Figure 7-8 shows the 2-phase clock signals required by the 6800 MPU. These two clock signals control every single action that takes place in the MPU and its peripheral devices. To illustrate this, the significant events that occur during the fetch and execution of the LDAA immediate instruction will be discussed. Recall that this is a 2-byte instruction. The first byte is the opcode (86_{16}). The second byte is the number that is to be loaded into accumulator A. This instruction requires two MPU cycles. During the first cycle, the opcode is fetched and decoded. During the second cycle, the operand is retrieved from memory and is placed in accumulator A.

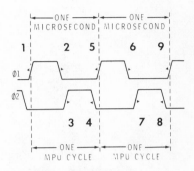

Figure 7-8.

Timing for the LDAA immediate instruction.

The significant events are illustrated. Notice that the events occur at the edges of the clock pulses. Assume that, prior to time 1, the program counter contains the address of the LDAA immediate instruction.

At time 1, the address is transferred from the program counter to the address bus via the memory address register. Notice that this occurs at the positive-going edge of the ϕ1 clock. If the VMA and R/$\overline{W}$ lines are not already at logic 1, they will be switched to logic 1. A logic 1 on VMA indicates to memory that this is a valid address. A logic 1 on R/$\overline{W}$ indicates to memory that the MPU wishes to read the byte at the indicated address.

Time 2 is the falling edge of the ϕ1 clock. At this time, the program counter will be incremented by one to the address of the next byte in memory. However, this will not change the address on the address bus. Remember that this address is latched into the memory address register. Thus, the output address is still that of the first byte of the LDAA instruction.

The events which occur during the ϕ1 clock are initiated from within the MPU itself. In fact, in most systems, the ϕ1 clock is applied *only* to the MPU. The ϕ2 clock, on the other hand, is applied to the peripheral circuits as well as the MPU. Thus, the RAMs, ROMs, etc., are controlled by the ϕ2 clock.

Time 3 is the rising edge of the $\phi 2$ clock. This positive-going edge forces memory to place the data from the indicated address onto the data bus. Recall that this is the opcode for the LDAA immediate instruction or 86_{16}. Notice that the address has had from time 1 to time 3 to stabilize.

Time 4 is the falling edge of the $\phi 2$ clock. At this time, the MPU accepts the byte from the data bus. Notice that the data bus has from time 3 to time 4 to stabilize. The MPU transfers this byte (86_{16}) to the instruction register. There, it is decoded and is interpreted as an LDAA immediate opcode. This tells the MPU that the next byte in memory is the operand that is to be loaded into accumulator A.

This completes the first MPU cycle. During this cycle, the opcode was simply read from memory and decoded. This corresponds to the fetch phase discussed earlier for our hypothetical MPU. Notice that an MPU cycle corresponds to one cycle of the clock. Now let's see what happens during the second cycle or execute phase of the instruction.

At time 5, the address of the operand is transferred from the program counter to the address bus. At time 6, the program counter is incremented by one in anticipation of the next fetch phase.

At time 7, the rising edge of the $\phi 2$ clock causes the operand to be transferred from memory to the data bus. At time 8, the operand is latched into the MPU where it is transferred to accumulator A. This completes the second MPU cycle and the execution phase of the instruction. Time 9 represents the start of the fetch phase for the next instruction. The LDAA immediate instruction required two MPU cycles or two cycles of the clock. Assuming a 1 MHz clock, two microseconds are required for this instruction.

Timing of Program Segment

Now that you are familiar with the timing of a single instruction, several instructions will be put together to form a sample program. You can then study the timing relationships between the bus signals, clock signals, the R/$\overline{W}$ line, etc.

Our sample program segment is shown in Figure 7-9. Using the immediate addressing mode, it loads 07_{16} into accumulator A and adds 21_{16}. The result is then stored in location 0001_{16}. Notice that the first instruction resides at address 0010_{16}.

HEX ADDRESS	HEX CONTENTS	MNEMONIC/ HEX CONTENTS	COMMENTS
0010	86	LDAA#	Load Accumulator A immediate with
0011	07	07	07.
0012	8B	ADDA#	Add to Accumulator A immediate
0013	21	21	21.
0014	97	STAA	Store the result
0015	01	01	at this address.
0016	. . .	. . .	Next Instruction

Figure 7-9

Sample program segment.

Figure 7-10 illustrates the timing relationships. At the top the $\emptyset$1 and $\emptyset$2 clock signals are shown. The information that appears on the buses and control lines for each clock period is shown at the bottom. This program segment requires eight clock or MPU cycles. These are numbered one through eight. Next, you will see what happens during each of these cycles.

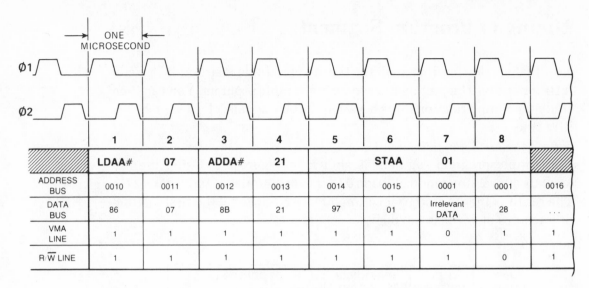

Figure 7-10

Timing of sample program segment.

Cycle 1. During the first cycle, the address of the LDAA# instruction (0010_{16}) is placed on the address bus. As a result, the opcode 86_{16} is read from that address and is picked up by the MPU. Since this was a read operation from a valid address, the VMA and $R/\overline{W}$ lines are at logic 1. The MPU decodes the opcode and recognizes that this is an LDAA# instruction. Consequently, it knows that the next byte in memory is the operand that is to be loaded into the accumulator. During this cycle, the program counter was incremented to 0011_{16} so that it now points at the operand.

Cycle 2. This is the execution phase of the LDAA# instruction. The address of the operand (0011_{16}) is placed on the address bus. The operand (07_{16}) is read out on the data bus and is placed in accumulator A. In the process, the program counter is incremented to 0012_{16}. This completes the execute phase of the first instruction.

Cycle 3. This is the fetch phase of the next instruction. The address 0012_{16} is placed on the address bus. The opcode at that address is read out and placed on the data bus. The MPU picks up the opcode, decodes it, and discovers that it is an ADDA# instruction. In the process, the program counter is incremented to 0013_{16}.

Cycle 4. Here, the address 0013_{16} is transferred to the address bus and the selected memory location is read out. Therefore, the operand 21_{16} is placed on the data bus. The operand is picked up by the MPU and is added to the contents of the accumulator. The sum 28_{16} is retained in accumulator A. The program counter is incremented to 0014_{16}.

Cycle 5. This is the fetch phase for the third instruction. The address 0014_{16} is placed on the address bus. The opcode for STAA is read out and decoded. The MPU recognizes that the direct address mode is used. Thus, it will interpret the next byte in memory as the address at which the sum is to be stored. The program counter is incremented to 0015_{16}.

Cycle 6. Address 0015_{16} is placed on the address bus. Notice that the contents of this location is the address at which the sum is to be stored. Thus, 01 is read out on the data bus where it is picked up by the MPU. Because the MPU recognized that direct addressing is indicated, it assumes that the address at which the sum is to be stored is 0001_{16}. This address is retained in the MPU. The program counter is incremented to 0016_{16}.

Cycle 7. During this cycle, the MPU prepares to store the sum. To do this, it must transfer the address 0001_{16} to the address register. Also, it must transfer the sum from the accumulator to the data register. While this is happening, the MPU must refrain from all external data transfers. To prevent unwanted data transfers, the MPU switches the VMA line low. This tells all peripheral devices that the address is not a valid one and that no data transfers should be initiated. Thus, the peripheral devices simply ignore the data and address buses for this cycle.

Cycle 8. The MPU is now ready to store the sum in memory. The address at which the sum is to be stored (0001_{16}) is placed on the address bus. The data to be stored (28_{16}) is placed on the data bus. The VMA line is switched high, indicating that this is a valid address. The R/$\overline{W}$ line is switched low, indicating that this is a store operation. Thus, the sum (28_{16}) is stored away in memory location 0001_{16}.

Of course, the computer does not stop here. During the next cycle, the next instruction is fetched and decoded. However, the eight machine cycles illustrated above should give you the idea. As you will see later, the timing relationships shown here become important when we interface the MPU with memory or I/O circuitry.

The 6800 Data Sheet

The preceding section has given you some information on the control lines and timing relationships of the 6800 microprocessor, but you may have some questions that have not been answered here. For this reason, a detailed data sheet on the 6800 microprocessor is included in Appendix B of this course. It explains in more technical language the capabilities of the 6800 microprocessor. At this point in your study, you should have little trouble understanding this data sheet. You may want to refer to this data sheet if you have a question that is not answered in the text.

Self-Test Review

1. What is a 3-state logic gate?

2. How is the non-inverting buffer shown in Figure 7-4A switched to its high impedance state?

3. In the 6800 MPU, how can the address bus be forced to the off state?

4. How can the data bus be forced to its off state?

5. What does a logic 0 on the VMA line indicate?

6. What does a logic 1 on the BA line indicate?

7. How can the MPU be stopped by hardware?

8. How does the MPU indicate that it wishes to store data in memory?

9. List three ways in which an interrupt request differs from a non-maskable interrupt.

10. The following is a list of the 6800 MPU's buses and control lines. Characterize each as either input, output, or bidirectional.

$\overline{\text{Halt}}$	_____	R/$\overline{\text{W}}$	_____
ϕ1	_____	DBE	_____
$\overline{\text{IRQ}}$	_____	ϕ2	_____
VMA	_____	TSC	_____
BA	_____	$\overline{\text{NMI}}$	_____
Address Bus	_____	Reset	_____
Data Bus	_____		

11. In reference to the clock signals, when is a new address placed on the address bus?

12. When is the program counter incremented?

13. When does memory place data on the address bus?

14. When does the MPU pick up or latch in data that is on the data bus?

Answers

1. A gate which has an off state in addition to the normal logic 1 and logic 0 states.

2. By applying a logic 0 to the enable/disable input.

3. By applying a logic 1 to the 3-state control (TSC) line.

4. By applying a logic 0 to the data bus enable (DBE) line.

5. That the address is not valid and should be ignored.

6. That the MPU has halted.

7. By applying a logic level 0 to the $\overline{\text{HALT}}$ input.

8. By switching the R/$\overline{\text{W}}$ line to low.

9. First, the interrupt request is maskable; $\overline{\text{NMI}}$ is not.
    Second, $\overline{\text{IRQ}}$ is level sensitive; $\overline{\text{NMI}}$ is edge sensitive.
    Third, $\overline{\text{IRQ}}$ uses the interrupt vector at address FFF8_{16} and FFF9_{16}, while $\overline{\text{NMI}}$ uses the vector at FFFC_{16} and FFFD_{16}.

10.

$\overline{\text{HALT}}$	—	input	R/$\overline{\text{W}}$ — output
ϕ1	—	input	DBE — input
$\overline{\text{IRQ}}$	—	input	ϕ2 — input
VMA	—	output	TSC — input
BA	—	output	$\overline{\text{NMI}}$ — input
Address Bus	—	output	Reset — input
Data Bus	—	bi-directional	

11. On the rising edge of the ϕ1 clock.

12. On the falling edge of the ϕ1 clock.

13. On the rising edge of the ϕ2 clock.

14. On the falling edge of the ϕ2 clock.

INTERFACING WITH RANDOM ACCESS MEMORY

The Cassette tape segment entitled "Semiconductor Memories" is an excellent overview of the types of memories encountered in microprocessor applications. If you have not already done so, you should complete this audio-visual activity at this time.

As shown in the audio-visual presentation, there are several different types of semiconductor memories. Today, the most popular type of memory used with microprocessors is the static RAM.

Recall that a RAM is a random access read/write memory. The static RAM uses bistable flip-flops to store data. Because the data is latched in these flip-flops, no refresh circuitry is required. That is, data can be maintained indefinitely without refreshing as long as power is applied.

Many different types of static RAMs are available. The smaller static RAMs use the bipolar TTL technique. Most of the larger RAMs use either MOS or CMOS technology. One of the most popular sizes of static RAMs is 1024 bits. This size RAM is packaged in a single IC having from 16 to 24 pins. Internally, the 1024 memory cells may be arranged as 128 8-bit words. Thus, a microprocessor system that requires 512 bytes of RAM would require four of these IC's. IC's of this type require eight pins as data lines. For this reason, 24-pin packages are often used. Since price is related to package size, a RAM of this type is often more expensive than a RAM that uses a smaller package.

A more popular scheme is to arrange the 1024 memory cells into 256 four-bit words. With this arrangement, only four data pins are required. Since the microprocessor works with 8-bit words, two of these RAMs must be used to form a 256 by 8-bit memory. As before, four packages are required to form the 512-byte memory. However, the four packages tend to be smaller and probably less expensive.

Another popular arrangement is the 1024 by 1-bit RAM. This scheme uses only one data line per package. Of course, eight of these packages must be used to form 8-bit bytes. Also, a problem arises if we wish to have a memory smaller than 1024 by 8.

The Static Ram Storage Cell

The basic storage cell for an MOS type static RAM is shown in Figure 7-11. Keep in mind that this cell stores a single bit of data. There may be 1024 of these along with address decoders and bus drivers in a single IC.

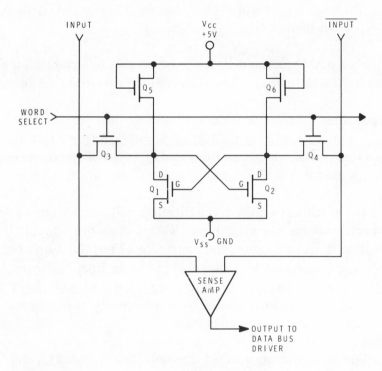

Figure 7-11
The static RAM storage cell.

The storage cell itself consists of the six MOS transistors. In keeping with current convention, the simplified symbol for the MOS transistor is used. Assume that these are N-channel enhancement type MOSFETs. Recall that an enhancement type MOSFET is normally off or non-conducting. However, since these are N-channel devices, they can be made to conduct by placing a positive voltage on the gate terminal. That is, when the gate is near ground potential, the transistor is off and represents a very high impedance. But, when the gate is high (near $+V_{cc}$), the transistor conducts and has a much lower impedance. If you keep these points in mind, the operation of the cell is easy to understand.

Transistors Q_1 and Q_2 are cross coupled so that they form a bistable latch or flip-flop. The bit of data is stored in this latch. Q_5 and Q_6 act as load resistors for Q_1 and Q_2 respectively. MOSFETs are used instead of physical resistors because they take up less chip space. Q_3 and Q_4 act as switches which connect input data to the latch during write operations. Also, they connect the data in the latch to the output sense amplifier during read operations. The word select line is connected to the gates of Q_3 and Q_4. A logic 1 on the word select line will turn Q_3 and Q_4 on. A logic 0 will keep them turned off.

Since this is a RAM storage cell, we must be able to write into it and to read from it. The following discussion will show how we write into it.

Write Operation. Before writing a bit of data into the cell, the discussion will first define what constitutes a 1 and 0. Assume that the latch contains a binary 1 when Q_2 conducts and Q_1 is cut off. And, of course, it contains a binary 0 when Q_1 conducts and Q_2 is cut off.

When power is initially applied, the flip-flop will latch in one condition or the other but we can never be sure of which. We write data into the cell by controlling the input, $\overline{\text{input}}$, and word select lines. To store a binary 1, we place a logic 1 (a positive voltage) at the input line. The $\overline{\text{input}}$ line is always the opposite state of the input line, so it will go to logic 0 (≈ 0 volts). The binary 1 is now stored by momentarily applying a logic 1 (positive pulse) to the word select line.

A positive pulse on the word select line will turn switches Q_3 and Q_4 on. Thus, the positive voltage on the input line is applied through Q_3 to the gate of Q_2. This forces Q_2 to conduct. When Q_2 conducts, its drain voltage falls to a low value. This reduced voltage is felt on the gate of Q_1, cutting Q_1 off. When Q_1 cuts off, its drain voltage goes high. This increased voltage is felt on the gate of Q_2, holding Q_2 in the on state.

When the word select line returns to logic 0, Q_3 and Q_4 cut off. However, the conduction of Q_2 keeps Q_1 cut off and the high drain voltage of Q_1 keeps Q_2 conducting. Thus, the binary 1 is latched in the flip-flop. It will remain there until power is removed or until a binary 0 is deliberately written in.

We can later write in a 0 if we like by applying a logic 0 to the input, a logic 1 to $\overline{\text{input}}$ and then pulsing the word select line. When the word select line goes high, Q_4 conducts, applying the logic 1 from $\overline{\text{input}}$ to the gate of Q_1. This tends to bring Q_1 out of cutoff. At the same time, Q_3 conducts, applying the logic 0 from the input to the gate of Q_2. This tends to cut off Q_2. As you can see, the flip-flop latches in the opposite state. This represents a binary 0.

The sense amplifier and output line (shown at the bottom) are disabled during this period by the read/write line (not shown).

Read Operation. The input and $\overline{\text{input}}$ lines are 3-state lines that are enabled or disabled by the read/write line. When the read/write line (not shown) is high, the input and $\overline{\text{input}}$ lines are effectively disconnected. During this period, we can read data from the storage cell by pulsing the word select line. Assume that the cell is presently storing a logic 1. This means that Q_1 is cut off and that Q_2 is conducting. Consequently Q_1's drain voltage is high (logic 1) while Q_2's drain voltage is low. When the word select line swings high, Q_3 conducts, connecting the high voltage at the drain of Q_1 to the left input of the sense amplifier. At the same time, Q_4 conducts, connecting the low voltage at the drain of Q_2 to the right input of the sense amplifier. The sense amplifier interprets this as a logic 1 condition and sets the output line accordingly.

If the flip-flop contains a logic 0 when the word select pulse occurs, the right input of the sense amplifier receives the higher voltage while the left input receives the lower. The sense amplifier interprets this as a logic 0.

A 128-Word by 8-Bit Ram

Because a storage cell can store only one bit of information, large numbers of these cells are required to form useful memory sizes. Figure 7-12 shows how 1024 cells can be arranged to form a 128-word by 8-bit RAM. Each of the squares represents one of the 6-transistor cells just discussed.

The word select lines are shown entering on the left. While only four are shown, there would actually be 128 of these lines—one for each word. Notice that word select line 00 connects to each of eight storage cells across the top of the figure. In an actual system, these eight storage cells might make up the 8-bit byte we call memory location 0000_{16}.

The input lines are shown at the top of the diagram. For simplicity, only four of the eight lines are shown. Notice that each input line is inverted so that complement inputs can be applied to each cell. Although the details are not shown, both the input and $\overline{\text{input}}$ lines are 3-state lines so that they are effectively disconnected except during a write operation.

The output lines are shown at the bottom of the diagram. These lines are disabled during a write operation but they are enabled during a read operation. One sense amplifier is required for each output line.

Keep in mind that Figure 7-12 does not show the complete RAM. It merely shows the memory storage matrix and the sense amplifiers. Some additional circuits are required to turn this into a working RAM. One of these is an address decoder.

The memory array is arranged as 128 bytes. An address decoder is required that can select any of these 128, 8-bit storage locations. Thus, a 1 of 128 decoder is required. The input to the decoder is the seven address lines from the MPU. Recall that seven bits can specify 128 different addresses.

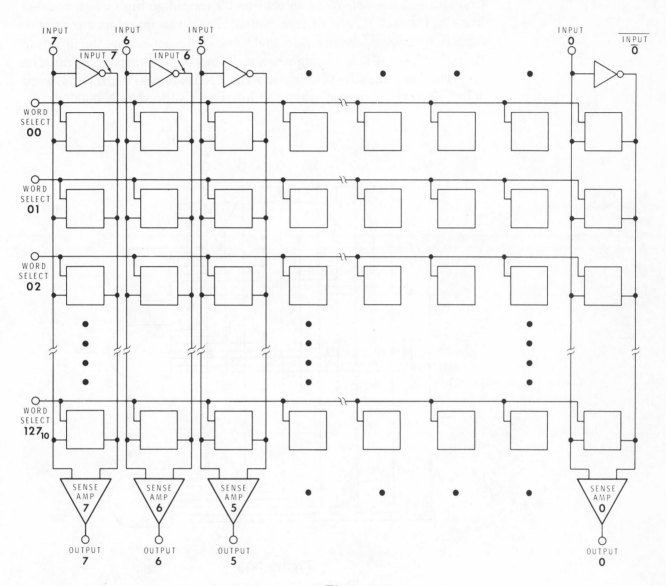

Figure 7-12
Here 1024 storage cells are arranged to
form a 128-byte by 8-bit RAM.

The address decoder is made up of 128 7-input AND gates. A simplified diagram is shown in Figure 7-13. Here, only three gates are shown — the first two and the last. Word select line 00 should go high when address lines A_0 through A_6 are all low. Notice that seven inverters are used to form $\overline{A_0}$ through $\overline{A_6}$. Notice also, that these complements are the inputs to the top AND gate. If A_0 through A_6 are all low, then $\overline{A_0}$ through $\overline{A_6}$ must be all high. Consequently, the output of the AND gate goes high. Thus, word select line 00 is selected when the low order address is 0000000_2.

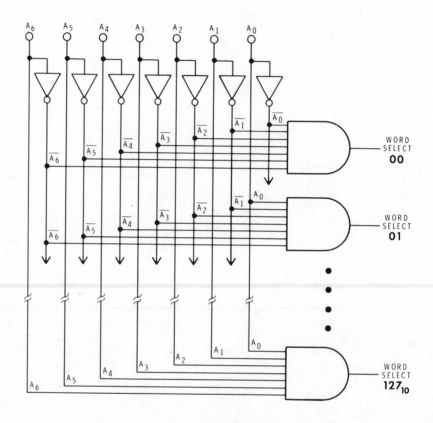

Figure 7-13
The 1 of 128 address decoder.

The 01 select line is activated when the address is 0000001_2. The next 125_{10} gates are not shown. Word select line 127_{10} is selected when A_0 through A_6 are all high. Thus, it is activated when the address is 1111111_2.

Most RAMs do not have separate input and output lines. Instead they have data lines which can serve either as inputs or outputs. This is possible because the MPU cannot read and write data simultaneously.

Figure 7-14 shows a simplified arrangement. The data lines are shown on the left. The 3-state input buffers are enabled by a high signal on the WRITE line. This line is controlled by the R/$\overline{\text{W}}$ signal and the chip enable (CE) signal. As you will see, the WRITE line is high when the MPU is writing data into memory. This enables the input buffers and allows data to be written into the selected address. The output buffers are disabled during this period by the low signal on the READ line.

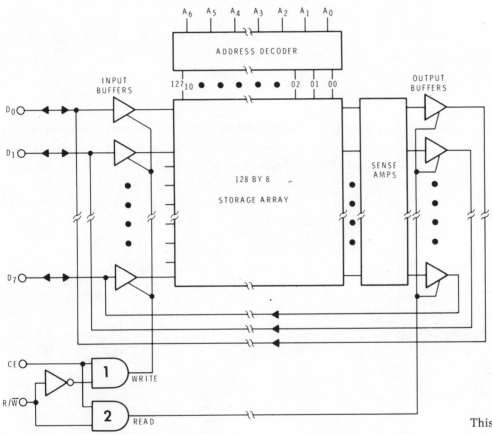

Figure 7-14

This RAM has bi-directional data lines.

When data is to be read from the RAM, the READ line is switched high and the WRITE line is switched low. This disables the input buffers and enables the output buffers. Thus, the data at the selected address is read out and placed on the data bus.

As Figure 7-14 illustrates, the READ and WRITE signals are controlled by the chip enable (CE) signal and the R/$\overline{\text{W}}$ line. The CE input line is switched high when this particular memory chip is selected. If this line is low, gates 1 and 2 are disabled. This causes both the READ and WRITE signals to go low, disabling both the input and output buffers. In effect, it disconnects this chip from the data bus.

However, when CE is high, the $R/\overline{W}$ line controls the READ and WRITE signals. This $R/\overline{W}$ line is connected to the $R/\overline{W}$ line of the MPU. Recall that the $R/\overline{W}$ line is low when the MPU is writing data into RAM, and high when the MPU is reading from RAM. When $R/\overline{W}$ is high, the output of gate 2 goes high, enabling the output buffers. The output of gate 1 is held low, disabling the input buffers. This places the RAM in the read mode.

When $R/\overline{W}$ goes low, the output of gate 1 goes high and the output of gate 2 goes low. This places the RAM in the write mode.

Some RAMs have a single chip enable line. In many RAMs, the chip enable line is labeled $\overline{CE}$, meaning that the chip is selected when the enable line is low. Some RAMs have several chip enable (CE) or chip select (CS) lines.

Figure 7-15 shows a 128 by 8 RAM that is designed to be used with the 6800 MPU. As shown in the simplified block diagram, this RAM has six chip select lines. The large number of chip selects allows this RAM to be used with little or no external address decoding. As shown in the pin assignment diagram, a 24-pin package is required. This RAM is called the 6810. Data sheets on this device are included in Appendix B of this course.

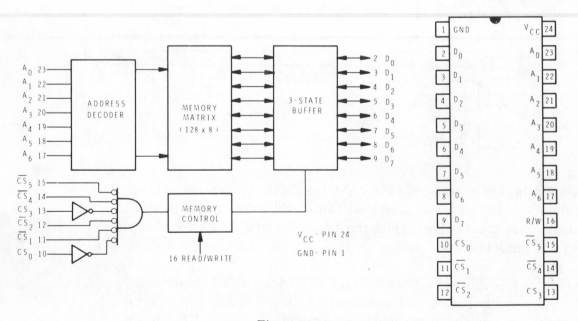

Figure 7-15
The 6810 is a 128-byte by 8-bit RAM.

A 256 by 4-Bit Ram

Figure 7-16 shows the block diagram of a popular 256 by 4-bit static RAM. In 8-bit systems, two of these would be required to form a 256_{10} byte memory. Like the 128_{10} by 8 RAM, this circuit has 1024_{10} storage cells. To simplify the address decoders, the cells are arranged in 32 rows of 32 cells each. The 32 cells in each row are further divided into 8 columns of 4 bits each. Thus, the array consists of 32 rows by 8 columns by 4 bits (or 256 by 4 bits).

Two address decoders are used. The row select decoder is a 1-of-32 decoder which chooses the row. Five address lines (A_0 through A_4) are used to specify the proper row.

A 1-of-8 column decoder is used to select the proper column. Three address lines (A_5 through A_7) are used to specify the proper column. The selected 4-bit word is at the point where the row and column lines intersect.

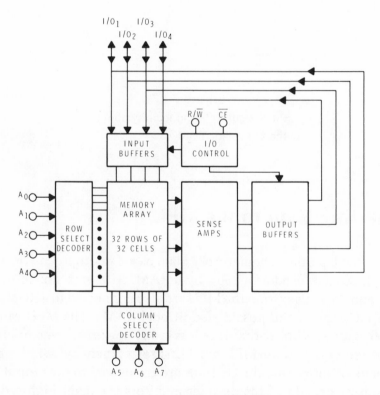

Figure 7-16
Block Diagram of a 256 by 4 RAM.

In this particular IC, the data lines are called I/O lines. The R/$\overline{W}$ line determines whether the IC is in the read or write mode. The $\overline{CE}$ line determines if this particular IC has been selected. If you count the pins shown and add one for V_{cc} and another for ground, you will see that a 16-pin package is required. Figure 7-17 shows the pin assignments and logic diagram of the popular 2112 static RAM. It has the same general arrangement as that shown in the block diagram.

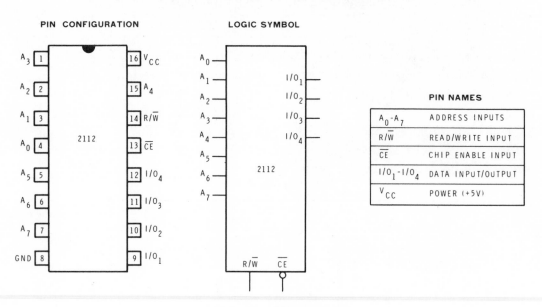

Figure 7-17

Pin assignments and logic symbol for the 2112 static RAM.

Connecting Ram to the MPU

Figure 7-18 is a partial schematic of a 6800 based microprocessor system. Two 2112 IC's are used as a 256_{10}-by-8 RAM. Although not shown, the address and data buses from the MPU are also connected to a ROM, input and output circuits, and possibly additional RAMs. The MPU can communicate with only one of these devices at any one time. To communicate with the two 2112 ICs, the MPU must first select them by switching their $\overline{CE}$ lines low. Notice that the $\overline{CE}$ lines are connected to the output of the RAM address decoder. This decoder monitors the eight high-order address lines. When the address of the RAM appears on these lines, the two 2112 chips are enabled.

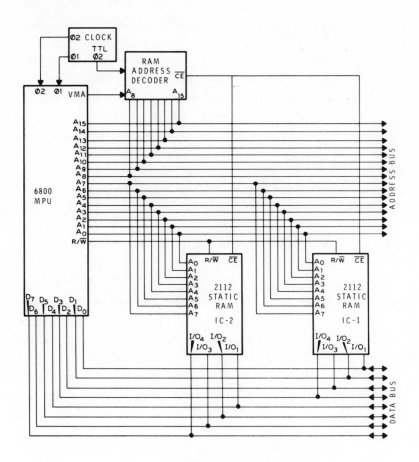

Figure 7-18

Partial schematic of a 6800 based microprocessor using two 2112 static RAMs.

The two 2112 IC's make up a 256 by 8-bit RAM. IC1 connects to the four least significant bits of the data bus (D_0 through D_3), while IC2 connects to the four most significant bits. Thus, when a byte of data is stored in the RAM, the four LSB's go in IC1, while the four MSB's go in IC2. This is possible because the two IC's are enabled at the same time. Notice that the address, $\overline{CE}$, and R/$\overline{W}$ lines of the two ICs are tied together.

The address lines of the IC's monitor the A_0 through A_7 lines from the MPU. Once the chips are enabled, any one of the 256 memory locations can be selected by placing the proper address on the lower eight address lines.

Address Decoding

The 256_{10}-byte RAM must be assigned some starting address. In 6800-based systems, a common practice is to assign RAM the lowest addresses. Thus, a 256_{10}-byte RAM would be given address 0000_{16} through $00FF_{16}$. In binary, these are addresses 0000 0000 0000 0000$_2$ through 0000 0000 1111 1111$_2$. Notice that the eight LSB's can specify any one of the 256_{10} memory locations. However, it is the upper eight bits that specify that the starting address is at the low end of memory. That is, the RAM must be enabled when the upper eight bits of the address bus are 0000 0000.

In Figure 7-18, the RAM address decoder monitors the upper eight bits of the address bus. When this decoder finds that the upper eight bits are all zeros, it switches the $\overline{CE}$ line low, enabling the RAM. However, notice that VMA and the $\emptyset2$ clock signals are also applied to the decoder. Recall that VMA is 1 when the address is valid. Thus, the decoder must also monitor the VMA line, since the RAM should not be enabled unless the address is valid. Recall also that the MPU must receive and transmit data only while the $\emptyset2$ clock is at logic 1. Thus, the decoder also monitors the $\emptyset2$ clock. If the high-order address lines are all zeros, the VMA line is high, and the $\emptyset2$ clock is high, the RAM will be enabled.

The address decoder can be any type of logic circuit that meets the above requirements. A typical circuit is shown in Figure 7-19. If you trace through the various logic levels, you will see that $\overline{CE}$ is low only when A_8 through A_{15} are low and VMA and $\emptyset2$ are high. NAND gate 1 produces a low at its output when VMA and $\emptyset2$ are high. The other inputs to NOR gate 2 and the inputs to NOR gates 3 and 4 are low when the high-order address is 0000 0000$_2$. The three NOR gates produce high outputs. Thus, the inputs to NAND gate 5 are all high. This forces the output of gate 5 low. As you can see, this circuit fulfills the requirements of the address decoder.

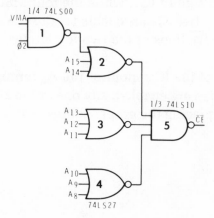

Figure 7-19

Address decoder using
discrete logic gates.

A memory location in the RAM shown in Figure 7-18 is selected by all 16 address lines. The low-order address lines connect directly to the RAM IC's, while the high-order lines connect to the RAM address decoder. Thus, each memory location in RAM has only one address. The addresses are said to be *fully decoded*.

We can save some decoding logic by only *partially decoding* the address. Figure 7-20 shows an address decoder that monitors only two of the address lines (A_{14} and A_{15}). If you trace the logic levels through, you will see that $\overline{CE}$ is low any time that A_{14} and A_{15} are low and VMA and $\emptyset 2$ are high. A_{14} and A_{15} will be low for any address at or below $3FFF_{16}$. If the $\overline{CE}$ line is used to enable a RAM that has fewer than $3FFF_{16}$ bytes, some of the addresses will be duplicated. To illustrate this point, assume that we replace the address decoder shown in Figure 7-18 with the circuit shown in Figure 7-20. Memory location 0000_{16} can be selected by placing address 0000_{16} on the address bus. However, location 0000_{16} is also selected when 0900_{16} is placed on the address bus. The reason for this is that the RAM is enabled because A_{14} and A_{15} are low. And, the lowest address in the RAM is read out because A_0 through A_7 are low. Actually, there are dozens of addresses that will select any given location. For example, addresses $3F00_{16}$, 2700_{16}, $1C00_{16}$, and many others will all select memory location 0000_{16}. This is the price that must be paid for saving a few gates in the address decoder.

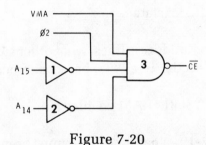

Figure 7-20
We can save gates by only partially decoding the address.

In practice, this does not actually cause many problems. All we have done is sacrifice the lower $16,384_{10}$ addresses to 256_{10} bytes of RAM. However, this still leaves three-fourths of the 65 K of addresses untouched. In most cases, this leaves more than enough addresses for I/O devices, ROMs, etc.

The fact that a given byte of data appears at several addresses is also no problem as long as we remember this limitation in our programming. Partial decoding schemes are frequently used because they save decoding logic.

Self-Test Review

15. List three common arrangements for a 1024-bit static RAM.

16. Using 256 by 4-bit static RAMs, what is the smallest 8-bit RAM possible?

17. What is the advantage of using two 256 by 4-bit RAMs to form 256 by 8-bit memory rather than using two 128 by 8-bit RAMs.

18. How many bits of data can be stored in the circuit shown in Figure 7-11?

19. Explain how data is written into this circuit.

20. Explain how data is read from this circuit.

21. Refer to Figure 7-13. Which address lines would connect to the input of the AND gate that drives word select line 02?

22. Refer to Figure 7-14. What is the state of the input and output buffers if CE is low?

23. When CE is high and R/$\overline{\text{W}}$ is low, the circuit shown in Figure 7-14 is in the _____ state.

24. In addition to some address lines, what other signals are connected to an address decoder in a 6800-based microcomputer system?

25. How is the 2112 static RAM enabled?

26. Refer to Figure 7-19. What conditions must be met before $\overline{\text{CE}}$ will go low?

27. What is the advantage and disadvantage of only partially decoding an address?

28. When each byte of memory has one and only one address, the memory is said to be _____ decoded.

Answers

15.   The most common arrangements for a 1024-bit static RAM are:

                1024 by 1-bit
                256 by 4-bits
                128 by 8-bits

16.   256 by 8-bits.

17.   Because the 128 by 8-bit RAM requires 8 data lines, it uses a larger and usually more expensive package.

18.   Only one at a time.

19.   The input data bit sets the INPUT and $\overline{\text{INPUT}}$ lines to the proper complementary states, then the word select line is pulsed high. This turns Q_3 and Q_4 on connecting the inputs to the flip-flop. This sets or resets the flip-flop to the proper state.

20.   The two input lines are tri-stated. The word select line is pulsed high turning on Q_3 and Q_4. This connects the outputs of the flip-flop to the sense amplifier. In turn, the sense amplifier sets the data line to the proper state.

21. $\overline{A_0}$, A_1, $\overline{A_2}$, $\overline{A_3}$, $\overline{A_4}$, $\overline{A_5}$, and $\overline{A_6}$.

22.   Both the input and output buffers are disabled.

23.   Write.

24.   The VMA line and the $\emptyset2$ clock signal.

25.   The 2112 static RAM is enabled by applying a logic 0 to the $\overline{\text{CE}}$ line.

26.   VMA and $\emptyset2$ must be high. At the same time, address lines A_8 through A_{15} must be low.

27.   The advantage is that generally fewer logic gates are required. The disadvantages are that it wastes addresses and that a given byte of data may be accessed at several different addresses.

28.   Fully.

INTERFACING WITH DISPLAYS

One of the most popular output devices used with the microprocessor is the 7-segment LED display. It can be used to display the decimal digits 0 through 9 or the hexadecimal digits 0 through F. It can also display many special characters. Its low cost and flexibility make the 7-segment LED display ideal for low cost microprocessor based systems.

The 7-Segment Display

The 7-segment display consists of seven LED's arranged in the pattern shown in Figure 7-21A. An eighth LED is generally included to act as a decimal point. By lighting the LED's in different combinations, 256_{10} patterns are possible. These range from a blank display (all segments off) to the digit 8 with a decimal point (all segments on). Figure 7-21B shows some of the patterns that can be formed.

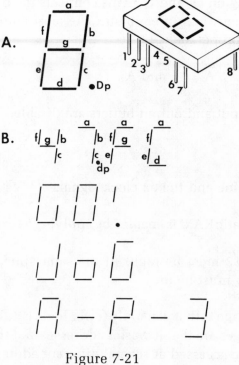

Figure 7-21

The 7-segment display can be used to form many numerals, letters, and symbols.

Two types of 7-segment displays are popular. One is called the common-anode type. As shown in Figure 7-22A, the anodes of the eight light-emitting diodes are tied together and connected to $+V_{cc}$. A diode is forward biased (turned on) by applying a low logic level to its cathode. An external series resistor is required to reduce the current to an acceptable level.

The other type is called the common-cathode type. As Figure 7-22B illustrates, the cathodes are tied together and connected to ground. In this case, a diode is forward biased (turned on) by applying a high logic level to its anode.

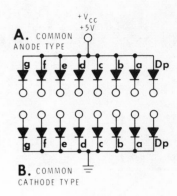

Figure 7-22

Two types of 7-segment displays.

Driving the 7-Segment Display

A number of IC's are especially designed to drive the 7-segment display. A typical example is the 7447 shown in Figure 7-23A. This is a BCD-to-7-segment decoder-driver. It receives a 4-bit binary number at inputs A, B, C, and D. It provides the proper patterns at outputs a through g to form the numerals 0 through 9 and six special characters as shown in Figure 7-23B.

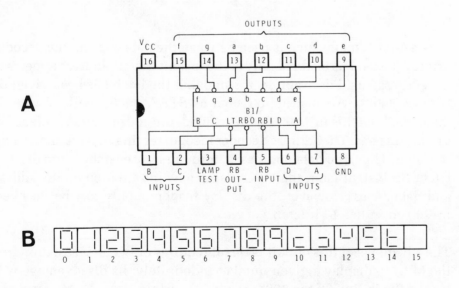

Figure 7-23

The 7447 seven segment decoder-driver and its resultant displays.

When used with a microprocessor, the MPU does not drive the decoder-driver directly. Recall that the information on the data bus is there for a microsecond or less. Since the 7447 has no latch capability, a separate latch must be used to store the data at the right instant. Figure 7-24 shows a representative circuit.

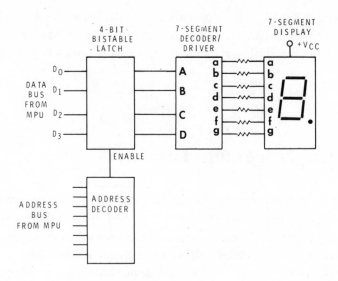

Figure 7-24
Using the decoder/driver.

Here a 4-bit bistable latch is used between the data bus and the decoder-driver. The latch is enabled only at the instant that its address appears on the address bus. For example, assume that the latch has been given the address 8000_{16}. An instruction such as STAA 8000_{16} will activate the display. When this instruction is executed, the address 8000 is placed on the address bus. The address decoder recognizes this address and enables the latch. Thus, the data on lines D_0 through D_3 are latched into the 4-bit latch. An instant later, the MPU places new information on the address and data buses. However, the display responds only to what has been preserved in the 4-bit latch.

The advantage of this circuit is that it requires only one instruction from the MPU to display a given number indefinitely. Its disadvantage is its lack of flexibility. Of the 256_{10} displays possible, only the 16_{10} provided by the decoder-driver can be used. Thus, this arrangement can display only those symbols shown in Figure 7-23B.

A more versatile way of driving a 7-segment display is shown in Figure 7-25. Here, a low current display is used so that the latch can drive the display directly. Notice that the BCD-to-7-segment decoder is eliminated. The seven segments of the display (and the decimal point) are now controlled directly by the eight bits of data on the data bus.

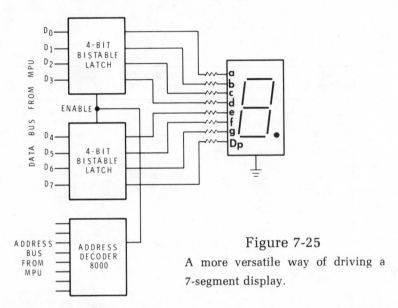

Figure 7-25

A more versatile way of driving a 7-segment display.

The display shown is a common-cathode type. Thus, a segment is turned on by applying a logic high to its input. Figure 7-26 shows the 8-bit pattern that is required to display the digit 1. Since this 8-bit pattern comes from the MPU, the microprocessor must do the decoding. This requires more MPU time and instructions but it greatly increases the versatility of the display. We can now use any of the 256_{10} possible displays by providing the proper 8-bit pattern.

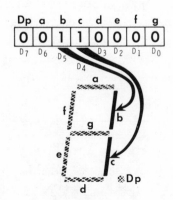

Figure 7-26

Each bit controls one segment of the display.

A display of this type is often used to display the hexadecimal digits 0 through F. The MPU must convert the binary numbers 0000 through 1111 into the proper 8-bit patterns to display the equivalent hexadecimal digit. The easiest way to do this is to use a "look-up" table. The 8-bit patterns are placed in 16_{10} consecutive memory locations. Assume that the starting address of the table is $FF96_{16}$ as shown in Figure 7-27.

HEX ADDRESS	HEX CONTENTS	MNEMONIC/ CONTENTS	COMMENTS
0010	97	STAA	Store the binary number at the
0011	16	16	variable offset.
0012	CE	LDX#	Load the index register
0013	FF	FF	with the starting address
0014	96	96	of the table.
0015	A6	LDAA,X	Load A indexed using the
0016	—	variable offset	variable offset
0017	B7	STAA	Store the 7-segment
0018	80	80	code at 8000_{16}.
0019	00	00	
.	.		
.	.		
.	.	D_p a b c d e f g	NEXT INSTRUCTION
FF96	7E	0 1 1 1 1 1 1 0	7-Segment pattern for 0
FF97	30	0 0 1 1 0 0 0 0	7-Segment pattern for 1
FF98	6D	0 1 1 0 1 1 0 1	7-Segment pattern for 2
FF99	79	0 1 1 1 1 0 0 1	7-Segment pattern for 3
FF9A	33	0 0 1 1 0 0 1 1	7-Segment pattern for 4
FF9B	5B	0 1 0 1 1 0 1 1	7-Segment pattern for 5
FF9C	5F	0 1 0 1 1 1 1 1	7-Segment pattern for 6
FF9D	70	0 1 1 1 0 0 0 0	7-Segment pattern for 7
FF9E	7F	0 1 1 1 1 1 1 1	7-Segment pattern for 8
FF9F	7B	0 1 1 1 1 0 1 1	7-Segment pattern for 9
FFA0	77	0 1 1 1 0 1 1 1	7-Segment pattern for A
FFA1	1F	0 0 0 1 1 1 1 1	7-Segment pattern for B
FFA2	4E	0 1 0 0 1 1 1 0	7-Segment pattern for C
FFA3	3D	0 0 1 1 1 1 0 1	7-Segment pattern for D
FFA4	4F	0 1 0 0 1 1 1 1	7-Segment pattern for E
FFA5	47	0 1 0 0 0 1 1 1	7-Segment pattern for F

Figure 7-27

Program segment and table for converting binary to 7-segment display format.

A program segment is required that will store the proper 7-segment pattern in the latches shown in Figure 7-25. Assume that the address of the latches is 8000_{16}. The program segment might look like that shown in Figure 7-27.

The program assumes that the binary number we wish to convert to its 7-segment hexadecimal equivalent is in accumulator A. The first instruction stores the binary number at address 0016_{16}. Assume that the number is $0000\ 0110_2$ or 06_{16}. Thus, this number is stored at address 0016_{16}. Notice that this number becomes the offset for the LDAA, X instruction at address 0015_{16}.

The second instruction loads the starting address of the table ($FF96_{16}$) into the index register. Then, accumulator A is loaded using indexed addressing. The offset, which is now 06_{16}, (by virtue of the first instruction) is added to the contents of the index register ($FF96_{16}$) to form the address of the operand ($FF9C_{16}$). Thus, the number at address $FF9C_{16}$ is loaded into accumulator A. This number is $5F_{16}$, which is the proper 7-segment code to form the numeral 6.

Finally, this number is stored at address 8000_{16}. This is the address of the latches that drive the display. Therefore, if 06_{16} is in accumulator A when this program segment is executed, the digit 6 will be displayed. Also, if 02_{16} is initially in accumulator A, the program segment will cause a 2 to be displayed.

Using this arrangement, two 4-bit latches are required for each display. There are eight bit latches available in a single IC. However, most come in 20 to 24-pin packages, which are relatively expensive. There is one type of 8-bit latch that comes in a 16-pin package. This device will be discussed next.

Using an Addressable Latch

Figure 7-28 shows the pin outs and schematic for the 8-bit addressable latch. It can store an 8-bit byte and drive a low current display. Its most striking characteristic is that data is entered into the device in serial form. That is, it has a single data input (pin 13). Thus, the eight bits of data must be entered into the device one bit at a time. This explains how the IC can get by with only 16 pins.

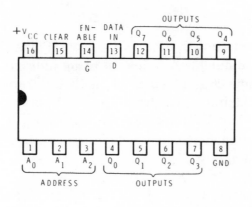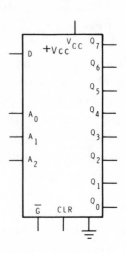

Figure 7-28

Pin outs and schematic diagram of the
74LS259 latch.

The addressable latch has an enable pin that allows it to be selected by an address decoder. A low at pin 14 will enable the latch and allow it to receive data. Actually, there are eight latches on the IC. They are numbered 0 through 7. The particular latch to which the input data bit is routed is determined by the 3-bit address at pins A_0, A_1, and A_2. Figure 7-29 shows which latch is selected for each address.

ADDRESS	INPUTS		LATCH SELECTED
A_2	A_1	A_0	
0	0	0	0
0	0	1	1
0	1	0	2
0	1	1	3
1	0	0	4
1	0	1	5
1	1	0	6
1	1	1	7

Figure 7-29.

Latch selection table.

How can this latch be used by the microprocessor to drive a display? Figure 7-30 shows a representative circuit. The three address lines on the addressable latch are connected to their corresponding lines on the address bus. The remaining lines of the address bus are connected to the address decoder. Assume that the address decoder is arranged so that the addressable latch is enabled for addresses $C160_{16}$ through $C167_{16}$. That is, the addressable latch is enabled for eight different addresses. Address $C160_{16}$ selects latch 0 of the addressable latch; $C161_{16}$ selects latch 1; and so forth.

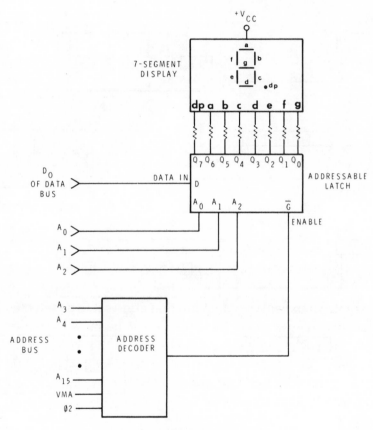

Figure 7-30.
Using the addressable latch to drive a
7-segment display.

The only data line connected to the addressable latch is D_0 from the microprocessor's data bus. The outputs of the eight latches (Q_0 through Q_7) drive the seven segments and the decimal point of the display.

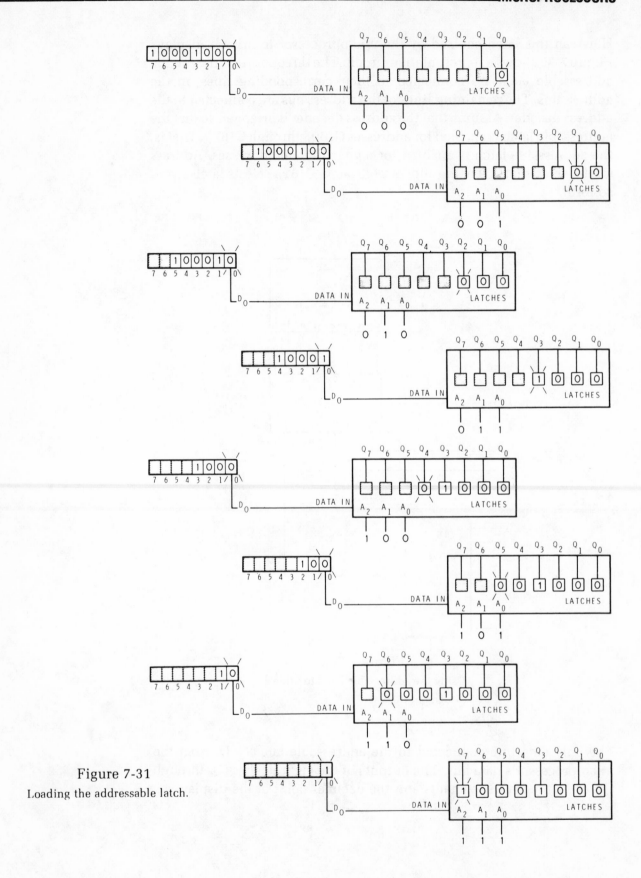

Figure 7-31
Loading the addressable latch.

While this arrangement results in an inexpensive circuit, it places an extra burden on the MPU. As in the previous example, the microprocessor must make the binary to 7-segment conversion. But in this case, it must also convert the parallel 7-segment code into a serial bit stream that is acceptable to the addressable latch. You are already familiar with the solution to the first problem. Now, the discussion will show how the MPU can convert parallel data to serial data.

The procedure is illustrated in Figure 7-31. The register on the left represents one of the accumulators. It contains the proper 7-segment code for displaying the letter A. This code must be transferred a bit at a time into the addressable latch shown on the right. Remember that the addressable latch actually contains eight latches and that the particular latch selected is determined by the 3-bit address at A_0 through A_2.

The first step is to store the contents of the accumulator at the basic latch address which is $C160_{16}$. If you convert this address to binary, you will find that address bits A_0, A_1, A_2 are all 0's. Since these lines connect to pins A_0, A_1, and A_2 on the addressable latch, latch 0 is selected as shown. Notice that the only data line used is D_0. Thus, the 0 in bit 0 of the accumulator is stored in latch 0.

Next, the contents of the accumulator are shifted to the right so that the next bit is available at D_0. The address of the latch is incremented by 1 and a store instruction is executed. Thus, the second bit is stored in latch 1.

This procedure continues as shown until all eight bits have been shifted from the accumulator to the addressable latch. Of course, a short program segment is required to control this operation. A typical program is shown in Figure 7-32. Step through the program and verify that it works. Remember that the 7-segment code must be in accumulator A before running the program.

The ET-3400 Microprocessor Trainer uses a method similar to this for driving the displays. The program shown in Figure 7-32 will light the left-most display. However, in the ET-3400 Microprocessor Trainer, the D_0 data line is inverted. Therefore, a 1 must be used in the accumulator for each segment that you wish to light. For example, the letter A is formed by placing 01110111_2 in accumulator A before you run the program.

HEX ADDRESS	HEX CONTENTS	MNEMONICS/ CONTENTS	COMMENTS
0010	CE	LDX #	Load the index register immediate
0011	C1	C1	with the address of the latch.
0012	60	60	
0013	A7	STAA, X	Store accumulator A in the latch.
0014	00	00	
0015	46	RORA	Get ready to send next bit.
0016	08	INX	Set up next address.
0017	8C	CPX#	Compare with final address.
0018	C1	C1	
0019	67	67	
001A	26	BNE	If a match does not occur, branch back
001B	F7	F7	to here.
001C	3E	Wait	Otherwise, wait.

Figure 7-32

A simple program for loading the addressable latch.

Multiplexing Displays

The previous approaches required one or more latches for each display. There is a method by which we can drive up to eight displays using only two 8-bit latches. However, it requires some additional components and a lot of microprocessor time.

A typical circuit is shown in Figure 7-33. Eight common cathode displays are used in this example. The display cannot light unless its associated transistor is turned on. The transistors are controlled by the contents of the digit select latch. In turn, this latch is loaded by the MPU. Q_1 is turned on by placing 1 in bit 7 of the digit latch; Q_2 is turned on by placing 1 in bit 6; etc. Generally, only one transistor at a time is turned on. A common procedure is to store 10000000 in the digit select latch and rotate the contents so that the 1 appears at each bit in turn.

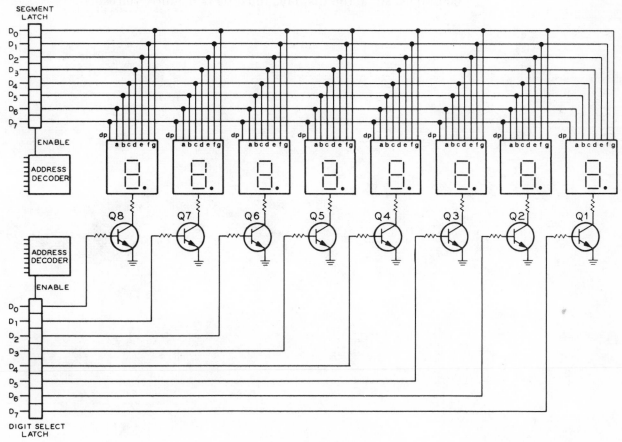

Figure 7-33
Multiplexing Displays.

The individual segments of each display are turned on by the segment latch. For example, to turn on the decimal point in the right-most display, the segment latch must contain a 1 at bit 7. At the same time, the digit select latch must turn on Q_1.

To display an 8-digit message, the procedure looks like this: Load the digit select latch with 10000000_2. Load the segment latch with the 7-segment information for the right-most display. This causes the right-most display to show the first digit. After a brief delay, the contents of the digit display latch are changed to 01000000. This turns on the second display. Next the contents of the segment latch must be changed to the 7-segment code for the second display. This procedure continues until all eight displays are lit. Because no two displays are lit simultaneously, the displays must be refreshed many times each second to give the illusion of a constant steady display.

The advantage of this technique is that a minimum amount of hardware is required. However, it requires more MPU time than the previous techniques since the displays must be constantly refreshed.

Self-Test Review

29. How do we turn on a common-anode type 7-segment display?

30. What is a disadvantage of using a decoder-driver, such as the 7447, to drive a display?

31. Why is a latch required between the MPU and the display?

32. When the latch drives the display directly, what performs the decoding function?

33. List four instructions that could be used to output data to a display.

34. Using the arrangement shown in Figure 7-26, what 8-bit code is required to form the letter P?

35. Refer to the program shown in Figure 7-27. If the number in accumulator A is 08_{16} when this program segment is run, what binary number will be outputted to the display?

36. What is the purpose of the program shown in Figure 7-27?

37. Refer to Figure 7-30. What determines which of the latches the input data bit goes into?

38. The program shown in Figure 7-32 converts _____ data to _____ data.

39. Refer to Figure 7-33. What determines which character is displayed?

40. Refer to Figure 7-33. What determines the display on which the character appears?

Answers

29. A common-anode type display is turned on by applying logic 0 to the proper cathode.

30. The pattern is limited to those provided by the decoder.

31. Because the output data is stable for only an instant, a latch must be used to capture the data and hold it for the display.

32. The microprocessor.

33. Any of the store instructions could be used to output data to a display. These include: STAA, STAB, STX, and STS.

34. $0110\ 0111_2$.

35. $0111\ 1111_2$. This is the 7-segment pattern for the numeral 8.

36. The program converts binary numbers between 0000 and 1111 to a 7-segment code to form the appropriate hexadecimal numeral.

37. The 3-bit address at A_0 through A_2.

38. parallel, serial.

39. The number in the segment latch.

40. The number in the digit select latch.

The hardware experiments are included in the Student Workbook. Go to the Student Workbook and perform experiments 11 through 14. Some of these experiments are quite involved and you should not attempt more than one experiment per sitting.

Unit 8

INTERFACING — PART 2

INTRODUCTION

In this unit, you will continue your study of interfacing the microprocessor with other circuits. The emphasis will be on interfacing with switches and displays, which are the most common input and output devices.

You will also be introduced to a special type of support IC called the peripheral interface adapter. As you will see, this device can greatly simplify many interfacing problems.

As you complete this unit, you will perform several interfacing experiments. As with Unit 7, a basic knowledge of electronics in general and digital techniques in particular is required to gain full benefit from these experiments.

UNIT OBJECTIVES

When you have completed this unit you will be able to:

1.   Draw a diagram showing how mechanical switches can be connected to an MPU.

2.   Explain how the MPU can eliminate the effects of contact bounce.

3.   Explain the operation of a program that detects contact closure of switches, provides for debouncing, and decodes a simple keyboard.

4.   Draw a simplified block diagram of a PIA and explain the purpose of the output, control, and data direction register.

5.   Write a simple program that will configure the PIA in any desired input-output combination.

6.   Explain how the PIA can be used to drive displays and encode keyboards.

INTERFACING WITH SWITCHES

The most popular input device used with the microprocessor is the switch. The operator of microprocessor-based equipment usually communicates with the MPU by using keyboard switches. However, in completely automated systems, the equipment being controlled often communicates with the MPU by limit switches, pressure switches, etc. In this section, you will examine some techniques used in interfacing with switches.

Interfacing Requirements

When interfacing with a switch, or switches, four operations are involved. First, the MPU must select or address the proper switch bank. Second, it must detect contact closure. Third, it must provide for debouncing (unless this is accomplished by external hardware). Finally, it must decode the input. The following information describes each of these operations in more detail.

Selecting the Switch   Figure 8-1 shows a simple arrangement for connecting eight switches to the MPU. Three-state buffers are used to interface the switches with the data bus. The buffers are enabled by the output of the address decoder. This decoder can use any of the decoding schemes discussed earlier. Assume that the decoder responds to address $C003_{16}$. Until the decoder receives this address, the buffers are disabled. This effectively disconnects the switches from the data bus.

To find out if a switch is closed, the MPU must read in the data from this address. An easy way to do this is with the LDAA instruction. When the LDAA C003 instruction is executed, the address C003 goes out on the address bus. The decoder detects this address and enables the three-state buffer. Thus, for an instant, the switch bank is connected to the data bus. The data from the switch bank is loaded into accumulator A.

Detecting Contact Closure   If none of the switches are closed, all the data lines will be high because of pull-up resistors R_0 through R_7. Thus, the data entered into accumulator A will be FF_{16}. To test for a switch closure, the contents of accumulator A can be compared with FF_{16}. That is, a CMPA#FF instruction could be used. If this is followed by a BNE instruction, the MPU will branch if a key is depressed. Otherwise, it will not. For example, suppose S_0 is closed. When the accumulator is loaded from address $C003_{16}$, the D_0 line will be low. Thus, the number loaded into the accumulator will be FE_{16}. The CMPA instruction clears the zero flag since no match occurs. Therefore, the BNE instruction causes the branch to occur.

Debouncing the Switch Most mechanical switches produce contact bounce. When the switch is closed, the contacts do not make an immediately solid electrical or mechanical connection. Instead, they "bounce" open and closed for a brief period of time. Figure 8-2 illustrates this effect.

While contact bounce may only last for a few milliseconds, this is long enough for the MPU to interpret the bounce as repeated switch closures. To overcome this bounce problem, some switches use cross-coupled NAND gates that will immediately latch in one state so that all contact bounce is ignored. However, this requires additional circuitry.

In many applications, a better approach is to let the MPU itself do the debouncing. A simple scheme is to wait about ten milliseconds and then read in the data from the switch bank again. If the same indication occurs, then the MPU can be certain that the switch is closed. The switch can be checked as many times as is necessary to ensure that contact bounce is eliminated.

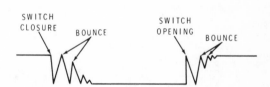

Figure 8-2
The effects of contact bounce.

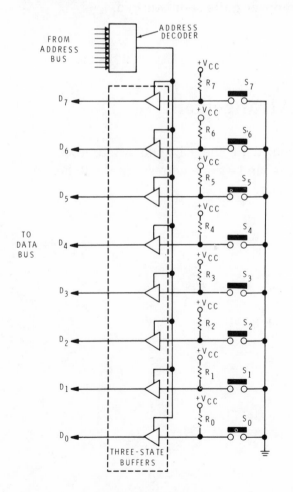

Figure 8-1
Interfacing a bank of switches to the MPU.

Decoding the Switches After the MPU determines that a switch has been closed, it must decide which switch it is. In most cases the switch closure represents a number. For example, the MPU should recognize an S_5 closure as the number 5. This, too, is easily accomplished by the proper subroutine.

Referring to Figure 8-1, you can see that each switch corresponds to one bit of the data line. When a switch is closed, the corresponding data line goes to 0. When loaded into the accumulator, the corresponding bit is also 0. The bit that is 0 can be detected by rotating the accumulator into the carry bit until the carry bit is cleared. By counting the number of rotations, the MPU can determine which switch is depressed.

In most applications, another job of the decoding procedure is to reject multiple switch closures. If two switches are closed simultaneously, the MPU should not accept data. If a second switch is closed before the first switch is released, the MPU may reject the data or accept only the first switch closure. By using a few extra programming steps, a very simple and inexpensive keyboard can appear quite sophisticated.

A Typical Keyboard Arrangement

The keyboard arrangement used with the ET-3400 Microprocessor Trainer is a good example of what can be done with simple switches. A simplified circuit is shown in Figure 8-3.

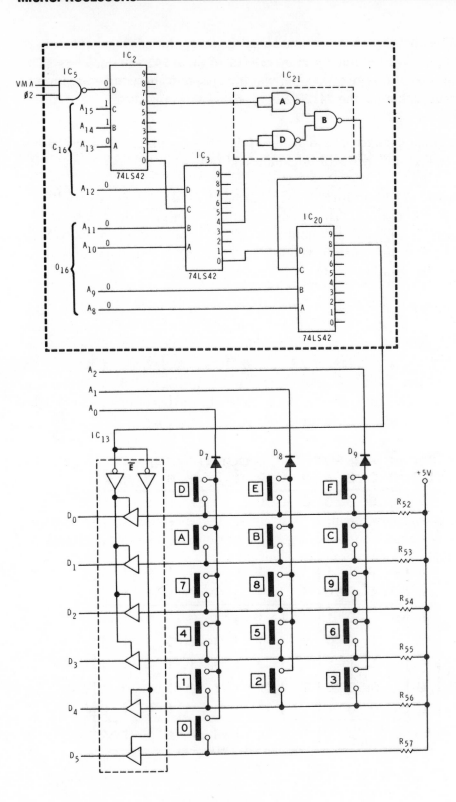

Figure 8-3
Keyboard arrangement of the ET-3400
Microprocessor Trainer.

The Circuit   The address decoder is shown in dotted lines at the top of the Figure. For the most part it consists of three 74LS42 decoders. (The operation of this type of decoder was discussed in an earlier experiment.) The truth table for the 74LS42 is repeated in Figure 8-4.

The address decoder is also used to select the 7-segment displays. However, in this unit, we will be concerned only with keyboard decoding.

The portion of the address decoder shown in Figure 8-3 monitors address lines A_8 through A_{15}. That is, it monitors the high order address. The keyboard is selected by enabling IC13. Normally, IC13 is in its high impedance state so that the keyboard is isolated from the data bus. IC13 is enabled by applying logic 0 to the enable line ($\overline{E}$).

The address decoder enables IC13 when the high order address is CO_{16}. With a high order address of CO_{16}, address lines A_{15} and A_{14} are at logic 1 while A_8 through A_{13} are at logic 0. Decoder IC2 is controlled by address lines A_{13}, A_{14}, A_{15}, and the VMA and $\phi2$ clock signal. When an instruction such as LDA C003 is executed, the inputs to IC2 will be as shown in Figure 8-3. The truth table for the decoder shows that output line 6 will be logic 0 while all other output lines will be logic 1.

DEC. NO.	D	C	B	A	0	1	2	3	4	5	6	7	8	9
0	0	0	0	0	0	1	1	1	1	1	1	1	1	1
1	0	0	0	1	1	0	1	1	1	1	1	1	1	1
2	0	0	1	0	1	1	0	1	1	1	1	1	1	1
3	0	0	1	1	1	1	1	0	1	1	1	1	1	1
4	0	1	0	0	1	1	1	1	0	1	1	1	1	1
5	0	1	0	1	1	1	1	1	1	0	1	1	1	1
6	0	1	1	0	1	1	1	1	1	1	0	1	1	1
7	0	1	1	1	1	1	1	1	1	1	1	0	1	1
8	1	0	0	0	1	1	1	1	1	1	1	1	0	1
9	1	0	0	1	1	1	1	1	1	1	1	1	1	0
>9	INVALID CODES				1	1	1	1	1	1	1	1	1	1

Figure 8-4
Truth table for the 74LS42 decoder.

The 1 at output 0 of IC2 is applied to IC3. Address lines A_{10} through A_{12} are also connected to IC3. With a high order address of CO, these lines will be at 0. With these inputs, the truth table shows that output line 4 of IC3 will be 0 while all other outputs will be 1. The 0 at output line 4 is inverted by IC21D. Simultaneously, the 0 at output 6 of IC2 is inverted by IC21A. These two signals are then NANDed together to form logic 0 at the output of IC21B. This 0 is applied to input C of IC20.

The other inputs to IC20 include a logic 1 from IC3, logic 0 from A_9, and logic 0 from A_8. The truth table shows that this will result in a logic 0 at output 8 of IC20. This logic 0 is applied to the enable input of IC13. This enables the three-state buffers and momentarily connects the keyboard to the data bus. Thus, the keyboard is momentarily connected to the data bus any time the high order address is CO_{16}.

The keyboard is divided into three columns. The center and right columns have five keys each while the left column has six keys. The RESET key is not shown since it is not addressed as the other keys are. The low order address determines which column of keys is selected. A_0 controls the left column and A_1 and A_2 control the center and right columns, respectively. A column is selected by choosing an address that will force the desired column line low, but will hold the unwanted column lines high. Address $C003_{16}$ fulfills these requirements for the right-hand column of keys. So do many other addresses, but consider this to be the address of that column. In the same way, the center column has an address of $C005_{16}$ and the left column has an address of $C006_{16}$.

Detecting and Encoding a Key Closure The monitor program in the ROM of the Trainer has a subroutine called ENCODE which starts at address $FDBB_{16}$. The purpose of this subroutine is to look over the keyboard, determine if a key has been depressed, and produce the proper hexadecimal value of the depressed key. The hexadecimal value is placed in accumulator A. Also, the carry flag will indicate whether or not a valid key entry has occurred. A valid entry is defined as one and only one key depressed. The C flag will be set if the entry was valid. It will be cleared for nonvalid entries or no entries at all.

The ENCODE subroutine is shown in Figure 8-5. The following explanation will refer to the instructions by the line numbers given on the left. Notice that the subroutine is written in assembly language.

The first instruction saves the original contents of accumulator B. As you will see later, the program normally comes here from another subroutine called INCH. When it does, B will hold a timing count that must not be lost.

LINE	ASSEMBLY CODE			COMMENTS
1	ENCODE	PSH B		Save contents of accumulator B.
2		LDA B	COL1	Load the right column into B.
3		LDA A	COL3	Load the left column into A.
4		ASL A		
5		ASL A		Get rid of "don't care" bits.
6		ASL A		
7		ROL B		Double precision shift left
8		ASL A		of accumulators A and B
9		ROL B		to get rid
10		ASL A		of "don't care" bits.
11		ROL B		
12		PSH B		Save contents of B.
13		LDA B	COL2	Load the center column into B.
14		AND B	#$1F	Mask off bits 5, 6, and 7.
15		ABA		Merge with A.
16		PUL B		Restore B.
17		COM A		After complementing the keyboard
18		COM B		pattern will be in A and B (1 = key closed).
19		STX	T0	Save contents of index register.
20		LDX	#HEXTAB-1	Point index register to table of hex values.
21		CBA		Which accumulator contains a 1?
22		BEQ	ENC3	Neither or both contain 1's (invalid entry).
23		BCC	ENC1	A contains a 1 so go to ENC1.
24		PSH A		B contains a 1 so
25		TBA		Swap the contents
26		PUL B		of A and B.
27		LDX	#HEXTAB+7	Point the index register to upper half of hex table.
28	ENC1	TST B		None of these keys should be closed.
29		BNE	ENC3	If they are, go to ENC3.
30	ENC2	INX		Otherwise, have the index register
31		ASLA		Scan up the table until it
32		BHI	ENC2	finds the proper hex value.
33		BEQ	ENC4	If only one key is depressed, entry is valid.
34	ENC3	CLC		Entry is not valid so clear C.
35	ENC4	LDA A	0,X	Load the hex value into accumulator A.
36		LDX	T0	Restore index register and
37		PUL B		accumulator B to their original values.
38		RTS		Return

Figure 8-5
ENCODE subroutine.

The next two instructions load A and B from the keyboard columns. After line 3, A and B will contain the data from the two outside keyboard columns. Figure 8-6A shows which keys are associated with which bits. The indicated bit will contain 0 if its associated key is depressed. Otherwise, it will contain a 1. The X's are shown in those bits that are not affected by the keys. The first step is to eliminate these "don't care" states. In accumulator A and the carry flag, this is done by shifting to the left. After line 6, the accumulators and carry flag will contain the keyboard patterns shown in Figure 8-6B.

Next A and B are shifted left together through the carry flag. Figure 8-6C shows the contents of these registers after line 11. The contents of B are then saved by pushing them into the stack. Accumulator B is now free to be loaded with the data from the center column of the keyboard. Bits 5, 6, and 7 are masked off leaving the registers as shown in Figure 8-6D. B is added to A so that the 0's in A are replaced with the states of keys 2, 5, 8, B, and E. When B is pulled from the stack (line 16), the registers will contain the keyboard pattern as shown in Figure 8-6E. Notice that each of the 16_{10} keys is represented by one of the bits in the accumulators. If no keys are depressed, all bits will be 1's. If a key is depressed, its corresponding bit will be 0.

In lines 17 and 18, the two accumulators are complemented. Thus, from this point on a depressed key is represented by a 1 while an open key is represented by a 0.

Assume that the D key is depressed. In this case, the accumulators will appear as shown in Figure 8-6F after line 18. In line 19, the contents of the index register are saved in a temporary location in RAM called TO. Next the index register is loaded with one less than the starting address of a hexadecimal table.

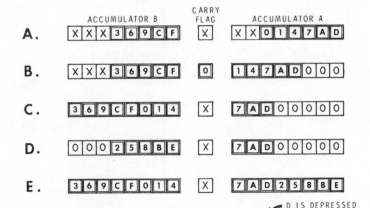

Figure 8-6
The keyboard bit pattern is placed in accumulators A and B.

The hexadecimal table is shown in Figure 8-7. Notice that the hex digits 00 through 0F are not in order in the table. However, compare the entries in the table to Figure 8-6E. The first eight entries in the table are in the same order as the keyboard pattern in accumulator A. The upper eight entries correspond to the key patterns in accumulator B. As you will see later, this is no accident.

Line 21 of the program compares the contents of accumulators A and B. With D depressed, the number in A will be larger. The result is that both the Z and C flags are cleared. The BEQ does not cause a branch because the Z flag is cleared. However, the BCC instruction does cause a branch because the C flag is cleared. Notice that the branch is to the point labelled ENC1 (line 28).

HEX ADDRESS	HEX CONTENTS	SYMBOLIC ADDRESS
FFA6	07	HEXTAB
FFA7	0A	
FFA8	0D	
FFA9	02	
FFAA	05	
FFAB	08	
FFAC	0B	
FFAD	0E	
FFAE	03	
FFAF	06	
FFB0	09	
FFB1	0C	
FFB2	0F	
FFB3	00	
FFB4	01	
FFB5	04	

Figure 8-7
The hexadecimal table (HEXTAB).

This part of the subroutine encodes the key closure and at the same time checks to see that no other keys are closed. The first step tests B. If the result is not zero, the MPU knows that a second key is closed and the entry is ignored by branching to ENC3. (The result of this will be shown later). Otherwise, the index register is incremented to the address of the first entry in the hex table, the contents of accumulator A is then shifted to the left, and the BHI instruction simultaneously checks both the C and Z flags. The branch is implemented if both C and Z are cleared. Both are cleared in this case so the program jumps back to ENC2 and the index register is incremented so that it points to the second entry in the table. Accumulator A is shifted left again. This places the 1 (that represents switch D being closed) into the MSB of the accumulator. C and Z are still cleared so the BHI instruction sends the program back to ENC2 again.

The index register is incremented again so that it now points to the third entry in the hex table. Notice that the third entry is OD_{16}. Thus, the index register is now pointing to the number that corresponds to the switch closure. Accumulator A is shifted left again so that the 1 (representing switch D) is placed in the carry flag. This sets the C flag and, consequently, the BHI instruction cannot cause a branch.

Because the BHI branch does not occur, the next instruction encountered is the BEQ instruction. If only one key is depressed, the contents of accumulator A should be zero. If it is zero, then only one key was depressed. Otherwise, a second key was depressed and the entry should be tagged not valid. If the entry is valid, the BEQ instruction causes the program to jump over the CLC instruction to ENC4 (line 35).

At ENC4, accumulator A is loaded with the third entry from the hex table. Thus, the program has fulfilled its requirements. A number corresponding to the key depressed is in accumulator A and the C flag is set indicating a valid entry. All that remains is to restore the original contents of the index register and accumulator B. Finally, the RTS instruction returns the program to the point where this subroutine was called.

If you step through this subroutine with a different key depressed, you will see that the proper hex code is always returned. If no keys are depressed or if two keys are depressed, the program will branch to ENC3. This clears the carry flag. Thus, the subroutine will end with C cleared, which indicates that the entry was not valid.

Eliminating Contact Bounce   A second subroutine is used to eliminate contact bounce. It is called INCH for "input character." Its starting address is FDF4 and it calls the ENCODE program just discussed 20_{16} different times. If for 20_{16} consecutive times, ENCODE tells INCH that a valid entry exists, INCH is convinced and accepts the entry. Since this process requires several milliseconds, any contact bounce is eliminated.

This subroutine is shown in Figure 8-8. The subroutine is divided into two nearly identical halves. The first half (lines 1 through 6) waits for the keyboard to be cleared (no keys depressed). It does this so that it does not mistake a previous key closure for a valid entry.

If a key is depressed upon entering this subroutine, first, the contents of B are saved; then B is loaded with a delaying count of 20_{16}. By counting this number down to zero, the program establishes a delay sufficient to "wait out" any contact bounce.

LINE	ASSEMBLY CODE		COMMENTS
1	INCH	PSH B	Save contents of accumulator B
2	INC1	LDA B #$20	Load B with a delaying count of 20_{16}.
3	INC2	BSR ENCODE	Branch to the ENCODE subroutine.
4		BCS INC1	If carry is set go to INC1.
5		DEC B	Otherwise decrement the count.
6		BNE INC2	If count is not zero go back to INC2.
7	INC3	LDA B #$20	Load B with a delaying count of 20_{16}.
8	INC4	BSR ENCODE	Branch to the ENCODE subroutine.
9		BCC INC3	If carry is clear, check again.
10		DEC B	Otherwise, decrement the count.
11		BNE INC4	If count is not zero go back to INC4.
12		PUL B	Restore the original contents of accumulator B.
13		RTS	Return.

Figure 8-8
INCH subroutine.

The BSR instruction sends the MPU off to the ENCODE subroutine. If a key is depressed, the C flag will be set when the program returns. The BCS instruction sends the program back to INC1 if the C flag is set. The program will stay in this loop until the ENCODE subroutine returns with the carry bit clear. Of course, this will happen only after a key is released. This prevents a single entry from being mistaken for two or more entries. An entry is accepted only after the previous entry is released.

Once a key is released, ENCODE will clear the carry flag. Thus, the BCS instruction will not cause a branch. Instead B is decremented and checked for zero. If not zero, the program branches back to INC2. This loop is repeated 20_{16} times and gets rid of any contact bounce associated with the release of the previous key. Once the program is convinced that the previous key has been released, it proceeds to the second half of the subroutine (lines 7 through 13).

Accumulator B is loaded with a delaying count of 20_{16} again and the BSR instruction calls the ENCODE subroutine. Upon return from this subroutine, the BCC instruction checks the carry flag. If it is clear, no valid entry is being received and the program branches back to INC3. In practice, the MPU in the ET-3400 Trainer spends most of its time caught in this loop waiting for a key closure to occur.

When a key closure does occur, the ENCODE subroutine sets the carry bit. This allows the MPU to escape the loop. It then enters the loop composed of lines 8 through 11. It repeats this loop 20_{16} times to eliminate any contact bounce. When it escapes this loop, we can be confident that the key closure is absolutely valid.

This is a good example of software-hardware trade offs. These subroutines make the keyboard appear quite sophisticated. A mechanical or electromechanical keyboard having all these features would be very expensive.

You will learn more about interfacing with switches later after you learn about the peripheral interface adapter. Also, in a later experiment you will gain some practical experience interfacing switches.

Self-Test Review

1. List four requirements that must be met when connecting mechanical switches to the MPU.

2. What type of circuit is often used between the switches and the data bus of the MPU?

3. Refer to Figure 8-1. If no switches are closed, what hexadecimal number is read from the switch bank?

4. Refer to Figure 8-1. If S_2 is closed, what hexadecimal number is read from the switch bank?

5. What two things can be determined by the hexadecimal number read in from the switch bank?

6. Why is debouncing required?

7. How can the MPU overcome the effects of contact bounce?

8. Refer to Figure 8-3. To what address does the center row of keys respond?

9. Refer to Figure 8-5. What is the purpose of the first 18 lines of the program?

10. What technique is used for finding the hexadecimal equivalent of the key that is depressed?

11. Refer to Figure 8-8. How does this routine overcome contact bounce?

ANSWERS

1. The MPU must: 1) Address the switches.
                     2) Detect contact closure.
                     3) Overcome contact bounce.
                     4) Decode the switches.

2. A three-state buffer.

3. FF_{16}.

4. FB_{16}.

5. The hexadecimal number read from the switch bank reveals
    1) If a switch is closed.
    2) Which switch is closed.

6. When a mechanical switch is closed, its contacts often bounce open
    and closed several times. Unless this is taken into consideration, a
    single switch closure can be mistaken for multiple switch closures.

7. The MPU can overcome the effects of contact bounce by rechecking
    the closed switch several times.

8. $C005_{16}$.

9. The first 18 lines of the program place the switch pattern into
    accumulators A and B.

10. They are looked up in a table.

11. By rechecking the closed switch. It must find the switch closed for
    20_{16} consecutive checks before the value is accepted as good.

THE PERIPHERAL INTERFACE ADAPTER (PIA)

Most microprocessors have a family of support chips that are used to simplify the problem of interfacing with the outside world. One of the most popular of these interfacing chips is the peripheral interface adapter (PIA). The PIA was developed to support the 6800 MPU. However, it is also being used in many microprocessor based designs using other MPU's.

While a complete discussion of support chips is beyond the scope of this course, detailed data sheets on several support IC's are included in Appendix B.

In this section, you will be introduced to the PIA. You will learn enough about it to use it in the experiments in the Student Workbook.

The block diagrams of two typical systems that use PIA's are shown in Figure 8-9. In Figure 8-9A a single PIA is used to drive both an input and an output device. This is possible since the PIA has two independent channels. Figure 8-9B shows a system that uses two PIA's. One controls an input device while the other controls an output device.

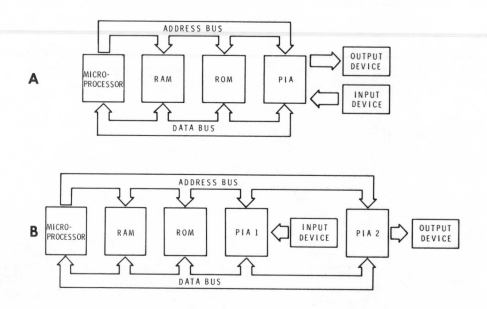

Figure 8-9
The PIA is used to interface input and
output devices to the MPU.

The purpose of the PIA is to simplify the problem of interfacing the MPU to external devices. Of course, any device can be interfaced with the MPU using conventional combinational logic. However, the conventional logic approach generally requires many IC's. This defeats one of the prime advantages of the microprocessor — a simple straightforward design requiring few IC's. The advantage of the PIA is that in many cases one or two IC's can do all the interfacing.

Because the PIA can do most routine peripheral control tasks, the MPU is freed to handle more important tasks. Also, the PIA allows the MPU to treat a peripheral device as a memory location. In addition, it acts as a buffer between the high-speed MPU and the low-speed I/O device. Since the PIA has some on board address decoding, a separate address decoder is not needed in many applications.

The PIA is superior to combinational logic in another way. The PIA is extremely flexible because it is programmable. That is, its configuration can be changed from one moment to the next by the program being executed. For example, an output port can be changed to an input port in the middle of a program. Later, you will see how this is done. But first, you will learn about the internal structure of the PIA.

I/O Diagram

The diagram of the PIA shown in Figure 8-10 shows its input and output lines. Since this is an interface device, one side connects to the MPU while the other side connects to one or more peripheral devices.

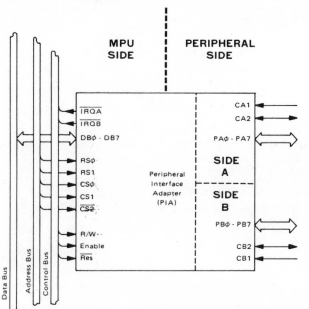

Figure 8-10
I/O diagram of the peripheral interface adapter.

On the MPU side, the PIA monitors several address, data, and control lines of the MPU. It monitors all eight data bus lines. Data is transferred to and from the PIA, a byte at a time, by the data bus. For this reason, the PIA is said to be "byte oriented." In this respect, the PIA is treated like memory. As you will see later, the PIA has four addresses that can be treated much like RAM.

The PIA can monitor five of the MPU's address lines. This is enough to partially decode the address. In many cases, no additional address decoding is necessary.

The PIA also connects to several control lines. The $R/\overline{W}$ line informs the PIA whether it is to receive data from the MPU or send data to the MPU. Once again, note the similarity between the PIA and RAM.

Another similarity is the enable line. Like RAM, the PIA is enabled by the $\phi2$ clock (often ANDed with VMA). This provides the basic timing signal for the PIA.

The reset line of the PIA is generally connected to the master system reset. This allows the PIA registers to be reset to a known condition at the same time the MPU is reset.

The PIA has two interrupt request lines. These allow the PIA to request service from the MPU. These may connect to either the IRQ or the NMI lines of the MPU. As you saw earlier, interrupts can be used to simplify I/O operations and to save MPU time. While the interrupt capability of the PIA is not discussed in this unit, the PIA data sheet in Appendix B briefly outlines these capabilities.

The peripheral side of the MPU has two nearly identical I/O channels. PA_0 through PA_7 make up a peripheral data bus for the A side of the PIA. CA_1 and CA_2 are two control/interface lines associated with the A side. Notice that the B side has comparable data and control lines. Do not confuse the peripheral data buses on the right with the MPU data bus on the left. Both buses will be referred to frequently in the following discussion.

PIA Registers

The A and B sides of the PIA are nearly identical. Except when noted, everything stated about one side of the PIA also applies to the other side.

Each side of the PIA has three main registers as shown in Figure 8-11. These include an output register (OR), a data direction register (DDR), and a control register (CR). The output register is used to hold a data byte that is being transferred to the peripheral data bus. It acts as a temporary storage location for data being transferred from the MPU to the peripheral device.

The data direction register sets up the individual lines in the peripheral data bus as either inputs or outputs. Each bit in the DDR controls the corresponding peripheral data line. A 1 in a specific bit of the DDR causes the corresponding peripheral data line to act as an output line. A 0 causes it to act as an input line.

To set up all eight peripheral data lines of the A side as inputs, we simply store 00_{16} in the DDR of the A side. By the same token, we can set up the B side as output data lines by storing FF_{16} in the DDR of the B side. The various data lines can be set up in any combination. Moreover, a peripheral data line can be changed from input to output simply by changing its corresponding bit in the data direction register. Keep in mind, that this change is made by software. No hardware change is necessary.

The control register allows you to program several other characteristics of the PIA. One of these will be discussed later. The others are explained in the PIA data sheets in Appendix B.

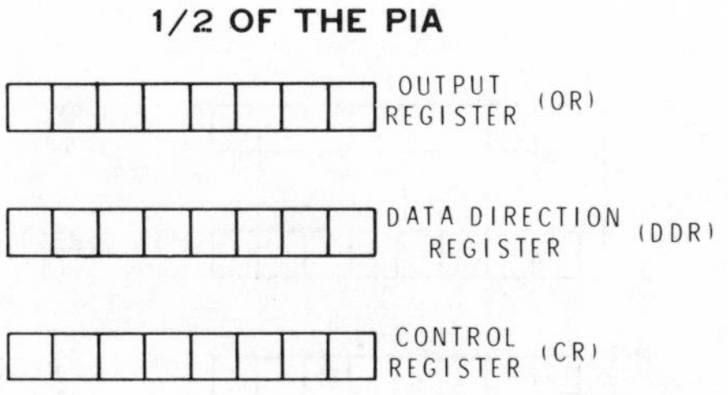

1/2 OF THE PIA

OUTPUT REGISTER (OR)

DATA DIRECTION REGISTER (DDR)

CONTROL REGISTER (CR)

Figure 8-11
Each side of the PIA has three main registers.

Addressing the PIA Registers

The PIA has six registers in which data can be stored and from which data can be read. The two control registers each have an address of their own. In a typical system, the control register on the A side may have an address of 4005_{16}. The control register on the B side may have an address of 4007_{16}. In this case, we could write data into the control register on the A side with the instruction STAA 4005_{16}. Or, we could read from the control register on the B side with LDAA 4007_{16}.

While the control register has an address of its own, the data direction register and the output register share a common address. Typically, the data direction and output register on the A side may share the address 4004_{16}. Those on the B side may share the address 4006_{16}. Thus, in a typical system, the PIA may have addresses assigned as shown in Figure 8-12.

Even though the data direction and output registers share the same address, each is still individually accessible. When address 4004 appears on the address bus, either ORA or DDRA will be selected depending on bit 2 of the control register. If bit 2 of CRA is a 1, then address 4004_{16} selects ORA. However, if bit 2 of CRA is 0, then address 4004 selects DDRA. In this same way, bit 2 of CRB determines which register is selected by address 4006_{16}. A 1 selects the output register; a 0 selects the data direction register.

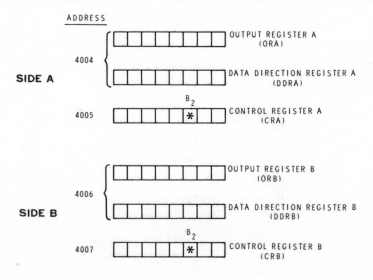

Figure 8-12
Typical address assignments of PIA
registers.

Initializing the PIA

Before the PIA can be used for input-output transfers, it must first be programmed to operate in the desired manner. For example, assume that you wish to use the A side of the PIA as an output port and the B side as an input port. Figure 8-13 shows a PIA that is configured in this manner. DDRA sets all A-side peripheral data lines as outputs and bit 2 of CRA has set the output register to respond to address 4004. DDRB sets all B-side peripheral data lines as inputs and bit 2 of CRB has set ORB to respond to address 4006. This state does not come about by accident. We must deliberately set up these conditions. This process is called initializing the PIA.

In most applications, the PIA is initialized after the system is reset. Once configured in a certain way, the PIA is normally left in this configuration. For this reason, you can assume that the initialization process starts immediately after the system is reset.

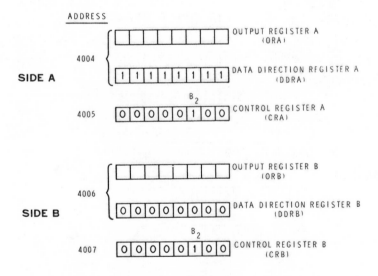

Figure 8-13
The A side is configured as an output
port; the B side, as an input port.

The PIA has a reset line that is normally connected to the system reset line. When the PIAs' reset line goes low, all the registers in the PIA are reset to zero as shown in Figure 8-14. With both data direction registers reset to zero, both peripheral data buses are configured as inputs. Also, with bit 2 of the control registers reset to 0, address 4004 selects DDRA while 4006 selects DDRB. To initialize the PIA, we must change the contents of its registers from that shown in Figure 8-14 to that shown in Figure 8-13.

A program that will accomplish this is:

LDAA	#FF
STAA	4004
LDAA	#04
STAA	4005
STAA	4007

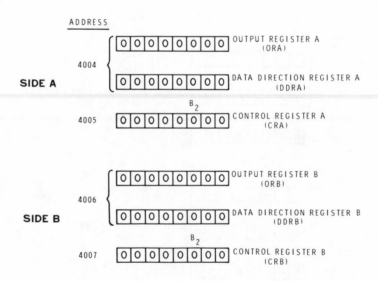

Figure 8-14
When the PIA is reset, all registers are
set to zero.

The first instruction loads accumulator A with all binary 1's. The second instruction stores this at location 4004_{16}. Since bit 2 of CRA is initially 0, FF is stored in DDRA. This configures the A-side peripheral data bus as outputs.

The third instruction loads 04_{16} into accumulator A. The next two instructions store 04_{16} at addresses 4005_{16} and 4007_{16}. These addresses are the control registers. Recall that 04_{16} is equal to $0000\ 0100_2$. This sets bit 2 of both control registers to 1. Consequently, address 4004_{16} now specifies ORA while 4006_{16} now specifies ORB.

As you can see, the PIA is now set up as shown in Figure 8-15. Notice that we did not have to change the contents of DDRB in this case because it was initially reset to zero.

Once the PIA is configured in this manner, the MPU can transfer data to the output port using the instruction: STAA 4004_{16}. Also, it can read data from the input port using the instruction: LDAA 4006_{16}.

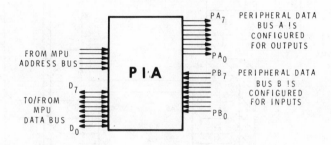

Figure 8-15
The initialization procedure configures the PIA as shown.

Addressing the PIA

Figure 8-16 shows how the PIA fits into a microprocessor system. Now consider how the PIA is addressed.

The PIA has three chip select lines (CS0, CS1, and $\overline{CS2}$). These three lines are used to select the PIA. In order for this particular PIA to be selected, CS0 and CS1 must be high while $\overline{CS2}$ must be low.

Notice that these three lines are connected to three of the address lines (A2, A14, and A15). In this application, the A14 line is ANDed with the VMA line. This ensures that the PIA is selected only if the address is valid. In the following discussion, assume that all addresses are valid.

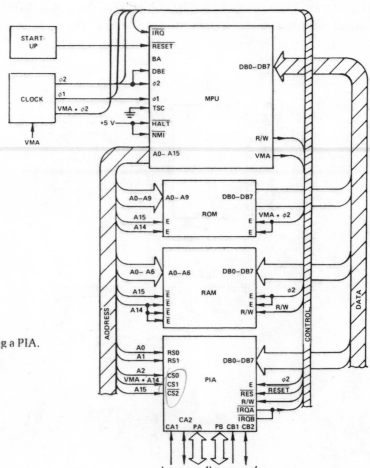

Figure 8-16
A microprocessor system using a PIA.

The PIA will be selected by any address in which A2 and A14 are high and A15 is low. Hexadecimal addresses like 4004, 5004, 6004, 7004, etc. will select the PIA because the above conditions are met. Actually, there are thousands of addresses that will select the PIA. Even so, in many systems this is no problem. In the application shown, any address below $3FFF_{16}$ will select the RAM. Many addresses between 4004_{16} and $7FFF_{16}$ select the PIA. Finally addresses above $C000_{16}$ select the ROM. Neither the ROM, the RAM, nor the PIA is fully decoded. Even so, their addresses are unique enough that each can be selected without additional decoding.

For programming purposes, we must assign the PIA four consecutive addresses. We will assume that these addresses are 4004_{16} through 4007_{16}. Notice that we could have just as easily selected addresses 6004_{16} through 6007_{16}.

In addition to the chip select lines, the PIA has two register select lines (RS0 and RS1) that also connect to the address bus. RS0 connects to A0 while RS1 connects to A1. The RS1 line determines which side of the PIA is selected. When RS1 is at logic 0, side A is selected. When RS1 is at logic 1, side B is selected.

The RS0 line selects the register on the affected side. When RS0 is 1, the control register is selected. When RS0 is 0, the data direction register or the output register is selected depending on the state of bit 2 of the control register.

HEX ADDRESS	BINARY EQUIVALENT OF LAST HEX DIGIT			REGISTER SELECTED
	CS0	RS1	RS0	
4004	0	1	0	0	DDRA or ORA*
4005	0	1	0	1	CRA
4006	0	1	1	0	DDRB or ORB*
4007	0	1	1	1	CRB

*Determined by bit 2 of CR
0 = DDR
1 = ORA

Figure 8-17
The relationship between the address
and the register selected.

The chart shown in Figure 8-17 shows why the various registers are selected for the addresses shown. For example, when the address is 4007_{16}, address lines 1 and 0 are both high. Thus, both RS0 and RS1 are at logic 1. The 1 at RS1 selects the B side of the PIA. The 1 at RS0 selects the control register. Thus, the address 4007_{16} selects the control register on the B side. Figure 8-18 illustrates the same thing in another way. It shows how the data path between the MPU and the PIA register is determined.

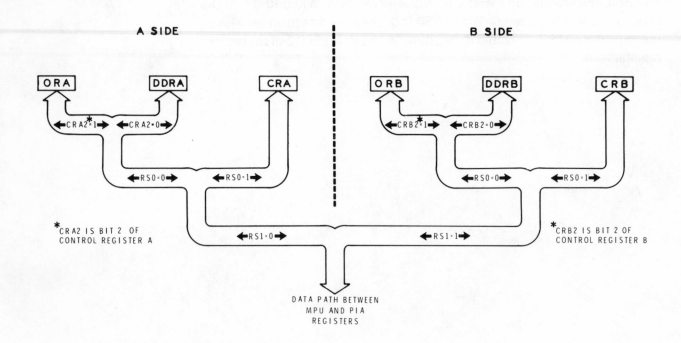

Figure 8-18
How the data path between the MPU
and the PIA register is determined.

Self-Test Review

12. What is the peripheral interface adapter (PIA)?

13. How is the PIA superior to combinational logic?

14. What is the internal structure of the PIA?

15. How is the PIA reset?

16. What are the contents of the PIA registers immediately after being reset?

17. How does the MPU decide which side of the PIA is selected?

18. Once the MPU has selected one side of the PIA, how does it determine which of the three registers is connected to the data bus?

19. Which pin of the PIA is normally connected to the A1 address line of the MPU?

20. Refer to Figure 8-16. Write a short routine that will initialize the PIA immediately after reset. Set up PA0 through PA3 and PB0 through PB3 as inputs. Set up PA4 through PA7 and PB4 through PB7 as outputs.

ANSWERS

12. The PIA is a 40-pin IC that is used to simplify the transfer of data between a microprocessor and the outside world.

13. In many cases, one or two PIAs can handle all interfacing requirements. Also, the PIA is extremely flexible since it can be programmed to perform in several different configurations.

14. The PIA has two nearly identical sides, each of which contains three registers: the output register, the data direction register, and the control register. The MPU can transfer data to or from either of these registers by way of the data bus.

15. The PIA is reset by pulling its $\overline{reset}$ line low.

16. When reset, the contents of all PIA registers are reset to 00_{16}.

17. The MPU selects the A side of the PIA by switching the PIA's RS1 line to 0 (low). The B side is selected by switching the RS1 line to 1.

18. If the RS0 line of the PIA is 1, the control register of the affected side is selected. If RS0 is 0, then the register selection is determined by bit 2 of the affected control register.

19. RS1 of the PIA is normally connected to address line A1 of the MPU.

20. A typical routine is:

LDAA	#F0
STAA	4004
STAA	4006
LDAA	#04
STAA	4005
STAA	4007

USING THE PIA

Now that you are familiar with the PIA, you are ready to examine some of the ways that the PIA can be used. In this section, you will see how the PIA can be used to handle displays and keyboards. You will start by examining how a PIA can be used to drive 7-segment displays.

Driving 7-Segment Displays

Figure 8-19 shows how a single PIA can be used to multiplex up to eight 7-segment displays. The PIA is configured to respond to addresses 4004_{16} through 4007_{16}. The A side of the PIA is used to supply the 7-segment code to the displays. Inverters are used to supply the current required by the displays. The B side is used to determine which display is selected. Here discrete transistors are used to provide the required current.

The displays are common cathode types. To light segment "a" of display 1, Q_1 must conduct through pin "a." Thus, a logic 1 must be applied to the base of Q_1 and to pin "a" of display 1.

Notice that both sides of the PIA must serve as outputs. Thus, during the initialization procedure, both data direction registers are set to FF_{16}. Then bit 2 of both control registers are set to 1's, so that data would be routed to the output registers.

All displays are blanked by storing FF_{16} in output register A. This sets PA0 through PA7 to 1's. The 1's are then inverted to 0's. Thus, no segments of any display can light.

To display a specific eight-character message, the displays must be turned on one at a time in sequence. This is controlled by the B side of the PIA. At the same time, the 7-segment character codes must be loaded into the A side of the PIA one at a time.

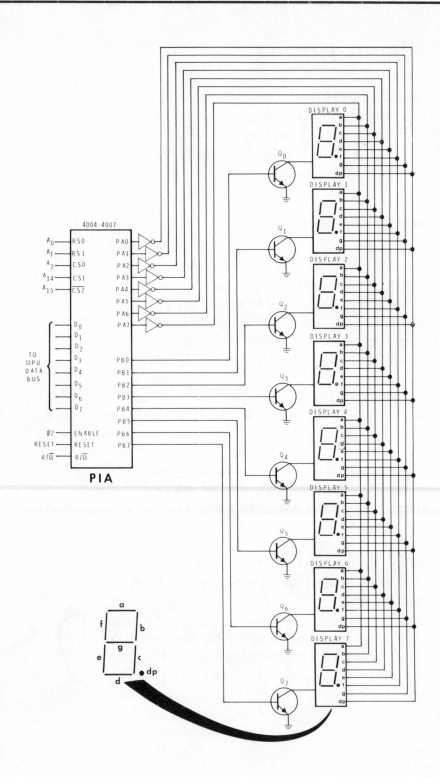

Figure 8-19
Using the PIA to multiplex displays.

A subroutine for multiplexing the displays is shown in Figure 8-20. It assumes that the eight 7-segment codes are already in RAM at consecutive addresses, SGCODE through SGCODE +7.

The first instruction loads the index register with one less than the address of the 7-segment code for the first character. Next, accumulator B is cleared and the carry flag is set to 1. Accumulator A is set to FF_{16} by first clearing to 00_{16} and then complementing. The FF_{16} in accumulator A is stored in the output register of the A side of the PIA. This sets PA0 through PA7 to 1's. The ones are inverted and blank all the displays. The displays are blanked by side A whenever the display pointer (side B) is being changed.

The next instructions rotate accumulator B to the left through the carry flag. Recall that accumulator B was originally cleared and that the carry flag was set. Thus, the 1 in the carry flag is rotated into bit 0 of accumulator B. The new contents of accumulator B are stored in the B side of the PIA. PB0 is set to 1 while PB1 through PB7 are reset to 0. The 1 at PB0 enables display 0. However, the display still does not light because the segment lines are still at logic 0.

LINE	ASSEMBLY CODE			COMMENTS
1	DISPLAY	LDX	#SGCODE−1	Point to first code minus one.
2		CLRB		Initialize the
3		SEC		display pointer
4	NXDIGIT	CLRA		Set ACCA
5		COMA		to FF
6		STAA	PIAORA	Turn off all displays
7		ROLB		Point to next display in sequence.
8		STAB	PIAORB	Enable next display in sequence.
9		BCC	NXTDSP	If last display has been lit,
10		RTS		exit. Otherwise,
11	LTDSP	INX		point to next 7-segment code
12		LDAA	O,X	Load code into ACCA.
13		STAA	PIAORA	Display the code.
14		CLRA		Leave this
15	DELAY	INCA		display lit for
16		BNE	DELAY	1536_{10} MPU cycles.
17		BRA	NXDIGIT	Go back and do it again.

Figure 8-20
Subroutine for multiplexing the displays.

The next instruction (BCC) checks the carry flag to see if it is cleared. It will be in this case because a 0 was rotated into it by the earlier ROLB instruction. Consequently, the RTS instruction is skipped over and the INX instruction is executed next.

The INX instruction increments the contents of the index register so that it now points at the 7-segment code for the first character that is to be displayed. The next instruction loads this character into accumulator A. Then the 7-segment code is stored in output register A of the PIA. The code is inverted and is applied to the segment lines of all eight displays. However, only display 0 is presently enabled. Thus, this is the only display that will be lit.

The next three instructions cause a delay of about 1536_{10} MPU cycles. In a typical system, this amounts to a delay of about 2 milliseconds. Finally, the BRA instruction branches the program back to the point called NXDIGIT.

At NXDIGIT, the displays are blanked again. Accumulator B is rotated to the left so that the 1 now appears at bit 1. This is stored at PIAORB, enabling display 1 and disabling all other displays. The carry flag is still cleared, so the RTS instruction is skipped. The next 7-segment code is selected and stored at PIAORA. Thus, the second code lights display 1. The display is held lit for about 2 milliseconds and the loop is repeated again.

The display loop continues until all eight displays have been lit. After the final display is lit, the program tries to repeat the loop again. However, this time, the 1 in accumulator B is rotated back into the carry flag. As a result, the BCC instruction does not cause a branch. The RTS instruction is executed and the program returns to wherever it came from.

In order to give the illusion of a constant display, this subroutine must be called several times each second. The display must be constantly refreshed by rewriting the same message over and over again.

Decoding Keyboards

Figure 8-21 illustrates how the PIA can be used to decode a 16-switch keyboard. The chip select lines are connected so that this PIA responds to addresses 4008_{16} through $400B_{16}$.

One switch is connected to each of the peripheral data lines of the PIA. When a switch is open, its corresponding peripheral data line is pulled up to logic 1 by the pull-up resistor. When a switch is closed, the corresponding peripheral data line falls to logic 0. In this application, both sides of the PIA act as input ports. Since they are automatically set up as inputs during reset, there is little to be done during initialization. Of course, bits 2 of the control registers must be set to 1 so that the input data from the keyboard can be read from addresses 4008_{16} and $400A_{16}$.

The problems associated with decoding the keyboard are the same as those discussed earlier. Because this keyboard does not use interrupts, the MPU must scan the keyboard at regular intervals. Typically, it would read from addresses 4008_{16} and $400A_{16}$ several times each second.

The MPU detects a switch closure by comparing the input data with FF_{16}. If the input data is anything other than FF_{16}, one (or more) of the switches is closed.

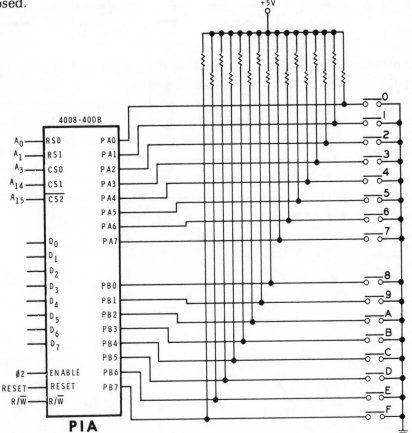

Figure 8-21
Using the PIA to monitor a keyboard.

The MPU overcomes the switch bounce problem in the same way discussed earlier. Also, the problems of rejecting multiple switch closures and producing an equivalent binary code can be accomplished using the same techniques discussed previously in this unit.

Decoding a Switch Matrix

The method shown in Figure 8-21 is a very straightforward technique of decoding switches. Using one PIA, this technique can handle up to 16 switches. There are other techniques that use the PIA to greater advantage. An example is shown in Figure 8-22. Here again, the PIA is handling 16 switches. However, this time only one side of the PIA is used.

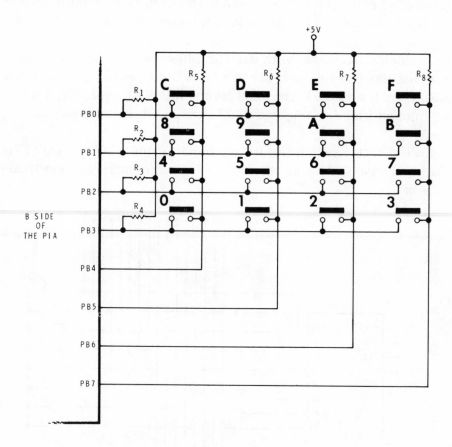

Figure 8-22
One side of the PIA can handle up to 16
switches.

The 16 switches are arranged in a 4 by 4 matrix. The B side of the PIA is used to interface with the switches. Lines PB0 through PB3 are configured as input lines while PB4 through PB7 are configured as output lines.

With no switches closed, PB0 through PB3 are pulled up to logic 1 by resistors R_1 through R_4. PB0 monitors switches C, D, E, and F. When all four switches are open, PB0 is at logic 1. Even with one of the switches closed, PB0 will still be at logic 1 if output lines PB4 through PB7 are at logic 1. And, these output lines (PB4 through PB7) are normally held at logic 1.

Periodically, the MPU scans the keyboard to see if any switch has been closed. It does this by applying logic 0 to one of the output lines and then checking for a logic 0 at one of the input lines.

A typical procedure might look like this. When the PIA is initialized, PB0 through PB3 are set up as inputs while PB4 through PB7 are set up as outputs. The MPU scans the keyboard in this manner. PB4 is reset to 0 by storing EF_{16} in output register B. Next, the B side is read out. If switch 0, 4, 8, or C is closed, its corresponding PIA input line will be low. For example, if switch 8 is closed, the 0 at PB4 will pull PB1 low. By examining lines PB0 through PB3, the MPU can tell which switch (if any) is closed.

If no switch is closed in the first column, PB5 is reset to 0 by storing DF_{16} in output register B. The MPU can now check to see if switch 1, 5, 9, or D is closed.

The technique just described allows the MPU to handle a large number of switches with a single PIA. Using both sides of the PIA, the MPU could handle an 8 by 8 matrix of 64_{10} switches. This technique will be explored in more detail in an interfacing experiment.

Self-Test Review

21. Refer to Figure 8-19. Write a short program that will initialize the PIA in the proper configuration.

22. Refer to Figure 8-19. Which side of the PIA determines which display is selected?

23. Refer to Figure 8-19. Assume that the PIA has been properly initialized. Write a simple program segment that will display the numeral 4 on display number 7.

24. Refer to Figure 8-21. In order for this scheme to work, both sides of the PIA must be configured as _____.

25. Refer to Figure 8-21. How does the MPU tell that switch 9 is closed?

26. How can the B side of the PIA be set up as shown in Figure 8-22?

27. Refer to Figure 8-22. How does the MPU tell that switch 7 is closed?

28. If both sides of the PIA are used, how many switches can be handled using the matrix technique?

ANSWERS

21. Assuming that the PIA was initially reset, a typical initialization routine would be:

    LDAA   #FF
    STAA   4004
    STAA   4006
    LDAA   #04
    STAA   4005
    STAA   4007

22. The B side.

23. Keep in mind that Q_7 must conduct and that pins b, c, g, and f must be high. Thus, the following instructions could be used:

    LDAA   #80
    STAA   4006
    LDAA   #99
    STAA   4004

24. inputs.

25. The MPU reads in data from both sides of the PIA and compares this data with several different bit patterns. If switch 9 is closed, the bit pattern from the B side will be FD_{16}.

26. The output register of the B side is configured in this manner during the initialization process by storing OF_{16} in the B side data direction register.

27. The MPU periodically resets line PB7 to 0. If PB2 is subsequently found to be 0, the MPU knows that switch 7 is closed.

28. Up to 64_{10}.

The interfacing experiments are included in the Student Workbook. Go to the Student Workbook and perform experiments 15 through 19. Some of these experiments are quite involved and you should not attempt more than one experiment per sitting.

Appendix A

DEFINITION OF THE
EXECUTABLE INSTRUCTIONS

A.1 Nomenclature

The following nomenclature is used in the subsequent definitions.

(a) *Operators*

( )	=	contents of
←	=	is transferred to
↑	=	"is pulled from stack"
↓	=	"is pushed into stack"
·	=	Boolean AND
⊙	=	Boolean (Inclusive) OR
⊕	=	Exclusive OR
≈	=	Boolean NOT

(b) *Registers in the MPU*

ACCA	=	Accumulator A
ACCB	=	Accumulator B
ACCX	=	Accumulator ACCA or ACCB
CC	=	Condition codes register
IX	=	Index register, 16 bits
IXH	=	Index register, higher order 8 bits
IXL	=	Index register, lower order 8 bits
PC	=	Program counter, 16 bits
PCH	=	Program counter, higher order 8 bits
PCL	=	Program counter, lower order 8 bits
SP	=	Stack pointer
SPH	=	Stack pointer high
SPL	=	Stack pointer low

(c) *Memory and Addressing*

M	=	A memory location (one byte)
M +1	=	The byte of memory at 0001 plus the address of the memory location indicated by "M."
Rel	=	Relative address (i.e. the two's complement number stored in the second byte of machine code corresponding to a branch instruction).

(d) *Bits 0 thru 5 of the Condition Codes Register*

C	=	Carry — borrow	bit — 0
V	=	Two's complement overflow indicator	bit — 1
Z	=	Zero indicator	bit — 2
N	=	Negative indicator	bit — 3
I	=	Interrupt mask	bit — 4
H	=	Half carry	bit — 5

(e) *Status of Individual Bits BEFORE Execution of an Instruction*

An	=	Bit n of ACCA (n=7,6,5,...,0)
Bn	=	Bit n of ACCB (n=7,6,5,...,0)
IXHn	=	Bit n of IXH (n=7,6,5,...,0)

$\qquad$ IXLn $\quad=\quad$ Bit n of IXL (n=7,6,5,...,0)

$\qquad$ Mn $\quad=\quad$ Bit n of M (n=7,6,5,...,0)

$\qquad$ SPHn $=$ Bit n of SPH (n=7,6,5,...,0)

$\qquad$ SPLn $=$ Bit n of SPL (n=7,6,5,...,0)

$\qquad$ Xn $\quad=\quad$ Bit n of ACCX (n=7,6,5,...,0)

(f) *Status of Individual Bits of the RESULT of Execution of an Instruction*

(i) For 8-bit Results

$\qquad$ Rn $\quad=$ Bit n of the result (n =7,6,5,...,0)

This applies to instructions which provide a result contained in a single byte of memory or in an 8-bit register.

(ii) For 16-bit Results

$\qquad$ RHn $\;=$ Bit n of the more significant byte of the result

$\qquad$ (n =7,6,5,...,0)

$\qquad$ RLn $\;=$ Bit n of the less significant byte of the result

$\qquad$ (n =7,6,5,...,0)

This applies to instructions which provide a result contained in two consecutive bytes of memory or in a 16-bit register.

A.2 Executable Instructions (definition of)

Detailed definitions of the 72 executable instructions of the source language are provided on the following pages.

Add Accumulator B to Accumulator A   **ABA**

Operation: ACCA ← (ACCA) + (ACCB)

Description: Adds the contents of ACCB to the contents of ACCA and places the result in ACCA.

Condition Codes:
- H: Set if there was a carry from bit 3; cleared otherwise.
- I: Not affected.
- N: Set if most significant bit of the result is set; cleared otherwise.
- Z: Set if all bits of the result are cleared; cleared otherwise.
- V: Set if there was two's complement overflow as a result of the operation; cleared otherwise.
- C: Set if there was a carry from the most significant bit of the result; cleared otherwise.

Boolean Formulae for Condition Codes:

$$H = A_3 \cdot B_3 + B_3 \cdot \bar{R}_3 + \bar{R}_3 \cdot A_3$$
$$N = R_7$$
$$Z = \bar{R}_7 \cdot \bar{R}_6 \cdot \bar{R}_5 \cdot \bar{R}_4 \cdot \bar{R}_3 \cdot \bar{R}_2 \cdot \bar{R}_1 \cdot \bar{R}_0$$
$$V = A_7 \cdot B_7 \cdot \bar{R}_7 + \bar{A}_7 \cdot \bar{B}_7 \cdot R_7$$
$$C = A_7 \cdot B_7 + B_7 \cdot \bar{R}_7 + \bar{R}_7 \cdot A_7$$

Addressing Modes, Execution Time, and Machine Code (hexadecimal/octal/decimal):

Addressing Modes	Execution Time (No. of cycles)	Number of bytes of machine code	Coding of First (or only) byte of machine code		
			HEX.	OCT.	DEC.
Inherent	2	1	1B	033	027

ADC

Add with Carry

Operation:	$ACCX \leftarrow (ACCX) + (M) + (C)$
Description:	Adds the contents of the C bit to the sum of the contents of ACCX and M, and places the result in ACCX.

Condition Codes:

H: Set if there was a carry from bit 3; cleared otherwise.
I: Not affected.
N: Set if most significant bit of the result is set; cleared otherwise.
Z: Set if all bits of the result are cleared; cleared otherwise.
V: Set if there was two's complement overflow as a result of the operation; cleared otherwise.
C: Set if there was a carry from the most significant bit of the result; cleared otherwise.

Boolean Formulae for Condition Codes:

$$H = X_3 \cdot M_3 + M_3 \cdot \bar{R}_3 + \bar{R}_3 \cdot X_3$$
$$N = R_7$$
$$Z = \bar{R}_7 \cdot \bar{R}_6 \cdot \bar{R}_5 \cdot \bar{R}_4 \cdot \bar{R}_3 \cdot \bar{R}_2 \cdot \bar{R}_1 \cdot \bar{R}_0$$
$$V = X_7 \cdot M_7 \cdot \bar{R}_7 + \bar{X}_7 \cdot \bar{M}_7 \cdot R_7$$
$$C = X_7 \cdot M_7 + M_7 \cdot \bar{R}_7 + \bar{R}_7 \cdot X_7$$

Addressing Formats:

See Table A-1

Addressing Modes, Execution Time, and Machine Code (hexadecimal/ octal/ decimal):

(DUAL OPERAND)

Addressing Modes	Execution Time (No. of cycles)	Number of bytes of machine code	Coding of First (or only) byte of machine code		
			HEX.	OCT.	DEC.
A IMM	2	2	89	211	137
A DIR	3	2	99	231	153
A EXT	4	3	B9	271	185
A IND	5	2	A9	251	169
B IMM	2	2	C9	311	201
B DIR	3	2	D9	331	217
B EXT	4	3	F9	371	249
B IND	5	2	E9	351	233

Add Without Carry   # ADD

Operation:	$ACCX \leftarrow (ACCX) + (M)$
Description:	Adds the contents of ACCX and the contents of M and places the result in ACCX.

Condition Codes: H: Set if there was a carry from bit 3; cleared otherwise.
                     I: Not affected.
                     N: Set if most significant bit of the result is set; cleared otherwise.
                     Z: Set if all bits of the result are cleared; cleared otherwise.
                     V: Set if there was two's complement overflow as a result of the operation; cleared otherwise.
                     C: Set if there was a carry from the most significant bit of the result; cleared otherwise.

Boolean Formulae for Condition Codes:

$$H = X_3 \cdot M_3 + M_3 \cdot \bar{R}_3 + \bar{R}_3 \cdot X_3$$
$$N = R_7$$
$$Z = \bar{R}_7 \cdot \bar{R}_6 \cdot \bar{R}_5 \cdot \bar{R}_4 \cdot \bar{R}_3 \cdot \bar{R}_2 \cdot \bar{R}_1 \cdot \bar{R}_0$$
$$V = X_7 \cdot M_7 \cdot \bar{R}_7 + \bar{X}_7 \cdot \bar{M}_7 \cdot R_7$$
$$C = X_7 \cdot M_7 + M_7 \cdot \bar{R}_7 + \bar{R}_7 \cdot X_7$$

Addressing Formats:

See Table A-1

Addressing Modes, Execution Time, and Machine Code (hexadecimal/octal/decimal):
(DUAL OPERAND)

Addressing Modes	Execution Time (No. of cycles)	Number of bytes of machine code	Coding of First (or only) byte of machine code		
			HEX.	OCT.	DEC.
A IMM	2	2	8B	213	139
A DIR	3	2	9B	233	155
A EXT	4	3	BB	273	187
A IND	5	2	AB	253	171
B IMM	2	2	CB	313	203
B DIR	3	2	DB	333	219
B EXT	4	3	FB	373	251
B IND	5	2	EB	353	235

AND

Logical AND

Operation: $\quad$ ACCX ← (ACCX) · (M)

Description: $\quad$ Performs logical "AND" between the contents of ACCX and the contents of M and places the result in ACCX. (Each bit of ACCX after the operation will be the logical "AND" of the corresponding bits of M and of ACCX before the operation.)

Condition Codes:
H: $\quad$ Not affected.
I: $\quad$ Not affected.
N: $\quad$ Set if most significant bit of the result is set; cleared otherwise.
Z: $\quad$ Set if all bits of the result are cleared; cleared otherwise.
V: $\quad$ Cleared.
C: $\quad$ Not affected.

Boolean Formulae for Condition Codes:

$$N = R_7$$
$$Z = \bar{R}_7 \cdot \bar{R}_6 \cdot \bar{R}_5 \cdot \bar{R}_4 \cdot \bar{R}_3 \cdot \bar{R}_2 \cdot \bar{R}_1 \cdot \bar{R}_0$$
$$V = 0$$

Addressing Formats:

See Table A-1

Addressing Modes, Execution Time, and Machine Code (hexadecimal/ octal/ decimal):

Addressing Modes	Execution Time (No. of cycles)	Number of bytes of machine code	Coding of First (or only) byte of machine code		
			HEX.	OCT.	DEC.
A IMM	2	2	84	204	132
A DIR	3	2	94	224	148
A EXT	4	3	B4	264	180
A IND	5	2	A4	244	164
B IMM	2	2	C4	304	196
B DIR	3	2	D4	324	212
B EXT	4	3	F4	364	244
B IND	5	2	E4	344	228

Arithmetic Shift Left   **ASL**

Operation:

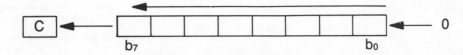

b_7 b_0

Description: Shifts all bits of the ACCX or M one place to the left. Bit 0 is loaded with a zero. The C bit is loaded from the most significant bit of ACCX or M.

Condition Codes:
H: Not affected.
I: Not affected.
N: Set if most significant bit of the result is set; cleared otherwise.
Z: Set if all bits of the result are cleared; cleared otherwise.
V: Set if, after the completion of the shift operation, EITHER (N is set and C is cleared) OR (N is cleared and C is set); cleared otherwise.
C: Set if, before the operation, the most significant bit of the ACCX or M was set; cleared otherwise.

Boolean Formulae for Condition Codes:

$N = R_7$

$Z = \bar{R}_7 \cdot \bar{R}_6 \cdot \bar{R}_5 \cdot \bar{R}_4 \cdot \bar{R}_3 \cdot \bar{R}_2 \cdot \bar{R}_1 \cdot \bar{R}_0$

$V = N \oplus C = [N \cdot \bar{C}] \odot [\bar{N} \cdot C]$

(the foregoing formula assumes values of N and C after the shift operation)

$C = M_7$

Addressing Formats

See Table A-3

Addressing Modes, Execution Time, and Machine Code (hexadecimal / octal / decimal):

Addressing Modes	Execution Time (No. of cycles)	Number of bytes of machine code	Coding of First (or only) byte of machine code		
			HEX.	OCT.	DEC.
A	2	1	48	110	072
B	2	1	58	130	088
EXT	6	3	78	170	120
IND	7	2	68	150	104

ASR
Arithmetic Shift Right

Operation:

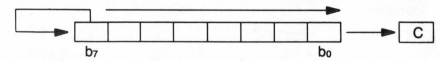

$$b_7 \qquad\qquad\qquad\qquad b_0$$

Description: Shifts all bits of ACCX or M one place to the right. Bit 7 is held constant. Bit 0 is loaded into the C bit.

Condition Codes:
H: Not affected.
I: Not affected.
N: Set if the most significant bit of the result is set; cleared otherwise.
Z: Set if all bits of the result are cleared; cleared otherwise.
V: Set if, after the completion of the shift operation, EITHER (N is set and C is cleared) OR (N is cleared and C is set); cleared otherwise.
C: Set if, before the operation, the least significant bit of the ACCX or M was set; cleared otherwise.

Boolean Formulae for Condition Codes:

$$N = R_7$$
$$Z = \bar{R}_7 \cdot \bar{R}_6 \cdot \bar{R}_5 \cdot \bar{R}_4 \cdot \bar{R}_3 \cdot \bar{R}_2 \cdot \bar{R}_1 \cdot \bar{R}_0$$
$$V = N \oplus C = [N \cdot \bar{C}] \odot [\bar{N} \cdot C]$$

(the foregoing formula assumes values of N and C after the shift operation)

$$C = M_0$$

Addressing Formats:

See Table A-3

Addressing Modes, Execution Time, and Machine Code (hexadecimal/ octal/ decimal):

Addressing Modes	Execution Time (No. of cycles)	Number of bytes of machine code	Coding of First (or only) byte of machine code		
			HEX.	OCT.	DEC.
A	2	1	47	107	071
B	2	1	57	127	087
EXT	6	3	77	167	119
IND	7	2	67	147	103

Branch if Carry Clear

BCC

Operation: $PC \leftarrow (PC) + 0002 + Rel$ if $(C)=0$

Description: Tests the state of the C bit and causes a branch if C is clear.

                    See BRA instruction for further details of the execution of the branch.

Condition Codes: Not affected.

Addressing Formats:

See Table A-8.

Addressing Modes, Execution Time, and Machine Code (hexadecimal/octal/decimal):

Addressing Modes	Execution Time (No. of cycles)	Number of bytes of machine code	Coding of First (or only) byte of machine code		
			HEX.	OCT.	DEC.
REL	4	2	24	044	036

BCS

Branch if Carry Set

Operation: $PC \leftarrow (PC) + 0002 + Rel$ if $(C)=1$

Description: Tests the state of the C bit and causes a branch if C is set.

See BRA instruction for further details of the execution of the branch.

Condition Codes: Not affected.

Addressing Formats:

See Table A-8.

Addressing Modes, Execution Time, and Machine Code (hexadecimal/octal/decimal):

Addressing Modes	Execution Time (No. of cycles)	Number of bytes of machine code	Coding of First (or only) byte of machine code		
			HEX.	OCT.	DEC.
REL	4	2	25	045	037

Branch if Equal **BEQ**

Operation:	PC ← (PC) + 0002 + Rel if (Z)=1
Description:	Tests the state of the Z bit and causes a branch if the Z bit is set.
	See BRA instruction for further details of the execution of the branch.
Condition Codes:	Not affected.
Addressing Formats:	
See Table A-8.	

Addressing Modes, Execution Time, and Machine Code (hexadecimal/octal/decimal):

Addressing Modes	Execution Time (No. of cycles)	Number of bytes of machine code	Coding of First (or only) byte of machine code		
			HEX.	OCT.	DEC.
REL	4	2	27	047	039

BGE

Branch if Greater than or Equal to Zero

Operation:

$$PC \leftarrow (PC) + 0002 + Rel \text{ if } (N) \oplus (V) = 0$$

$$\text{i.e. if } (ACCX) \geqslant (M)$$

(Two's complement numbers)

Description:

Causes a branch if (N is set and V is set) OR (N is clear and V is clear).

If the BGE instruction is executed immediately after execution of any of the instructions CBA, CMP, SBA, or SUB, the branch will occur if and only if the two's complement number represented by the minuend (i.e. ACCX) was greater than or equal to the two's complement number represented by the subtrahend (i.e. M).

See BRA instruction for details of the branch.

Condition Codes: Not affected.

Addressing Formats:

See Table A-8.

Addressing Modes, Execution Time, and Machine Code (hexadecimal/ octal/ decimal):

Addressing Modes	Execution Time (No. of cycles)	Number of bytes of machine code	Coding of First (or only) byte of machine code		
			HEX.	OCT.	DEC.
REL	4	2	2C	054	044

Branch if Greater than Zero **BGT**

Operation: $PC \leftarrow (PC) + 0002 + Rel$ if $(Z) \odot [(N) \oplus (V)] = 0$

i.e. if $(ACCX) > (M)$

(two's complement numbers)

Description: Causes a branch if [Z is clear] AND [(N is set and V is set) OR (N is clear and V is clear)].

If the BGT instruction is executed immediately after execution of any of the instructions CBA, CMP, SBA, or SUB, the branch will occur if and only if the two's complement number represented by the minuend (i.e. ACCX) was greater than the two's complement number represented by the subtrahend (i.e. M).

See BRA instruction for details of the branch.

Condition Codes: Not affected.

Addressing Formats:

See Table A-8.

Addressing Modes, Execution Time, and Machine Code (hexadecimal/ octal/ decimal):

Addressing Modes	Execution Time (No. of cycles)	Number of bytes of machine code	Coding of First (or only) byte of machine code		
			HEX.	OCT.	DEC.
REL	4	2	2E	056	046

BHI

Branch if Higher

Operation: $PC \leftarrow (PC) + 0002 + Rel$ if $(C) \cdot (Z) = 0$

i.e. if $(ACCX) > (M)$
(unsigned binary numbers)

Description: Causes a branch if (C is clear) AND (Z is clear).

If the BHI instruction is executed immediately after execution of any of the instructions CBA, CMP, SBA, or SUB, the branch will occur if and only if the unsigned binary number represented by the minuend (i.e. ACCX) was greater than the unsigned binary number represented by the subtrahend (i.e. M).

See BRA instruction for details of the execution of the branch.

Condition Codes: Not affected.

Addressing Formats:

See Table A-8.

Addressing Modes, Execution Time, and Machine Code (hexadecimal/octal/decimal):

Addressing Modes	Execution Time (No. of cycles)	Number of bytes of machine code	Coding of First (or only) byte of machine code		
			HEX.	OCT.	DEC.
REL	4	2	22	042	034

Bit Test   **BIT**

Operation: $(ACCX) \cdot (M)$

Description: Performs the logical "AND" comparison of the contents of ACCX and the contents
                     of M and modifies condition codes accordingly. Neither the contents of ACCX or M
                     operands are affected. (Each bit of the result of the "AND" would be the logical
                     "AND" of the corresponding bits of M and ACCX.)

Condition Codes: H: Not affected.
                   I: Not affected.
                   N: Set if the most significant bit of the result of the "AND" would be set; cleared
                        otherwise.
                   Z: Set if all bits of the result of the "AND" would be cleared; cleared otherwise.
                   V: Cleared.
                   C: Not affected.

Boolean Formulae for Condition Codes:
$$N = R_7$$
$$Z = \overline{R}_7 \cdot \overline{R}_6 \cdot \overline{R}_5 \cdot \overline{R}_4 \cdot \overline{R}_3 \cdot \overline{R}_2 \cdot \overline{R}_1 \cdot \overline{R}_0$$
$$V = 0$$

Addressing Formats:

See Table A-1.

Addressing Modes, Execution Time, and Machine Code (hexadecimal/ octal/ decimal):

Addressing Modes	Execution Time (No. of cycles)	Number of bytes of machine code	Coding of First (or only) byte of machine code		
			HEX.	OCT.	DEC.
A IMM	2	2	85	205	133
A DIR	3	2	95	225	149
A EXT	4	3	B5	265	181
A IND	5	2	A5	245	165
B IMM	2	2	C5	305	197
B DIR	3	2	D5	325	213
B EXT	4	3	F5	365	245
B IND	5	2	E5	345	229

BLE

Branch if Less than or Equal to Zero

Operation: $PC \leftarrow (PC) + 0002 + Rel$ if $(Z) \odot [(N) \oplus (V)] = 1$

i.e. if $(ACCX) \leqslant (M)$

(two's complement numbers)

Description: Causes a branch if [Z is set] OR [(N is set and V is clear) OR (N is clear and V is set)].

If the BLE instruction is executed immediately after execution of any of the instructions CBA, CMP, SBA, or SUB, the branch will occur if and only if the two's complement number represented by the minuend (i.e. ACCX) was less then or equal to the two's complement number represented by the subtrahend (i.e. M).

See BRA instruction for details of the branch.

Condition Codes: Not affected.

Addressing Formats:

See Table A-8.

Addressing Modes, Execution Time, and Machine Code (hexadecimal/octal/decimal):

Addressing Modes	Execution Time (No. of cycles)	Number of bytes of machine code	Coding of First (or only) byte of machine code		
			HEX.	OCT.	DEC.
REL	4	2	2F	057	047

Branch if Lower or Same　　　　　　　　　　　　　　　　　　**BLS**

Operation:　　　　　$PC \leftarrow (PC) + 0002 + Rel$ if $(C) \odot (Z) = 1$

i.e. if $(ACCX) \leq (M)$

(unsigned binary numbers)

Description:　　　Causes a branch if (C is set) OR (Z is set).

If the BLS instruction is executed immediately after execution of any of the instructions CBA, CMP, SBA, or SUB, the branch will occur if and only if the unsigned binary number represented by the minuend (i.e. ACCX) was less than or equal to the unsigned binary number represented by the subtrahend (i.e. M).

See BRA instruction for details of the execution of the branch.

Condition Codes:　Not affected.

Addressing Formats:

See Table A-8.

Addressing Modes, Execution Time, and Machine Code (hexadecimal/ octal/ decimal):

Addressing Modes	Execution Time (No. of cycles)	Number of bytes of machine code	Coding of First (or only) byte of machine code		
			HEX.	OCT.	DEC.
REL	4	2	23	043	035

BLT

Branch if Less than Zero

Operation: $PC \leftarrow (PC) + 0002 + Rel$ if $(N) \oplus (V) = 1$

i.e. if $(ACCX) < (M)$

(two's complement numbers)

Description: Causes a branch if (N is set and V is clear) OR (N is clear and V is set).

If the BLT instruction is executed immediately after execution of any of the instructions CBA, CMP, SBA, or SUB, the branch will occur if and only if the two's complement number represented by the minuend (i.e. ACCX) was less than the two's complement number represented by the subtrahend (i.e. M).

See BRA instruction for details of the branch.

Condition Codes: Not affected.

Addressing Formats:

See Table A-8.

Addressing Modes, Execution Time, and Machine Code (hexadecimal / octal / decimal):

Addressing Modes	Execution Time (No. of cycles)	Number of bytes of machine code	Coding of First (or only) byte of machine code		
			HEX.	OCT.	DEC.
REL	4	2	2D	055	045

Branch if Minus **BMI**

Operation: PC← (PC) + 0002 + Rel if (N) =1

Description: Tests the state of the N bit and causes a branch if N is set.

See BRA instruction for details of the execution of the branch.

Condition Codes: Not affected.

Addressing Formats:

See Table A-8.

Addressing Modes, Execution Time, and Machine Code (hexadecimal/ octal/ decimal):

Addressing Modes	Execution Time (No. of cycles)	Number of bytes of machine code	Coding of First (or only) byte of machine code		
			HEX.	OCT.	DEC.
REL	4	2	2B	053	043

BNE

Branch if Not Equal

Operation: $PC \leftarrow (PC) + 0002 + Rel$ if $(Z) = 0$

Description: Tests the state of the Z bit and causes a branch if the Z bit is clear.

See BRA instruction for details of the execution of the branch.

Condition Codes: Not affected.

Addressing Formats:

See Table A-8.

Addressing Modes, Execution Time, and Machine Code (hexadecimal/ octal/ decimal):

Addressing Modes	Execution Time (No. of cycles)	Number of bytes of machine code	Coding of First (or only) byte of machine code		
			HEX.	OCT.	DEC.
REL	4	2	26	046	038

Branch if Plus

BPL

Operation: PC ← (PC) + 0002 + Rel if (N) =0

Description: Tests the state of the N bit and causes a branch if N is clear.

        See BRA instruction for details of the execution of the branch.

Condition Codes: Not affected.

Addressing Formats:

See Table A-8.

Addressing Modes, Execution Time, and Machine Code (hexadecimal / octal / decimal):

Addressing Modes	Execution Time (No. of cycles)	Number of bytes of machine code	Coding of First (or only) byte of machine code		
			HEX.	OCT.	DEC.
REL	4	2	2A	052	042

BRA

Branch Always

Operation: $PC \leftarrow (PC) + 0002 + Rel$

Description: Unconditional branch to the address given by the foregoing formula, in which R is the relative address stored as a two's complement number in the second byte of machine code corresponding to the branch instruction.

Note: The source program specifies the destination of any branch instruction by its absolute address, either as a numerical value or as a symbol or expression which can be numerically evaluated by the assembler. The assembler obtains the relative address R from the absolute address and the current value of the program counter PC.

Condition Codes: Not affected.

Addressing Formats:

See Table A-8.

Addressing Modes, Execution Time, and Machine Code (hexadecimal/octal/decimal):

Addressing Modes	Execution Time (No. of cycles)	Number of bytes of machine code	Coding of First (or only) byte of machine code		
			HEX.	OCT.	DEC.
REL	4	2	20	040	032

Branch to Subroutine **BSR**

Operation: $PC \leftarrow (PC) + 0002$

$\downarrow (PCL)$

$SP \leftarrow (SP) - 0001$

$\downarrow (PCH)$

$SP \leftarrow (SP) - 0001$

$PC \leftarrow (PC) + Rel$

Description: The program counter is incremented by 2. The less significant byte of the contents of the program counter is pushed into the stack. The stack pointer is then decremented (by 1). The more significant byte of the contents of the program counter is then pushed into the stack. The stack pointer is again decremented (by 1). A branch then occurs to the location specified by the program.

See BRA instruction for details of the execution of the branch.

Condition Codes: Not affected.

Addressing Formats:

See Table A-8.

Addressing Modes, Execution Time, and Machine Code (hexadecimal / octal / decimal):

Addressing Modes	Execution Time (No. of cycles)	Number of bytes of machine code	Coding of First (or only) byte of machine code		
			HEX.	OCT.	DEC.
REL	8	2	8D	215	141

BRANCH TO SUBROUTINE EXAMPLE

			Memory Location	Machine Code (Hex)	Assembler Language		
					Label	Operator	Operand
A.	*Before*						
	PC	←	$1000	8D		BSR	CHARLI
			$1001	50			
	SP	←	$EFFF				
B.	*After*						
	PC	←	$1052	**	CHARLI	***	*****
	SP	←	$EFFD				
			$EFFE	10			
			$EFFF	02			

BVC

Branch if Overflow Clear

Operation: $PC \leftarrow (PC) + 0002 + Rel$ if $(V) = 0$

Description: Tests the state of the V bit and causes a branch if the V bit is clear.

                                  See BRA instruction for details of the execution of the branch.

Condition Codes: Not affected.

Addressing Formats:

See Table A-8.

Addressing Modes, Execution Time, and Machine Code (hexadecimal/ octal/ decimal):

Addressing Modes	Execution Time (No. of cycles)	Number of bytes of machine code	Coding of First (or only) byte of machine code		
			HEX.	OCT.	DEC.
REL	4	2	28	050	040

Branch if Overflow Set   **BVS**

Operation: $PC \leftarrow (PC) + 0002 + Rel$ if $(V) = 1$

Description: Tests the state of the V bit and causes a branch if the V bit is set.

           See BRA instruction for details of the execution of the branch.

Condition Codes: Not affected.

Addressing Formats:

See Table A-8.

Addressing Modes, Execution Time, and Machine Code (hexadecimal/ octal/ decimal):

Addressing Modes	Execution Time (No. of cycles)	Number of bytes of machine code	Coding of First (or only) byte of machine code		
			HEX.	OCT.	DEC.
REL	4	2	29	051	041

CBA

Compare Accumulators

Operation: (ACCA) − (ACCB)

Description: Compares the contents of ACCA and the contents of ACCB and sets the condition codes, which may be used for arithmetic and logical conditional branches. Both operands are unaffected.

Condition Codes: H: Not affected.
                  I: Not affected.
                  N: Set if the most significant bit of the result of the subtraction would be set; cleared otherwise.
                  Z: Set if all bits of the result of the subtraction would be cleared; cleared otherwise.
                  V: Set if the subtraction would cause two's complement overflow; cleared otherwise.
                  C: Set if the subtraction would require a borrow into the most significant bit of the result; clear otherwise.

Boolean Formulae for Condition Codes:

$$N = R_7$$
$$Z = \overline{R_7} \cdot \overline{R_6} \cdot \overline{R_5} \cdot \overline{R_4} \cdot \overline{R_3} \cdot \overline{R_2} \cdot \overline{R_1} \cdot \overline{R_0}$$
$$V = A_7 \cdot \overline{B_7} \cdot \overline{R_7} + \overline{A_7} \cdot B_7 \cdot R_7$$
$$C = \overline{A_7} \cdot B_7 + B_7 \cdot R_7 + R_7 \cdot \overline{A_7}$$

Addressing Modes, Execution Time, and Machine Code (hexadecimal/ octal/ decimal):

Addressing Modes	Execution Time (No. of cycles)	Number of bytes of machine code	Coding of First (or only) byte of machine code		
			HEX.	OCT.	DEC.
INHERENT	2	1	11	021	017

CLC

Clear Carry

Operation: C bit ← 0

Description: Clears the carry bit in the processor condition codes register.

Condition Codes: H: Not affected.
                           I: Not affected.
                           N: Not affected.
                           Z: Not affected.
                           V: Not affected.
                           C: Cleared

Boolean Formulae for Condition Codes:
                           C = 0

Addressing Modes, Execution Time, and Machine Code (hexadecimal/octal/decimal):

Addressing Modes	Execution Time (No. of cycles)	Number of bytes of machine code	Coding of First (or only) byte of machine code		
			HEX.	OCT.	DEC.
INHERENT	2	1	0C	014	012

CLI

Clear Interrupt Mask

Operation: I bit ← 0

Description: Clears the interrupt mask bit in the processor condition codes register. This enables the microprocessor to service an interrupt from a peripheral device if signalled by a high state of the "Interrupt Request" control input.

Condition Codes: H: Not affected.
                  I: Cleared.
                  N: Not affected.
                  Z: Not affected.
                  V: Not affected.
                  C: Not affected.

Boolean Formulae for Condition Codes:

$I = 0$

Addressing Modes, Execution Time, and Machine Code (hexadecimal/ octal/ decimal):

Addressing Modes	Execution Time (No. of cycles)	Number of bytes of machine code	Coding of First (or only) byte of machine code		
			HEX.	OCT.	DEC.
INHERENT	2	1	0E	016	014

Clear **CLR**

Operation:	ACCX ← 00
or:	M ← 00

Description: The contents of ACCX or M are replaced with zeros.

Condition Codes:
- H: Not affected.
- I: Not affected.
- N: Cleared
- Z: Set
- V: Cleared
- C: Cleared

Boolean Formulae for Condition Codes:

$$N = 0$$
$$Z = 1$$
$$V = 0$$
$$C = 0$$

Addressing Formats:

See Table A-3.

Addressing Modes, Execution Time, and Machine Code (hexadecimal/octal/decimal):

Addressing Modes	Execution Time (No. of cycles)	Number of bytes of machine code	Coding of First (or only) byte of machine code		
			HEX.	OCT.	DEC.
A	2	1	4F	117	079
B	2	1	5F	137	095
EXT	6	3	7F	177	127
IND	7	2	6F	157	111

CLV
Clear Two's Complement Overflow Bit

Operation: V bit ← 0

Description: Clears the two's complement overflow bit in the processor condition codes register.

Condition Codes: H: Not affected.
                           I: Not affected.
                          N: Not affected.
                          Z: Not affected.
                          V: Cleared.
                          C: Not affected.

Boolean Formulae for Condition Codes:
         $V = 0$

Addressing Modes, Execution Time, and Machine Code (hexadecimal/ octal/ decimal):

Addressing Modes	Execution Time (No. of cycles)	Number of bytes of machine code	Coding of First (or only) byte of machine code		
			HEX.	OCT.	DEC.
INHERENT	2	1	0A	012	010

Compare **CMP**

Operation: $(ACCX) - (M)$

Description: Compares the contents of ACCX and the contents of M and determines the condition codes, which may be used subsequently for controlling conditional branching. Both operands are unaffected.

Condition Codes:
H: Not affected.
I: Not affected.
N: Set if the most significant bit of the result of the subtraction would be set; cleared otherwise.
Z: Set if all bits of the result of the subtraction would be cleared; cleared otherwise.
V: Set if the subtraction would cause two's complement overflow; cleared otherwise.
C: Carry is set if the absolute value of the contents of memory is larger than the absolute value of the accumulator; reset otherwise.

Boolean Formulae for Condition Codes:

$$N = R_7$$
$$Z = \overline{R_7} \cdot \overline{R_6} \cdot \overline{R_5} \cdot \overline{R_4} \cdot \overline{R_3} \cdot \overline{R_2} \cdot \overline{R_1} \cdot \overline{R_0}$$
$$V = X_7 \cdot \overline{M_7} \cdot \overline{R_7} + \overline{X_7} \cdot M_7 \cdot R_7$$
$$C = \overline{X_7} \cdot M_7 + M_7 \cdot R_7 + R_7 \cdot \overline{X_7}$$

Addressing Formats:

See Table A-1.

Addressing Modes, Execution Time, and Machine Code (hexadecimal / octal / decimal):

(DUAL OPERAND)

Addressing Modes	Execution Time (No. of cycles)	Number of bytes of machine code	Coding of First (or only) byte of machine code		
			HEX.	OCT.	DEC.
A IMM	2	2	81	201	129
A DIR	3	2	91	221	145
A EXT	4	3	B1	261	177
A IND	5	2	A1	241	161
B IMM	2	2	C1	301	193
B DIR	3	2	D1	321	209
B EXT	4	3	F1	361	241
B IND	5	2	E1	341	225

COM
Complement

Operation: $ACCX \leftarrow \approx (ACCX) = FF - (ACCX)$

or: $M \leftarrow \approx (M) = FF - (M)$

Description: Replaces the contents of ACCX or M with its one's complement. (Each bit of the contents of ACCX or M is replaced with the complement of that bit.)

Condition Codes: H: Not affected.
                    I: Not affected.
                   N: Set if most significant bit of the result is set; cleared otherwise.
                   Z: Set if all bits of the result are cleared; cleared otherwise.
                   V: Cleared.
                   C: Set.

Boolean Formulae for Condition Codes:

$$N = R_7$$
$$Z = \bar{R}_7 \cdot \bar{R}_6 \cdot \bar{R}_5 \cdot \bar{R}_4 \cdot \bar{R}_3 \cdot \bar{R}_2 \cdot \bar{R}_1 \cdot \bar{R}_0$$
$$V = 0$$
$$C = 1$$

Addressing Formats:

See Table A-3.

Addressing Modes, Execution Time, and Machine Code (hexadecimal / octal / decimal):

Addressing Modes	Execution Time (No. of cycles)	Number of bytes of machine code	Coding of First (or only) byte of machine code		
			HEX.	OCT.	DEC.
A	2	1	43	103	067
B	2	1	53	123	083
EXT	6	3	73	163	115
IND	7	2	63	143	099

Compare Index Register   **CPX**

Operation: (IXL) − (M+1)
                    (IXH) − (M)

Description: The more significant byte of the contents of the index register is compared with the contents of the byte of memory at the address specified by the program. The less significant byte of the contents of the index register is compared with the contents of the next byte of memory, at one plus the address specified by the program. The Z bit is set or reset according to the results of these comparisons, and may be used subsequently for conditional branching.

The N and V bits, though determined by this operation, are not intended for conditional branching.

The C bit is not affected by this operation.

Condition Codes: H: Not affected.
                    I: Not affected.
                    N: Set if the most significant bit of the result of the subtraction from the more significant byte of the index register would be set; cleared otherwise.
                    Z: Set if all bits of the results of both subtractions would be cleared; cleared otherwise.
                    V: Set if the subtraction from the more significant byte of the index register would cause two's complement overflow; cleared otherwise.
                    C: Not affected.

Boolean Formulae for Condition Codes:

$$N = RH_7$$
$$Z = (\overline{RH_7} \cdot \overline{RH_6} \cdot \overline{RH_5} \cdot \overline{RH_4} \cdot \overline{RH_3} \cdot \overline{RH_2} \cdot \overline{RH_1} \cdot \overline{RH_0}) \cdot$$
$$(\overline{RL_7} \cdot \overline{RL_6} \cdot \overline{RL_5} \cdot \overline{RL_4} \cdot \overline{RL_3} \cdot \overline{RL_2} \cdot \overline{RL_1} \cdot \overline{RL_0})$$
$$V = IXH_7 \cdot \overline{M_7} \cdot \overline{RH_7} + \overline{IXH_7} \cdot M_7 \cdot RH_7$$

Addressing Formats:

See Table A-5.

Addressing Modes, Execution Time, and Machine Code (hexadecimal/octal/decimal):

Addressing Modes	Execution Time (No. of cycles)	Number of bytes of machine code	Coding of First (or only) byte of machine code		
			HEX.	OCT.	DEC.
IMM	3	3	8C	214	140
DIR	4	2	9C	234	156
EXT	5	3	BC	274	188
IND	6	2	AC	254	172

DAA
Decimal Adjust ACCA

Operation: Adds hexadecimal numbers 00, 06, 60, or 66 to ACCA, and may also set the carry bit, as indicated in the following table:

State of C-bit before DAA (Col. 1)	Upper Half-byte (bits 4-7) (Col. 2)	Initial Half-carry H-bit (Col.3)	Lower to ACCA (bits 0-3) (Col. 4)	Number Added after by DAA (Col. 5)	State of C-bit DAA (Col. 6)
0	0-9	0	0-9	00	0
0	0-8	0	A-F	06	0
0	0-9	1	0-3	06	0
0	A-F	0	0-9	60	1
0	9-F	0	A-F	66	1
0	A-F	1	0-3	66	1
1	0-2	0	0-9	60	1
1	0-2	0	A-F	66	1
1	0-3	1	0-3	66	1

Note: Columns (1) through (4) of the above table represent all possible cases which can result from any of the operations ABA, ADD, or ADC, with initial carry either set or clear, applied to two binary-coded-decimal operands. The table shows hexadecimal values.

Description: If the contents of ACCA and the state of the carry-borrow bit C and the half-carry bit H are all the result of applying any of the operations ABA, ADD, or ADC to binary-coded-decimal operands, with or without an initial carry, the DAA operation will function as follows.

Subject to the above condition, the DAA operation will adjust the contents of ACCA and the C bit to represent the correct binary-coded-decimal sum and the correct state of the carry.

Condition Codes: H: Not affected.
I: Not affected.
N: Set if most significant bit of the result is set; cleared otherwise.
Z: Set if all bits of the result are cleared; cleared otherwise.
V: Not defined.
C: Set or reset according to the same rule as if the DAA and an immediately preceding ABA, ADD, or ADC were replaced by a hypothetical binary-coded-decimal addition.

Boolean Formulae for Condition Codes:

$$N = R_7$$
$$Z = \bar{R}_7 \cdot \bar{R}_6 \cdot \bar{R}_5 \cdot \bar{R}_4 \cdot \bar{R}_3 \cdot \bar{R}_2 \cdot \bar{R}_1 \cdot \bar{R}_0$$
$$C = \text{See table above.}$$

Addressing Modes, Execution Time, and Machine Code (hexadecimal/octal/decimal):

Addressing Modes	Execution Time (No. of cycles)	Number of bytes of machine code	Coding of First (or only) byte of machine code		
			HEX.	OCT.	DEC.
INHERENT	2	1	19	031	025

DEC

Decrement

Operation:	$ACCX \leftarrow (ACCX) - 01$
or:	$M \leftarrow (M) - 01$

Description: Subtract one from the contents of ACCX or M.

The N, Z, and V condition codes are set or reset according to the results of this operation.

The C bit is not affected by the operation.

Condition Codes:
H: Not affected.
I: Not affected.
N: Set if most significant bit of the result is set; cleared otherwise.
Z: Set if all bits of the result are cleared; cleared otherwise.
V: Set if there was two's complement overflow as a result of the operation; cleared otherwise. Two's complement overflow occurs if and only if (ACCX) or (M) was 80 before the operation.
C: Not affected.

Boolean Formulae for Condition Codes:

$N = R_7$

$Z = \overline{R}_7 \cdot \overline{R}_6 \cdot \overline{R}_5 \cdot \overline{R}_5 \cdot \overline{R}_4 \cdot \overline{R}_3 \cdot \overline{R}_2 \cdot \overline{R}_1 \cdot \overline{R}_0$

$V = X_7 \cdot \overline{X}_6 \cdot \overline{X}_5 \cdot \overline{X}_4 \cdot \overline{X}_3 \cdot \overline{X}_2 \cdot \overline{X}_0 = \overline{R}_7 \cdot R_6 \cdot R_5 \cdot R_4 \cdot R_3 \cdot R_2 \cdot R_1 \cdot R_0$

Addressing Formats:

See Table A-3.

Addressing Modes, Execution Time, and Machine Code (hexadecimal/octal/decimal):

Addressing Modes	Execution Time (No. of cycles)	Number of bytes of machine code	Coding of First (or only) byte of machine code		
			HEX.	OCT.	DEC.
A	2	1	4A	112	074
B	2	1	5A	132	090
EXT	6	3	7A	172	122
IND	7	2	6A	152	106

Decrement Stack Pointer

DES

Operation: SP ← (SP) − 0001

Description: Subtract one from the stack pointer.

Condition Codes: Not affected.

Addressing Modes, Execution Time, and Machine Code (hexadecimal/ octal/ decimal):

Addressing Modes	Execution Time (No. of cycles)	Number of bytes of machine code	Coding of First (or only) byte of machine code		
			HEX.	OCT.	DEC.
INHERENT	4	1	34	064	052

DEX

Decrement Index Register

Operation: $IX \leftarrow (IX) - 0001$

Description: Subtract one from the index register.

Only the Z bit is set or reset according to the result of this operation.

Condition Codes: H: Not affected.
I: Not affected.
N: Not affected.
Z: Set if all bits of the result are cleared; cleared otherwise.
V: Not affected.
C: Not affected.

Boolean Formulae for Condition Codes:

$$Z = (\overline{RH_7} \cdot \overline{RH_6} \cdot \overline{RH_5} \cdot \overline{RH_4} \cdot \overline{RH_3} \cdot \overline{RH_2} \cdot \overline{RH_1} \cdot \overline{RH_0}) \cdot$$
$$(\overline{RL_7} \cdot \overline{RL_6} \cdot \overline{RL_5} \cdot \overline{RL_4} \cdot \overline{RL_3} \cdot \overline{RL_2} \cdot \overline{RL_1} \cdot \overline{RL_0})$$

Addressing Modes, Execution Time, and Machine Code (hexadecimal/octal/decimal):

Addressing Modes	Execution Time (No. of cycles)	Number of bytes of machine code	Coding of First (or only) byte of machine code		
			HEX.	OCT.	DEC.
INHERENT	4	1	09	011	009

Exclusive OR

EOR

Operation: $\quad\quad\quad$ ACCX ← (ACCX) ⊕ (M)

Description: $\quad\quad$ Perform logical "EXCLUSIVE OR" between the contents of ACCX and the contents of M, and place the result in ACCX. (Each bit of ACCX after the operation will be the logical "EXCLUSIVE OR" of the corresponding bit of M and ACCX before the operation.)

Condition Codes: $\quad$ H: $\quad$ Not affected.

$\quad\quad\quad\quad\quad\quad\quad$ I: $\quad$ Not affected.

$\quad\quad\quad\quad\quad\quad\quad$ N: $\quad$ Set if most significant bit of the result is set; cleared otherwise.

$\quad\quad\quad\quad\quad\quad\quad$ Z: $\quad$ Set if all bits of the result are cleared; cleared otherwise.

$\quad\quad\quad\quad\quad\quad\quad$ V: $\quad$ Cleared

$\quad\quad\quad\quad\quad\quad\quad$ C: $\quad$ Not affected.

Boolean Formulae for Condition Codes:

$$N = R_7$$
$$Z = \bar{R}_7 \cdot \bar{R}_6 \cdot \bar{R}_5 \cdot \bar{R}_4 \cdot \bar{R}_3 \cdot \bar{R}_2 \cdot \bar{R}_1 \cdot \bar{R}_0$$
$$V = 0$$

Addressing Formats:

See Table A-1.

Addressing Modes, Execution Time, and Machine Code (hexadecimal / octal / decimal):

Addressing Modes	Execution Time (No. of cycles)	Number of bytes of machine code	Coding of First (or only) byte of machine code		
			HEX.	OCT.	DEC.
A IMM	2	2	88	210	136
A DIR	3	2	98	230	152
A EXT	4	3	B8	270	184
A IND	5	2	A8	250	168
B IMM	2	2	C8	310	200
B DIR	3	2	D8	330	216
B EXT	4	3	F8	370	248
B IND	5	2	E8	350	232

INC

Increment

Operation:	ACCX ← (ACCX) + 01
or:	M ← (M) + 01
Description:	Add one to the contents of ACCX or M.

The N, Z, and V condition codes are set or reset according to the results of this operation.

The C bit is not affected by the operation.

Condition Codes:
H: Not affected.
I: Not affected.
N: Set if most significant bit of the result is set; cleared otherwise.
Z: Set if all bits of the result are cleared; cleared otherwise.
V: Set if there was two's complement overflow as a result of the operation; cleared otherwise. Two's complement overflow will occur if and only if (ACCX) or (M) was 7F before the operation.
C: Not affected.

Boolean Formulae for Condition Codes:

$$N = R_7$$
$$Z = \overline{R}_7 \cdot \overline{R}_6 \cdot \overline{R}_5 \cdot \overline{R}_4 \cdot \overline{R}_3 \cdot \overline{R}_2 \cdot \overline{R}_1 \cdot \overline{R}_0$$
$$V = \overline{X}_7 \cdot X_6 \cdot X_5 \cdot X_4 \cdot X_3 \cdot X_2 \cdot X_1 \cdot X_0$$
$$C = \overline{R}_7 \cdot \overline{R}_6 \cdot \overline{R}_5 \cdot \overline{R}_4 \cdot \overline{R}_3 \cdot \overline{R}_2 \cdot \overline{R}_1 \cdot \overline{R}_0$$

Addressing Formats:

See Table A-3.

Addressing Modes, Execution Time, and Machine Code (hexadecimal/ octal/ decimal):

Addressing Modes	Execution Time (No. of cycles)	Number of bytes of machine code	Coding of First (or only) byte of machine code		
			HEX.	OCT.	DEC.
A	2	1	4C	114	076
B	2	1	5C	134	092
EXT	6	3	7C	174	124
IND	7	2	6C	154	108

Increment Stack Pointer **INS**

Operation: $SP \leftarrow (SP) + 0001$

Description: Add one to the stack pointer.

Condition Codes: Not affected.

Addressing Modes, Execution Time, and Machine Code (hexadecimal/octal/decimal):

Addressing Modes	Execution Time (No. of cycles)	Number of bytes of machine code	Coding of First (or only) byte of machine code		
			HEX.	OCT.	DEC.
INHERENT	4	1	31	061	049

INX

Operation: IX ← (IX) + 0001

Description: Add one to the index register.

Only the Z bit is set or reset according to the result of this operation.

Condition Codes: H: Not affected.
I: Not affected.
N: Not affected.
Z: Set if all 16 bits of the result are cleared; cleared otherwise.
V: Not affected.
C: Not affected.

Boolean Formulae for Condition Codes:

$$Z = (\overline{RH_7} \cdot \overline{RH_6} \cdot \overline{RH_5} \cdot \overline{RH_4} \cdot \overline{RH_3} \cdot \overline{RH_2} \cdot \overline{RH_1} \cdot \overline{RH_0}) \cdot$$
$$(\overline{RL_7} \cdot \overline{RL_6} \cdot \overline{RL_5} \cdot \overline{RL_4} \cdot \overline{RL_3} \cdot \overline{RL_2} \cdot \overline{RL_1} \cdot \overline{RL_0})$$

Addressing Modes, Execution Time, and Machine Code (hexadecimal / octal / decimal):

Addressing Modes	Execution Time (No. of cycles)	Number of bytes of machine code	Coding of First (or only) byte of machine code		
			HEX.	OCT.	DEC.
INHERENT	4	1	08	010	008

Jump   JMP

Operation: PC ← numerical address

Description: A jump occurs to the instruction stored at the numerical address. The numerical address is obtained according to the rules for EXTended or INDexed addressing.

Condition Codes: Not affected.

Addressing Formats:

See Table A-7.

Addressing Modes, Execution Time, and Machine Code (hexadecimal/ octal/ decimal):

Addressing Modes	Execution Time (No. of cycles)	Number of bytes of machine code	Coding of First (or only) byte of machine code		
			HEX.	OCT.	DEC.
EXT	3	3	7E	176	126
IND	4	2	6E	156	110

JSR
Jump to Subroutine

Operation:

Either:	PC ← (PC) + 0003 (for EXTended addressing)
or:	PC ← (PC) + 0002 (for INDexed addressing)
Then:	↓ (PCL)
	SP ← (SP) − 0001
	↓ (PCH)
	SP ← (SP) − 0001
	PC ← numerical address

Description: The program counter is incremented by 3 or by 2, depending on the addressing mode, and is then pushed onto the stack, eight bits at a time. The stack pointer points to the next empty location in the stack. A jump occurs to the instruction stored at the numerical address. The numerical address is obtained according to the rules for EXTended or INDexed addressing.

Condition Codes: Not affected.

Addressing Formats:

See Table A-7.

Addressing Modes, Execution Time, and Machine Code (hexadecimal/ octal/ decimal):

Addressing Modes	Execution Time (No. of cycles)	Number of bytes of machine code	Coding of First (or only) byte of machine code		
			HEX.	OCT.	DEC.
EXT	9	3	BD	275	189
IND	8	2	AD	255	173

JUMP TO SUBROUTINE EXAMPLE (extended mode)

		Memory Location		Machine Code (Hex)	Assembler Language		
					Label	Operator	Operand
A.	*Before:*						
	PC	→	$0FFF	BD		JSR	CHARLI
			$1000	20			
			$1001	77			
	SP	←	$EFFF				
B.	*After:*						
	PC	→	$2077	**	CHARLI	***	*****
	SP	→	$EFFD				
			$EFFE	10			
			$EFFF	02			

Load Accumulator   # LDA

Operation: $ACCX \leftarrow (M)$

Description: Loads the contents of memory into the accumulator. The condition codes are set according to the data.

Condition Codes: H: Not affected.

                       I: Not affected.

                       N: Set if most significant bit of the result is set; cleared otherwise.

                       Z: Set if all bits of the result are cleared; cleared otherwise.

                       V: Cleared.

                       C: Not affected.

Boolean Formulae for Condition Codes:

$$N = R_7$$
$$Z = \bar{R}_7 \cdot \bar{R}_6 \cdot \bar{R}_5 \cdot \bar{R}_4 \cdot \bar{R}_3 \cdot \bar{R}_2 \cdot \bar{R}_1 \cdot \bar{R}_0$$
$$V = 0$$

Addressing Formats:

See Table A-1.

Addressing Modes, Execution Time, and Machine Code (hexadecimal/octal/decimal):

(DUAL OPERAND)

Addressing Modes	Execution Time (No. of cycles)	Number of bytes of machine code	Coding of First (or only) byte of machine code		
			HEX.	OCT.	DEC.
A IMM	2	2	86	206	134
A DIR	3	2	96	226	150
A EXT	4	3	B6	266	182
A IND	5	2	A6	246	166
B IMM	2	2	C6	306	198
B DIR	3	2	D6	326	214
B EXT	4	3	F6	366	246
B IND	5	2	E6	346	230

LDS

Load Stack Pointer

Operation: SPH ← (M)
SPL ← (M+1)

Description: Loads the more significant byte of the stack pointer from the byte of memory at the address specified by the program, and loads the less significant byte of the stack pointer from the next byte of memory, at one plus the address specified by the program.

Condition Codes: H: Not affected.
I: Not affected.
N: Set if the most significant bit of the stack pointer is set by the operation; cleared otherwise.
Z: Set if all bits of the stack pointer are cleared by the operation; cleared otherwise.
V: Cleared.
C: Not affected.

Boolean Formulae for Condition Codes:

$N = RH_7$

$Z = (\overline{RH_7} \cdot \overline{RH_6} \cdot \overline{RH_5} \cdot \overline{RH_4} \cdot \overline{RH_3} \cdot \overline{RH_2} \cdot \overline{RH_1} \cdot \overline{RH_0}) \cdot$
$ (\overline{RL_7} \cdot \overline{RL_6} \cdot \overline{RL_5} \cdot \overline{RL_4} \cdot \overline{RL_3} \cdot \overline{RL_2} \cdot \overline{RL_1} \cdot \overline{RL_0})$

$V = 0$

Addressing Formats:

See Table A-5.

Addressing Modes, Execution Time, and Machine Code (hexadecimal/ octal/ decimal):

Addressing Modes	Execution Time (No. of cycles)	Number of bytes of machine code	Coding of First (or only) byte of machine code		
			HEX.	OCT.	DEC.
IMM	3	3	8E	216	142
DIR	4	2	9E	236	158
EXT	5	3	BE	276	190
IND	6	2	AE	256	174

Load Index Register

LDX

Operation:

$IXH \leftarrow (M)$

$IXL \leftarrow (M+1)$

Description: Loads the more significant byte of the index register from the byte of memory at the address specified by the program, and loads the less significant byte of the index register from the next byte of memory, at one plus the address specified by the program.

Condition Codes:
H: Not affected.

I: Not affected.

N: Set if the most significant bit of the index register is set by the operation; cleared otherwise.

Z: Set if all bits of the index register are cleared by the operation; cleared otherwise.

V: Cleared.

C: Not affected.

Boolean Formulae for Condition Codes:

$N = RH_7$

$Z = (\overline{RH_7} \cdot \overline{RH_6} \cdot \overline{RH_5} \cdot \overline{RH_4} \cdot \overline{RH_3} \cdot \overline{RH_2} \cdot \overline{RH_1} \cdot \overline{RH_0}) \cdot$
$(\overline{RL_7} \cdot \overline{RL_6} \cdot \overline{RL_5} \cdot \overline{RL_4} \cdot \overline{RL_3} \cdot \overline{RL_2} \cdot \overline{RL_1} \cdot \overline{RL_0})$

$V = 0$

Addressing Formats:

See Table A-5.

Addressing Modes, Execution Time, and Machine Code (hexadecimal / octal / decimal):

Addressing Modes	Execution Time (No. of cycles)	Number of bytes of machine code	Coding of First (or only) byte of machine code		
			HEX.	OCT.	DEC.
IMM	3	3	CE	316	206
DIR	4	2	DE	336	222
EXT	5	3	FE	376	254
IND	6	2	EE	356	238

LSR

Logical Shift Right

Operation:

Description: Shifts all bits of ACCX or M one place to the right. Bit 7 is loaded with a zero. The C bit is loaded from the least significant bit of ACCX or M.

Condition Codes:
H: Not affected.
I: Not affected.
N: Cleared.
Z: Set if all bits of the result are cleared; cleared otherwise.
V: Set if, after the completion of the shift operation, EITHER (N is set and C is cleared) OR (N is cleared and C is set); cleared otherwise.
C: Set if, before the operation, the least significant bit of the ACCX or M was set; cleared otherwise.

Boolean Formulae for Condition Codes:

$$N = 0$$
$$Z = \overline{R}_7 \cdot \overline{R}_6 \cdot \overline{R}_5 \cdot \overline{R}_4 \cdot \overline{R}_3 \cdot \overline{R}_2 \cdot \overline{R}_1 \cdot \overline{R}_0$$
$$V = N \oplus C = [N \cdot \overline{C}] \odot [\overline{N} \cdot C]$$

(the foregoing formula assumes values of N and C after the shift operation).

$$C = M_0$$

Addressing Formats:

See Table A-3.

Addressing Modes, Execution Time, and Machine Code (hexadecimal/octal/decimal):

Addressing Modes	Execution Time (No. of cycles)	Number of bytes of machine code	Coding of First (or only) byte of machine code		
			HEX.	OCT.	DEC.
A	2	1	44	104	068
B	2	1	54	124	084
EXT	6	3	74	164	116
IND	7	2	64	144	100

Negate   # NEG

Operation:	ACCX ← − (ACCX) = 00 − (ACCX)
or:	M ← − (M) = 00 − (M)

Description: Replaces the contents of ACCX or M with its two's complement. Note that 80 is left unchanged.

Condition Codes:
- H: Not affected.
- I: Not affected.
- N: Set if most significant bit of the result is set; cleared otherwise.
- Z: Set if all bits of the result are cleared; cleared otherwise.
- V: Set if there would be two's complement overflow as a result of the implied subtraction from zero; this will occur if and only if the contents of ACCX or M is 80.
- C: Set if there would be a borrow in the implied subtraction from zero; the C bit will be set in all cases except when the contents of ACCX or M is 00.

Boolean Formulae for Condition Codes:

$$N = R_7$$
$$Z = \overline{R_7} \cdot \overline{R_6} \cdot \overline{R_5} \cdot \overline{R_4} \cdot \overline{R_3} \cdot \overline{R_2} \cdot \overline{R_1} \cdot \overline{R_0}$$
$$V = R_7 \cdot \overline{R_6} \cdot \overline{R_5} \cdot \overline{R_4} \cdot \overline{R_3} \cdot \overline{R_2} \cdot \overline{R_1} \cdot \overline{R_0}$$
$$C = R_7 + R_6 + R_5 + R_4 + R_3 + R_2 + R_1 + R_0$$

Addressing Formats:

See Table A-3.

Addressing Modes, Execution Time, and Machine Code (hexadecimal/ octal/ decimal):

Addressing Modes	Execution Time (No. of cycles)	Number of bytes of machine code	Coding of First (or only) byte of machine code		
			HEX.	OCT.	DEC.
A	2	1	40	100	064
B	2	1	50	120	080
EXT	6	3	70	160	112
.IND	7	2	60	140	096

NOP

No Operation

Description: This is a single-word instruction which causes only the program counter to be incremented. No other registers are affected.

Condition Codes: Not affected.

Addressing Modes, Execution Time, and Machine Code (hexadecimal/ octal/ decimal):

Addressing Modes	Execution Time (No. of cycles)	Number of bytes of machine code	Coding of First (or only) byte of machine code		
			HEX.	OCT.	DEC.
INHERENT	2	1	01	001	001

Inclusive OR

ORA

Operation: $\text{ACCX} \leftarrow (\text{ACCX}) \odot (\text{M})$

Description: Perform logical "OR" between the contents of ACCX and the contents of M and places the result in ACCX. (Each bit of ACCX after the operation will be the logical "OR" of the corresponding bits of M and of ACCX before the operation).

Condition Codes: H: Not affected.

                     I: Not affected.

                     N: Set if most significant bit of the result is set; cleared otherwise.

                     Z: Set if all bits of the result are cleared; cleared otherwise.

                     V: Cleared.

                     C: Not affected.

Boolean Formulae for Condition Codes:

$$N = R_7$$
$$Z = \bar{R}_7 \cdot \bar{R}_6 \cdot \bar{R}_5 \cdot \bar{R}_4 \cdot \bar{R}_3 \cdot \bar{R}_2 \cdot \bar{R}_1 \cdot \bar{R}_0$$
$$V = 0$$

Addressing Formats:

See Table A-1.

Addressing Modes, Execution Time, and Machine Code (hexadecimal / octal / decimal):

(DUAL OPERAND)

Addressing Modes	Execution Time (No. of cycles)	Number of bytes of machine code	Coding of First (or only) byte of machine code		
			HEX.	OCT.	DEC.
A IMM	2	2	8A	212	138
A DIR	3	2	9A	232	154
A EXT	4	3	BA	272	186
A IND	5	2	AA	252	170
B IMM	2	2	CA	312	202
B DIR	3	2	DA	332	218
B EXT	4	3	FA	372	250
B IND	5	2	EA	352	234

PSH

Operation:	↓ (ACCX)
	SP ← (SP) − 0001
Description:	The contents of ACCX is stored in the stack at the address contained in the stack pointer. The stack pointer is then decremented.
Condition Codes:	Not affected.
Addressing Formats:	

See Table A-4.

Addressing Modes, Execution Time, and Machine Code (hexadecimal/ octal/ decimal):

Addressing Modes	Execution Time (No. of cycles)	Number of bytes of machine code	Coding of First (or only) byte of machine code		
			HEX.	OCT.	DEC.
A	4	1	36	066	054
B	4	1	37	067	055

Pull Data from Stack

PUL

Operation:	$SP \leftarrow (SP) + 0001$ $\uparrow ACCX$
Description:	The stack pointer is incremented. The ACCX is then loaded from the stack, from the address which is contained in the stack pointer.
Condition Codes:	Not affected.

Addressing Formats:

See Table A-4.

Addressing Modes, Execution Time, and Machine Code (hexadecimal / octal / decimal):

Addressing Modes	Execution Time (No. of cycles)	Number of bytes of machine code	Coding of First (or only) byte of machine code		
			HEX.	OCT.	DEC.
A	4	1	32	062	050
B	4	1	33	063	051

ROL

Rotate Left

Operation:

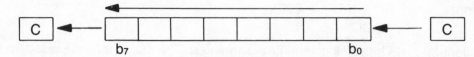

b_7 b_0

Description: Shifts all bits of ACCX or M one place to the left. Bit 0 is loaded from the C bit. The C bit is loaded from the most significant bit of ACCX or M.

Condition Codes: H: Not affected.

                I: Not affected.

                N: Set if most significant bit of the result is set; cleared otherwise.

                Z: Set if all bits of the result are cleared; cleared otherwise.

                V: Set if, after the completion of the operation, EITHER (N is set and C is cleared) OR (N is cleared and C is set); cleared otherwise.

                C: Set if, before the operation, the most significant bit of the ACCX or M was set; cleared otherwise.

Boolean Formulae for Condition Codes:

$$N = R_7$$
$$Z = \bar{R}_7 \cdot \bar{R}_6 \cdot \bar{R}_5 \cdot \bar{R}_4 \cdot \bar{R}_3 \cdot \bar{R}_2 \cdot \bar{R}_1 \cdot \bar{R}_0$$
$$V = N \oplus C = [N \cdot \bar{C}] \odot [\bar{N} \cdot C]$$

(the foregoing formula assumes values of N and C after the rotation)

$$C = M_7$$

Addressing Formats:

See Table A-3

Addressing Modes, Execution Time, and Machine Code (hexadecimal/ octal/ decimal):

Addressing Modes	Execution Time (No. of cycles)	Number of bytes of machine code	Coding of First (or only) byte of machine code		
			HEX.	OCT.	DEC.
A	2	1	49	111	073
B	2	1	59	131	089
EXT	6	3	79	171	121
IND	7	2	69	151	105

Rotate Right   **ROR**

Operation:

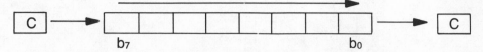

Description: Shifts all bits of ACCX or M one place to the right. Bit 7 is loaded from the C bit. The
C bit is loaded from the least significant bit of ACCX or M.

Condition Codes: H: Not affected.
I: Not affected.
N: Set if most significant bit of the result is set; cleared otherwise.
Z: Set if all bits of the result are cleared; cleared otherwise.
V: Set if, after the completion of the operation, EITHER (N is set and C is
cleared) OR (N is cleared and C is set); cleared otherwise.
C: Set if, before the operation, the least significant bit of the ACCX or M was set;
cleared otherwise.

Boolean Formulae for Condition Codes:

$$N = R_7$$
$$Z = \bar{R}_7 \cdot \bar{R}_6 \cdot \bar{R}_5 \cdot \bar{R}_4 \cdot \bar{R}_3 \cdot \bar{R}_2 \cdot \bar{R}_1 \cdot \bar{R}_0$$
$$V = N \oplus C = [N \cdot \bar{C}] \odot [\bar{N} \cdot C]$$
(the foregoing formula assumes values of N and C after the rotation)
$$C = M_0$$

Addressing Formats:

See Table A-3

Addressing Modes, Execution Time, and Machine Code (hexadecimal/octal/decimal):

Addressing Modes	Execution Time (No. of cycles)	Number of bytes of machine code	Coding of First (or only) byte of machine code		
			HEX.	OCT.	DEC.
A	2	1	46	106	070
B	2	1	56	126	086
EXT	6	3	76	166	118
IND	7	2	66	146	102

RTI

Operation:

$SP \leftarrow (SP) + 0001 , \uparrow CC$

$SP \leftarrow (SP) + 0001 , \uparrow ACCB$

$SP \leftarrow (SP) + 0001 , \uparrow ACCA$

$SP \leftarrow (SP) + 0001 , \uparrow IXH$

$SP \leftarrow (SP) + 0001 , \uparrow IXL$

$SP \leftarrow (SP) + 0001 , \uparrow PCH$

$SP \leftarrow (SP) + 0001 , \uparrow PCL$

Description:
The condition codes, accumulators B and A, the index register, and the program counter, will be restored to a state pulled from the stack. Note that the interrupt mask bit will be reset if and only if the corresponding bit stored in the stack is zero.

Condition Codes: Restored to the states pulled from the stack.

Addressing Modes, Execution Time, and Machine Code (hexadecimal/ octal/ decimal):

Addressing Modes	Execution Time (No. of cycles)	Number of bytes of machine code	Coding of First (or only) byte of machine code		
			HEX.	OCT.	DEC.
INHERENT	10	1	3B	073	059

Return from Interrupt

Example

		Memory Location	Machine Code (Hex)	Assembler Language Label	Operator	Operand
A.	*Before*					
	PC →	$D066	3B		RTI	
	SP →	$EFF8				
		$EFF9	11HINZVC	(binary)		
		$EFFA	12			
		$EFFB	34			
		$EFFC	56			
		$EFFD	78			
		$EFFE	55			
		$EFFF	67			
B.	*After*					
	PC →	$5567	**		***	*****
		$EFF8				
		$EFF9	11HINZVC	(binary)		
		$EFFA	12			
		$EFFB	34			
		$EFFC	56			
		$EFFD	78			
		$EFFE	55			
	SP →	$EFFF	67			

CC = HINZVC (binary)

ACCB = 12 (Hex)   IXH = 56 (Hex)

ACCA = 34 (Hex)   IXL = 78 (Hex)

Return from Subroutine **RTS**

Operation: SP ← (SP) + 0001
              ↑ PCH
              SP ← (SP) + 0001
              ↑ PCL

Description: The stack pointer is incremented (by 1). The contents of the byte of memory, at the address now contained in the stack pointer, are loaded into the 8 bits of highest significance in the program counter. The stack pointer is again incremented (by 1). The contents of the byte of memory, at the address now contained in the stack pointer, are loaded into the 8 bits of lowest significance in the program counter.

Condition Codes: Not affected.

Addressing Modes, Execution Time, and Machine Code (hexadecimal/ octal/ decimal):

Addressing Modes	Execution Time (No. of cycles)	Number of bytes of machine code	Coding of First (or only) byte of machine code		
			HEX.	OCT.	DEC.
INHERENT	5	1	39	071	057

Return from Subroutine

EXAMPLE

		Memory Location	Machine Code (Hex)	Assembler Language		
				Label	Operator	Operand
A.	*Before*					
	PC	$30A2	39		RTS	
	SP	$EFFD				
		$EFFE	10			
		$EFFF	02			
B.	*After*					
	PC	$1002	**		***	*****
		$EFFD				
		$EFFE	10			
	SP	$EFFF	02			

SBA

Subtract Accumulators

Operation: ACCA ← (ACCA) − (ACCB)

Description: Subtracts the contents of ACCB from the contents of ACCA and places the result in ACCA. The contents of ACCB are not affected.

Condition Codes:
- H: Not affected.
- I: Not affected.
- N: Set if most significant bit of the result is set; cleared otherwise.
- Z: Set if all bits of the result are cleared; cleared otherwise.
- V: Set if there was two's complement overflow as a result of the operation.
- C: Carry is set if the absolute value of accumulator B plus previous carry is larger than the absolute value of accumulator A; reset otherwise.

Boolean Formulae for Condition Codes:

$$N = R_7$$
$$Z = \overline{R_7} \cdot \overline{R_6} \cdot \overline{R_5} \cdot \overline{R_4} \cdot \overline{R_3} \cdot \overline{R_2} \cdot \overline{R_1} \cdot \overline{R_0}$$
$$V = A_7 \cdot \overline{B_7} \cdot \overline{R_7} + \overline{A_7} \cdot B_7 \cdot R_7$$
$$C = \overline{A_7} \cdot B_7 + B_7 \cdot R_7 + R_7 \cdot \overline{A_7}$$

Addressing Modes, Execution Time, and Machine Code (hexadecimal/octal/decimal):

Addressing Modes	Execution Time (No. of cycles)	Number of bytes of machine code	Coding of First (or only) byte of machine code		
			HEX.	OCT.	DEC.
INHERENT	2	1	10	020	016

Subtract with Carry

SBC

Operation: $\quad$ ACCX $\leftarrow$ (ACCX) $-$ (M) $-$ (C)

Description: $\quad$ Subtracts the contents of M and C from the contents of ACCX and places the result in ACCX.

Condition Codes: $\quad$ H: $\quad$ Not affected.

I: $\quad$ Not affected.

N: $\quad$ Set if most significant bit of the result is set; cleared otherwise.

Z: $\quad$ Set if all bits of the result are cleared; cleared otherwise.

V: $\quad$ Set if there was two's complement overflow as a result of the operation; cleared otherwise.

C: $\quad$ Carry is set if the absolute value of the contents of memory plus previous carry is larger than the absolute value of the accumulator; reset otherwise.

Boolean Formulae for Condition Codes:

$$N = R_7$$
$$Z = \overline{R_7} \cdot \overline{R_6} \cdot \overline{R_5} \cdot \overline{R_4} \cdot \overline{R_3} \cdot \overline{R_2} \cdot \overline{R_1} \cdot \overline{R_0}$$
$$V = X_7 \cdot \overline{M_7} \cdot \overline{R_7} + \overline{X_7} \cdot M_7 \cdot R_7$$
$$C = \overline{X_7} \cdot M_7 + M_7 \cdot R_7 + R_7 \cdot \overline{X_7}$$

Addressing Formats:

See Table A-1.

Addressing Modes, Execution Time, and Machine Code (hexadecimal/octal/decimal):

(DUAL OPERAND)

Addressing Modes	Execution Time (No. of cycles)	Number of bytes of machine code	Coding of First (or only) byte of machine code		
			HEX.	OCT.	DEC.
A IMM	2	2	82	202	130
A DIR	3	2	92	222	146
A EXT	4	3	B2	262	178
A IND	5	2	A2	242	162
B IMM	2	2	C2	302	194
B DIR	3	2	D2	322	210
B EXT	4	3	F2	362	242
B IND	5	2	E2	342	226

SEC

Set Carry

Operation: C bit ← 1

Description: Sets the carry bit in the processor condition codes register.

Condition Codes: H: Not affected.
                   I: Not affected.
                   N: Not affected.
                   Z: Not affected.
                   V: Not affected.
                   C: Set.

Boolean Formulae for Condition Codes:
                   C = 1

Addressing Modes, Execution Time, and Machine Code (hexadecimal/ octal/ decimal):

Addressing Modes	Execution Time (No. of cycles)	Number of bytes of machine code	Coding of First (or only) byte of machine code		
			HEX.	OCT.	DEC.
INHERENT	2	1	0D	015	013

Set Interrupt Mask   **SEI**

Operation: I bit ← 1

Description: Sets the interrupt mask bit in the processor condition codes register. The microprocessor is inhibited from servicing an interrupt from a peripheral device, and will continue with execution of the instructions of the program, until the interrupt mask bit has been cleared.

Condition Codes: H: Not affected.
                     I: Set.
                     N: Not affected.
                     Z: Not affected.
                     V: Not affected.
                     C: Not affected.

Boolean Formulae for Condition Codes:

I = 1

Addressing Modes, Execution Time, and Machine Code (hexadecimal/octal/decimal):

Addressing Modes	Execution Time (No. of cycles)	Number of bytes of machine code	Coding of First (or only) byte of machine code		
			HEX.	OCT.	DEC.
INHERENT	2	1	0F	017	015

SEV

Set Two's Complement Overflow Bit

Operation: V bit ← 1

Description: Sets the two's complement overflow bit in the processor condition codes register.

Condition Codes:
- H: Not affected.
- I: Not affected.
- N: Not affected.
- Z: Not affected.
- V: Set.
- C: Not affected.

Boolean Formulae for Condition Codes:

$$V = 1$$

Addressing Modes, Execution Time, and Machine Code (hexadecimal/ octal/ decimal):

Addressing Modes	Execution Time (No. of cycles)	Number of bytes of machine code	Coding of First (or only) byte of machine code		
			HEX.	OCT.	DEC.
INHERENT	2	1	0B	013	011

Store Accumulator

STA

Operation: $M \leftarrow (ACCX)$

Description: Stores the contents of ACCX in memory. The contents of ACCX remains unchanged.

Condition Codes:
H: Not affected.
I: Not affected.
N: Set if the most significant bit of the contents of ACCX is set; cleared otherwise.
Z: Set if all bits of the contents of ACCX are cleared; cleared otherwise.
V: Cleared.
C: Not affected.

Boolean Formulae for Condition Codes:

$$N = X_7$$
$$Z = \overline{X_7} \cdot \overline{X_6} \cdot \overline{X_5} \cdot \overline{X_4} \cdot \overline{X_3} \cdot \overline{X_2} \cdot \overline{X_1} \cdot \overline{X_0}$$
$$V = 0$$

Addressing Formats:

See Table A-2.

Addressing Modes, Execution Time, and Machine Code (hexadecimal/octal/decimal):

Addressing Modes	Execution Time (No. of cycles)	Number of bytes of machine code	Coding of First (or only) byte of machine code		
			HEX.	OCT.	DEC.
A DIR	4	2	97	227	151
A EXT	5	3	B7	267	183
A IND	6	2	A7	247	167
B DIR	4	2	D7	327	215
B EXT	5	3	F7	367	247
B IND	6	2	E7	347	231

STS

Operation: $M \leftarrow (SPH)$
$M + 1 \leftarrow (SPL)$

Description: Stores the more significant byte of the stack pointer in memory at the address specified by the program, and stores the less significant byte of the stack pointer at the next location in memory, at one plus the address specified by the program.

Condition Codes: H: Not affected.
I: Not affected.
N: Set if the most significant bit of the stack pointer is set; cleared otherwise.
Z: Set if all bits of the stack pointer are cleared; cleared otherwise.
V: Cleared.
C: Not affected.

Boolean Formulae for Condition Codes:

$N = SPH_7$
$Z = (\overline{SPH_7} \cdot \overline{SPH_6} \cdot \overline{SPH_5} \cdot \overline{SPH_4} \cdot \overline{SPH_3} \cdot \overline{SPH_2} \cdot \overline{SPH_1} \cdot \overline{SPH_0})$
$(\overline{SPL_7} \cdot \overline{SPL_6} \cdot \overline{SPL_5} \cdot \overline{SPL_4} \cdot \overline{SPL_3} \cdot \overline{SPL_2} \cdot \overline{SPL_1} \cdot \overline{SPL_0})$
$V = 0$

Addressing Formats:

See Table A-6.

Addressing Modes, Execution Time, and Machine Code (hexadecimal/octal/decimal):

Addressing Modes	Execution Time (No. of cycles)	Number of bytes of machine code	Coding of First (or only) byte of machine code		
			HEX.	OCT.	DEC.
DIR	5	2	9F	237	159
EXT	6	3	BF	277	191
IND	7	2	AF	257	175

Store Index Register

STX

Operation: $M \leftarrow (IXH)$

$M + 1 \leftarrow (IXL)$

Description: Stores the more significant byte of the index register in memory at the address specified by the program, and stores the less significant byte of the index register at the next location in memory, at one plus the address specified by the program.

Condition Codes:
- H: Not affected.
- I: Not affected.
- N: Set if the most significant bite of the index register is set; cleared otherwise.
- Z: Set if all bits of the index register are cleared; cleared otherwise.
- V: Cleared.
- C: Not affected.

Boolean Formulae for Condition Codes:

$N = IXH_7$

$Z = (\overline{IXH_7} \cdot \overline{IXH_6} \cdot \overline{IXH_5} \cdot \overline{IXH_4} \cdot \overline{IXH_3} \cdot \overline{IXH_2} \cdot \overline{IXH_1} \cdot \overline{IXH_0}) \cdot$
$(\overline{IXL_7} \cdot \overline{IXL_6} \cdot \overline{IXL_5} \cdot \overline{IXL_4} \cdot \overline{IXL_3} \cdot \overline{IXL_2} \cdot \overline{IXL_1} \cdot \overline{IXL_0})$

$V = 0$

Addressing Formats:

See Table A-6.

Addressing Modes, Execution Time, and Machine Code (hexadecimal/octal/decimal):

Addressing Modes	Execution Time (No. of cycles)	Number of bytes of machine code	Coding of First (or only) byte of machine code		
			HEX.	OCT.	DEC.
DIR	5	2	DF	337	223
EXT	6	3	FF	377	255
IND	7	2	EF	357	239

SUB

Subtract

Operation:	$ACCX \leftarrow (ACCX) - (M)$
Description:	Subtracts the contents of M from the contents of ACCX and places the result in ACCX.

Condition Codes:
- H: Not affected.
- I: Not affected.
- N: Set if most significant bit of the result is set; cleared otherwise.
- Z: Set if all bits of the result are cleared; cleared otherwise.
- V: Set if there was two's complement overflow as a result of the operation; cleared otherwise.
- C: Set if the absolute value of the contents of memory are larger than the absolute value of the accumulator; reset otherwise.

Boolean Formulae for Condition Codes:

$$N = R_7$$
$$Z = \overline{R_7} \cdot \overline{R_6} \cdot \overline{R_5} \cdot \overline{R_4} \cdot \overline{R_3} \cdot \overline{R_2} \cdot \overline{R_1} \cdot \overline{R_0}$$
$$V = X_7 \cdot \overline{M_7} \cdot \overline{R_7} \cdot \overline{X_7} \cdot M_7 \cdot R_7$$
$$C = \overline{X_7} \cdot M_7 + M_7 \cdot R_7 + R_7 \cdot \overline{X_7}$$

Addressing Formats:

See Table A-1.

Addressing Modes, Execution Time, and Machine Code (hexadecimal/octal/decimal):

(DUAL OPERAND)

Addressing Modes	Execution Time (No. of cycles)	Number of bytes of machine code	Coding of First (or only) byte of machine code		
			HEX.	OCT.	DEC.
A IMM	2	2	80	200	128
A DIR	3	2	90	220	144
A EXT	4	3	B0	260	176
A IND	5	2	A0	240	160
B IMM	2	2	C0	300	192
B DIR	3	2	D0	320	208
B EXT	4	3	F0	360	240
B IND	5	2	E0	340	224

Software Interrupt

SWI

Operation:
$$PC \leftarrow (PC) + 0001$$
$$\downarrow (PCL), SP \leftarrow (SP)-0001$$
$$\downarrow (PCH), SP \leftarrow (SP)-0001$$
$$\downarrow (IXL), SP \leftarrow (SP)-0001$$
$$\downarrow (IXH), SP \leftarrow (SP)-0001$$
$$\downarrow (ACCA), SP \leftarrow (SP)-0001$$
$$\downarrow (ACCB), SP \leftarrow (SP)-0001$$
$$\downarrow (CC), SP \leftarrow (SP)-0001$$
$$I \leftarrow 1$$
$$PCH \leftarrow (n-0005)$$
$$PCL \leftarrow (n-0004)$$

Description: The program counter is incremented (by 1). The program counter, index register, and accumulator A and B, are pushed into the stack. The condition codes register is then pushed into the stack, with condition codes H, I, N, Z, V, C going respectively into bit positions 5 thru 0, and the top two bits (in bit positions 7 and 6) are set (to the 1 state). The stack pointer is decremented (by 1) after each byte of data is stored in the stack.

The interrupt mask bit is then set. The program counter is then loaded with the address stored in the software interrupt pointer at memory locations (n-5) and (n-4), where n is the address corresponding to a high state on all lines of the address bus.

Condition Codes:
H: Not affected.
I: Set.
N: Not affected.
Z: Not affected.
V: Not affected.
C: Not affected.

Boolean Formula for Condition Codes:
$$I = 1$$

Addressing Modes, Execution Time, and Machine Code (hexadecimal/ octal/ decimal):

Addressing Modes	Execution Time (No. of cycles)	Number of bytes of machine code	Coding of First (or only) byte of machine code		
			HEX.	OCT.	DEC.
INHERENT	12	1	3F	077	063

Software Interrupt
EXAMPLE
A. *Before:*

CC = HINZVC (binary)
ACCB = 12 (Hex)   IXH = 56 (Hex)
ACCA = 34 (Hex)   IXL = 78 (Hex)

		Memory Location	Machine Code (Hex)	Assembler Language		
				Label	Operator	Operand
PC	→	$5566	3F		SWI	
SP	→	$EFFF				
		$FFFA	D0			
		$FFFB	55			

B. *After:*

		Memory Location	Machine Code (Hex)			
PC	→	$D055				
SP	→	$EFF8				
		$EFF9	11HINZVC	(binary)		
		$EFFA	12			
		$EFFB	34			
		$EFFC	56			
		$EFFD	78			
		$EFFE	55			
		$EFFF	67			

Note: This example assumes that FFFF is the memory location addressed when all lines of the address bus go to the high state.

Transfer from Accumulator A to Accumulator B   **TAB**

Operation: ACCB ← (ACCA)

Description: Moves the contents of ACCA to ACCB. The former contents of ACCB are lost. The contents of ACCA are not affected.

Condition Codes: H: Not affected.
                   I: Not affected.
                   N: Set if the most significant bit of the contents of the accumulator is set; cleared otherwise.
                   Z: Set if all bits of the contents of the accumulator are cleared; cleared otherwise.
                   V: Cleared.
                   C: Not affected.

Boolean Formulae for Condition Codes:

$$N = R_7$$
$$Z = \overline{R}_7 \cdot \overline{R}_6 \cdot \overline{R}_5 \cdot \overline{R}_4 \cdot \overline{R}_3 \cdot \overline{R}_2 \cdot \overline{R}_1 \cdot \overline{R}_0$$
$$V = 0$$

Addressing Modes, Execution Time, and Machine Code (hexadecimal/ octal/ decimal):

Addressing Modes	Execution Time (No. of cycles)	Number of bytes of machine code	Coding of First (or only) byte of machine code		
			HEX.	OCT.	DEC.
INHERENT	2	1	16	026	022

TAP

**Transfer from Accumulator A
to Processor Condition Codes Register**

Operation: CC ← (ACCA)

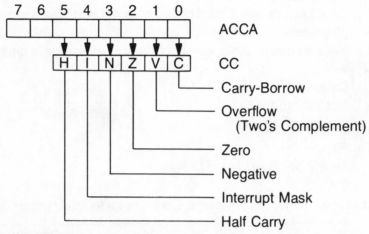

Bit Positions

Description: Transfers the contents of bit positions 0 thru 5 of accumulator A to the corresponding bit positions of the processor condition codes register. The contents of accumulator A remain unchanged.

Condition Codes: Set or reset according to the contents of the respective bits 0 thru 5 of accumulator A.

Addressing Modes, Execution Time, and Machine Code (hexadecimal/octal/decimal):

Addressing Modes	Execution Time (No. of cycles)	Number of bytes of machine code	Coding of First (or only) byte of machine code		
			HEX.	OCT.	DEC.
INHERENT	2	1	06	006	006

Transfer from Accumulator B to Accumulator A **TBA**

Operation: ACCA ← (ACCB)

Description: Moves the contents of ACCB to ACCA. The former contents of ACCA are lost. The contents of ACCB are not affected.

Condition Codes: H: Not affected.
I: Not affected.
N: Set if the most significant accumulator bit is set; cleared otherwise.
Z: Set if all accumulator bits are cleared; cleared otherwise.
V: Cleared.
C: Not affected.

Boolean Formulae for Condition Codes:

$$N = R_7$$
$$Z = \bar{R}_7 \cdot \bar{R}_6 \cdot \bar{R}_5 \cdot \bar{R}_4 \cdot \bar{R}_3 \cdot \bar{R}_2 \cdot \bar{R}_1 \cdot \bar{R}_0$$
$$V = 0$$

Addressing Modes, Execution Time, and Machine Code (hexadecimal/octal/decimal):

Addressing Modes	Execution Time (No. of cycles)	Number of bytes of machine code	Coding of First (or only) byte of machine code		
			HEX.	OCT.	DEC.
INHERENT	2	1	17	027	023

TPA

Transfer from Processor Condition Codes Register to Accumulator A

Operation: ACCA ← (CC)

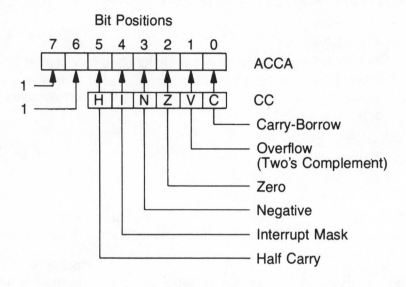

Description: Transfers the contents of the processor condition codes register to corresponding bit positions 0 thru 5 of accumulator A. Bit positions 6 and 7 of accumulator A are set (i.e. go to the "1" state). The processor condition codes register remains unchanged.

Condition Codes: Not affected.

Addressing Modes, Execution Time, and Machine Code (hexadecimal/ octal/ decimal):

Addressing Modes	Execution Time (No. of cycles)	Number of bytes of machine code	Coding of First (or only) byte of machine code		
			HEX.	OCT.	DEC.
INHERENT	2	1	07	007	007

Test

TST

Operation:	(ACCX) − 00
	(M) − 00
Description:	Set condition codes N and Z according to the contents of ACCX or M.
Condition Codes:	H: Not affected.
	I: Not affected.
	N: Set if most significant bit of the contents of ACCX or M is set; cleared otherwise.
	Z: Set if all bits of the contents of ACCX or M are cleared; cleared otherwise.
	V: Cleared.
	C: Cleared.

Boolean Formulae for Condition Codes:

$$N = M_7$$
$$Z = \overline{M_7} \cdot \overline{M_6} \cdot \overline{M_5} \cdot \overline{M_4} \cdot \overline{M_3} \cdot \overline{M_2} \cdot \overline{M_1} \cdot \overline{M_0}$$
$$V = 0$$
$$C = 0$$

Addressing Formats:

See Table A-3.

Addressing Modes, Execution Time, and Machine Code (hexadecimal/octal/decimal):

Addressing Modes	Execution Time (No. of cycles)	Number of bytes of machine code	Coding of First (or only) byte of machine code		
			HEX.	OCT.	DEC.
A	2	1	4D	115	077
B	2	1	5D	135	093
EXT	6	3	7D	175	125
IND	7	2	6D	155	109

TSX

Transfer from Stack Pointer to Index Register

Operation: IX ← (SP) + 0001

Description: Loads the index register with one plus the contents of the stack pointer. The contents of the stack pointer remain unchanged.

Condition Codes: Not affected.

Addressing Modes, Execution Time, and Machine Code (hexadecimal/octal/decimal):

Addressing Modes	Execution Time (No. of cycles)	Number of bytes of machine code	Coding of First (or only) byte of machine code		
			HEX.	OCT.	DEC.
INHERENT	4	1	30	060	048

Transfer From Index Register to Stack Pointer   **TXS**

Operation: $SP \leftarrow (IX) - 0001$

Description: Loads the stack pointer with the contents of the index register, minus one.
                  The contents of the index register remain unchanged.

Condition Codes: Not affected.

Addressing Modes, Execution Time, and Machine Code (hexadecimal/octal/decimal):

Addressing Modes	Execution Time (No. of cycles)	Number of bytes of machine code	Coding of First (or only) byte of machine code		
			HEX.	OCT.	DEC.
INHERENT	4	1	35	065	053

WAI

Wait for Interrupt

Operation:

PC ← (PC) + 0001
↓ (PCL) , SP ← (SP)-0001
↓ (PCH) , SP ← (SP)-0001
↓ (IXL) , SP ← (SP)-0001
↓ (IXH) , SP ← (SP)-0001
↓ (ACCA) , SP ← (SP)-0001
↓ (ACCB) , SP ← (SP)-0001
↓ (CC) , SP ← (SP)-0001

Condition Codes: Not affected.

Description:

The program counter is incremented (by 1). The program counter, index register, and accumulators A and B, are pushed into the stack. The condition codes register is then pushed into the stack, with condition codes H, I, N, Z, V, C going respectively into bit positions 5 thru 0, and the top two bits (in bit positions 7 and 6) are set (to the 1 state). The stack pointer is decremented (by 1) after each byte of data is stored in the stack.

Execution of the program is then suspended until an interrupt from a peripheral device is signalled, by the interrupt request control input going to a low state.

When an interrupt is signalled on the interrupt request line, and provided the I bit is clear, execution proceeds as follows. The interrupt mask bit is set. The program counter is then loaded with the address stored in the internal interrupt pointer at memory locations (n-7) and (n-6), where n is the address corresponding to a high state on all lines of the address bus.

Condition Codes:
H: Not affected.
I: Not affected until an interrupt request signal is detected on the interrupt request control line. When the interrupt request is received the I bit is set and further execution takes place, provided the I bit was initially clear.
N: Not affected.
Z: Not affected.
V: Not affected.
C: Not affected.

Addressing Modes, Execution Time, and Machine Code (hexadecimal/ octal/ decimal):

Addressing Modes	Execution Time (No. of cycles)	Number of bytes of machine code	Coding of First (or only) byte of machine code		
			HEX.	OCT.	DEC.
INHERENT	9	1	3E	076	062

Addressing Mode of Second Operand	First Operand	
	Accumulator A	Accumulator B
IMMediate	CCC A #number CCC A #symbol CCC A #expression CCC A #'C	CCC B #number CCC B #symbol CCC B #expression CCC B #'C
DIRect or EXTended	CCC A number CCC A symbol CCC A expression	CCC B number CCC B symbol CCC B expression
INDexed	CCC A X CCC Z ,X CCC A number,X CCC A symbol,X CCC A expression,X	CCC B X CCC B ,X CCC B number,X CCC B symbol,X CCC B expression,X

Notes: 1. CCC = mnemonic operator of source instruction.
      2. "symbol" may be the special symbol "*".
      3. "expression" may contain the special symbol "*".
      4. space may be omitted before A or B.

Applicable to the following source instructions:

ADC ADD AND BIT CMP
EOR LDA ORA SBC SUB

*Special symbol indicating program-counter.

TABLE A-1. Addressing Formats (1)

Addressing Mode of Second Operand	First Operand	
	Accumulator A	Accumulator B
DIRect or EXTended	STA A number STA A symbol STA A expression	STA B number STA B symbol STA B expression
INDexed	STA A X STA A ,X STA A number,X STA A symbol,X STA A expression,X	STA B X STA B ,X STA B number,X STA B symbol,X STA B expression,X

Notes: 1. "symbol" may be the special symbol "*".
      2. "expression" may contain the special symbol "*".
      3. Space may be omitted before A or B.

Applicable to the source instruction:

STA

*Special symbol indicating program-counter.

TABLE A-2. Addressing Formats (2)

Operand or Addressing Mode	Formats
Accumulator A	CCC A
Accumulator B	CCC B
EXTended	CCC number CCC symbol CCC expression
INDexed	CCC X CCC ,X CCC number,X CCC symbol,X CCC expression,X

Notes: 1. CCC = mnemonic operator of source instruction.
2. "symbol" may be the special symbol "*".
3. "expression" may contain the special symbol "*".
4. Space may be omitted before A or B.

Applicable to the following source instructions:

ASL ASR CLR COM DEC INC
LSR NEG ROL ROR TST

*Special symbol indicating program-counter.

TABLE A-3. Addressing Formats (3)

Operand	Formats
Accumulator A	CCC A
Accumulator B	CCC B

Notes: 1. CCC = mnemonic operator of source instruction.
2. Space may be omitted before A or B.

Applicable to the following source instructions:

PSH PUL

TABLE A-4. Addressing Formats (4)

Addressing Mode	Formats
IMMediate	CCC #number CCC #symbol CCC #expression CCC #'C
DIRect or EXTended	CCC number CCC symbol CCC expression
INDexed	CCC X CCC ,X CCC number,X CCC symbol,X CCC expression,X

Notes: 1. CCC = mnemonic operator of source instruction.
2. "symbol" may be the special symbol "*".
3. "expression" may contain the special symbol "*".

Applicable to the following source instructions:

CPX   LDS   LDX

*Special symbol indicating program-counter.

TABLE A-5. Addressing Formats (5)

Addressing Mode	Formats
DIRect or EXTended	CCC number CCC symbol CCC expression
INDexed	CCC X CCC ,X CCC number,X CCC symbol,X CCC expression,X

Notes: 1. CCC = mnemonic operator of source instruction.
2. "symbol" may be the special symbol "*".
3. "expression" may contain the special symbol "*".

Applicable to the following source instructions:

STS   STX

*Special symbol indicating program-counter.

TABLE A-6. Addressing Formats (6)

Addressing Mode	Formats
EXTended	CCC number CCC symbol CCC expression
INDexed	CCC X CCC ,X CCC number,X CCC symbol,X CCC expression,X

Notes: 1. CCC = mnemonic operator of source instruction.
2. "symbol" may be the special symbol "*".
3. "expression" may contain the special symbol "*".

Applicable to the following source instructions:

JMP   JSR

*Special symbol indicating program-counter.

TABLE A-7. Addressing Formats (7)

Addressing Mode	Formats
RELative	CCC number CCC symbol CCC expression

Notes: 1. CCC = mnemonic operator of source instruction.
2. "symbol" may be the special symbol "*".
3. "expression" may contain the special symbol "*".

Applicable to the following source instructions:

BCC BCS BEQ BGE BGT BHI BLE BLS
BLT BMI BNE BPL BRA BSR BVC BVS

*Special symbol indicating program-counter.

TABLE A-8. Addressing Formats (8)

Appendix B

DATA SHEETS

Courtesy of
Motorola Semiconductor
Products, Inc.

MOTOROLA Semiconductors

BOX 20912 • PHOENIX, ARIZONA 85036

MC6800

(0 to 70°C; L or P Suffix)

MC6800C

(-40 to 85°C; L Suffix only)

MICROPROCESSING UNIT (MPU)

The MC6800 is a monolithic 8-bit microprocessor forming the central control function for Motorola's M6800 family. Compatible with TTL, the MC6800, as with all M6800 system parts, requires only one +5.0-volt power supply, and no external TTL devices for bus interface.

The MC6800 is capable of addressing 65K bytes of memory with its 16-bit address lines. The 8-bit data bus is bidirectional as well as 3-state, making direct memory addressing and multiprocessing applications realizable.

- Eight-Bit Parallel Processing
- Bi-Directional Data Bus
- Sixteen-Bit Address Bus — 65K Bytes of Addressing
- 72 Instructions — Variable Length
- Seven Addressing Modes — Direct, Relative, Immediate, Indexed, Extended, Implied and Accumulator
- Variable Length Stack
- Vectored Restart
- Maskable Interrupt Vector
- Separate Non-Maskable Interrupt — Internal Registers Saved In Stack
- Six Internal Registers — Two Accumulators, Index Register, Program Counter, Stack Pointer and Condition Code Register
- Direct Memory Addressing (DMA) and Multiple Processor Capability
- Clock Rates as High as 1 MHz
- Simple Bus Interface Without TTL
- Halt and Single Instruction Execution Capability

MOS

(N-CHANNEL, SILICON-GATE)

MICROPROCESSOR

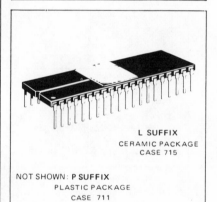

L SUFFIX
CERAMIC PACKAGE
CASE 715

NOT SHOWN: **P SUFFIX**
PLASTIC PACKAGE
CASE 711

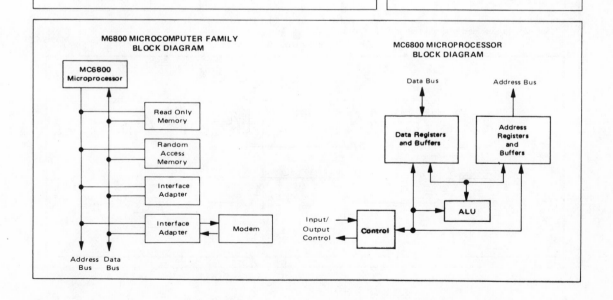

M6800 MICROCOMPUTER FAMILY BLOCK DIAGRAM

MC6800 MICROPROCESSOR BLOCK DIAGRAM

MC6800

ELECTRICAL CHARACTERISTICS (V_{CC} = 5.0 V ± 5%, V_{SS} = 0, T_A = 0 to 70°C unless otherwise noted.)

Characteristic		Symbol	Min	Typ	Max	Unit
Input High Voltage	Logic	V_{IH}	V_{SS} + 2.0	—	V_{CC}	Vdc
	$\phi1,\phi2$	V_{IHC}	V_{CC} − 0.3	—	V_{CC} + 0.1	
Input Low Voltage	Logic	V_{IL}	V_{SS} − 0.3	—	V_{SS} + 0.8	Vdc
	$\phi1,\phi2$	V_{ILC}	V_{SS} − 0.1	—	V_{SS} + 0.3	
Clock Overshoot/Undershoot — Input High Level		V_{OS}	V_{CC} − 0.5	—	V_{CC} + 0.5	Vdc
— Input Low Level			V_{SS} − 0.5	—	V_{SS} + 0.5	
Input Leakage Current		I_{in}				µAdc
(V_{in} = 0 to 5.25 V, V_{CC} = max)	Logic*		—	1.0	2.5	
(V_{in} = 0 to 5.25 V, V_{CC} = 0.0 V)	$\phi1,\phi2$		—	—	100	
Three-State (Off State) Input Current	D0-D7	I_{TSI}	—	2.0	10	µAdc
(V_{in} 0.4 to 2.4 V, V_{CC} = max)	A0-A15,R/W		—		100	
Output High Voltage		V_{OH}				Vdc
(I_{Load} = −205 µAdc, V_{CC} = min)	D0-D7		V_{SS} + 2.4	—	—	
(I_{Load} = −145 µAdc, V_{CC} = min)	A0-A15,R/W,VMA		V_{SS} + 2.4	--	—	
(I_{Load} = −100 µAdc, V_{CC} = min)	BA		V_{SS} + 2.4	—	—	
Output Low Voltage		V_{OL}	—	—	V_{SS} + 0.4	Vdc
(I_{Load} = 1.6 mAdc, V_{CC} = min)						
Power Dissipation		P_D	—	0.600	1.2	W
Capacitance #	$\phi1,\phi2$	C_{in}	80	120	160	pF
(V_{in} = 0, T_A = 25°C, f = 1.0 MHz)	TSC		—	—	15	
	DBE		—	7.0	10	
	D0-D7		—	10	12.5	
	Logic Inputs		—	6.5	8.5	
	A0-A15,R/W,VMA	C_{out}	—	—	12	pF
Frequency of Operation		f	0.1	—	1.0	MHz
Clock Timing (Figure 1)						
Cycle Time		t_{cyc}	1.0	—	10	µs
Clock Pulse Width		$PW_{\phi H}$				ns
(Measured at V_{CC} − 0.3 V)	$\phi1$		430	—	4500	
	$\phi2$		450	—	4500	
Total $\phi1$ and $\phi2$ Up Time		t_{ut}	940	—	—	ns
Rise and Fall Times	$\phi1,\phi2$	$t_{\phi r}, t_{\phi f}$	5.0	—	50	ns
(Measured between V_{SS} + 0.3 V and V_{CC} − 0.3 V)						
Delay Time or Clock Separation		t_d	0	—	9100	ns
(Measured at V_{OV} = V_{SS} + 0.5 V)						
Overshoot Duration		t_{OS}	0	—	40	ns

*Except $\overline{IRQ}$ and $\overline{NMI}$, which require 3 kΩ pullup load resistors for wire-OR capability at optimum operation.
#Capacitances are periodically sampled rather than 100% tested.

FIGURE 1 – CLOCK TIMING WAVEFORM

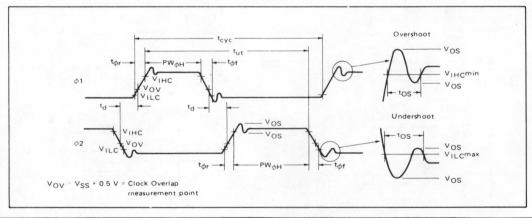

V_{OV} - V_{SS} + 0.5 V = Clock Overlap measurement point

MC6800

MAXIMUM RATINGS

Rating	Symbol	Value	Unit
Supply Voltage	V_{CC}	−0.3 to +7.0	Vdc
Input Voltage	V_{in}	−0.3 to +7.0	Vdc
Operating Temperature Range	T_A	0 to +70	°C
Storage Temperature Range	T_{stg}	−55 to +150	°C
Thermal Resistance	θ_{JA}	70	°C/W

This device contains circuitry to protect the inputs against damage due to high static voltages or electric fields; however, it is advised that normal precautions be taken to avoid application of any voltage higher than maximum rated voltages to this high impedance circuit.

READ/WRITE TIMING   Figures 2 and 3, f = 1.0 MHz, Load Circuit of Figure 6.

Characteristic	Symbol	Min	Typ	Max	Unit
Address Delay	t_{AD}	—	220	300	ns
Peripheral Read Access Time $t_{acc} = t_{ut} − (t_{AD} + t_{DSR})$	t_{acc}	—	—	540	ns
Data Setup Time (Read)	t_{DSR}	100	—	—	ns
Input Data Hold Time	t_H	10	—	—	ns
Output Data Hold Time	t_H	10	25	—	ns
Address Hold Time (Address, R/W, VMA)	t_{AH}	50	75	—	ns
Enable High Time for DBE Input	t_{EH}	450	—	—	ns
Data Delay Time (Write)	t_{DDW}	—	165	225	ns
Processor Controls*					
Processor Control Setup Time	t_{PCS}	200	—	—	ns
Processor Control Rise and Fall Time	t_{PCr}, t_{PCf}	—	—	100	ns
Bus Available Delay	t_{BA}	—	—	300	ns
Three State Enable	t_{TSE}	—	—	40	ns
Three State Delay	t_{TSD}	—	—	700	ns
Data Bus Enable Down Time During φ1 Up Time (Figure 3)	$t_{\overline{DBE}}$	150	—	—	ns
Data Bus Enable Delay (Figure 3)	t_{DBED}	300	—	—	ns
Data Bus Enable Rise and Fall Times (Figure 3)	t_{DBEr}, t_{DBEf}	—	—	25	ns

*Additional information is given in Figures 12 through 16 of the Family Characteristics — see pages 17 through 20.

FIGURE 2 – READ DATA FROM MEMORY OR PERIPHERALS

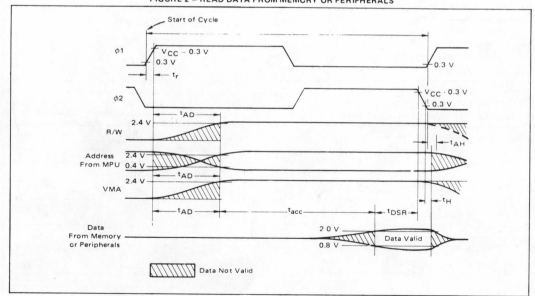

 MOTOROLA *Semiconductor Products Inc.*

MC6800

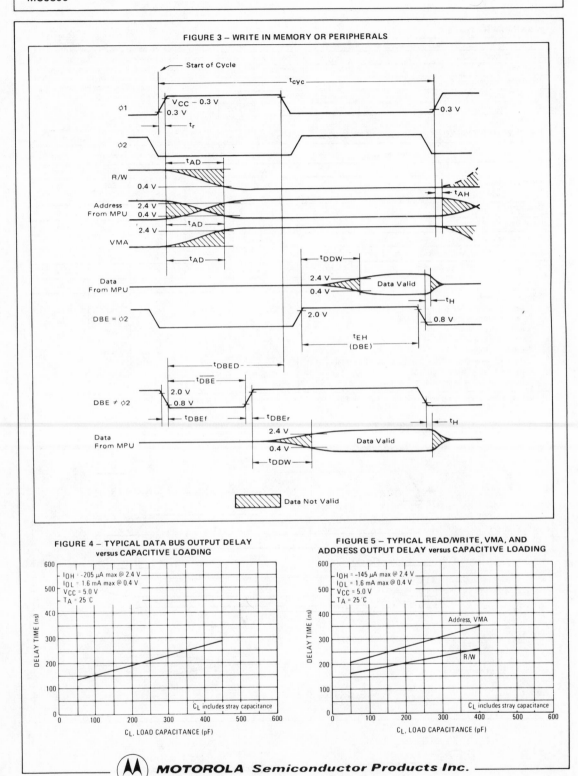

FIGURE 3 — WRITE IN MEMORY OR PERIPHERALS

FIGURE 4 — TYPICAL DATA BUS OUTPUT DELAY
versus CAPACITIVE LOADING

FIGURE 5 — TYPICAL READ/WRITE, VMA, AND
ADDRESS OUTPUT DELAY versus CAPACITIVE LOADING

MOTOROLA *Semiconductor Products Inc.*

MC6800

FIGURE 6 – BUS TIMING TEST LOAD

TYPICAL POWER SUPPLY CURRENT

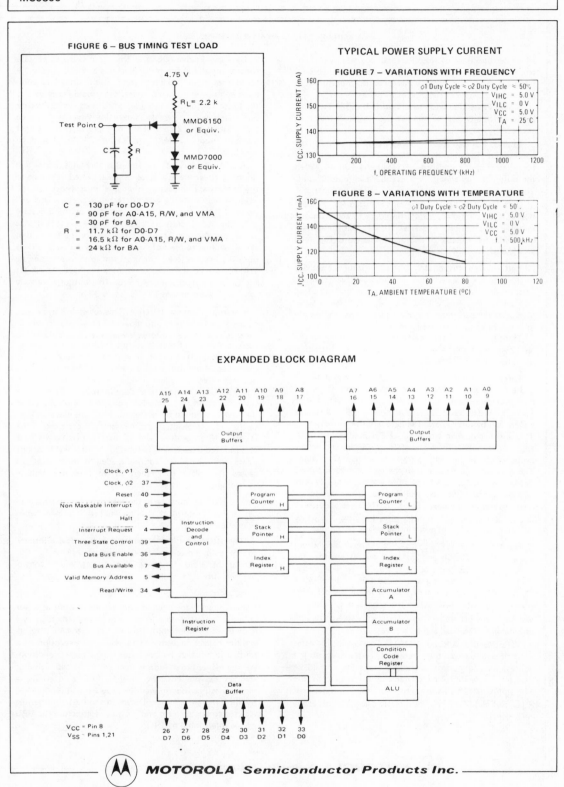

C = 130 pF for D0-D7
  = 90 pF for A0-A15, R/W, and VMA
  = 30 pF for BA
R = 11.7 kΩ for D0-D7
  = 16.5 kΩ for A0-A15, R/W, and VMA
  = 24 kΩ for BA

FIGURE 7 – VARIATIONS WITH FREQUENCY

FIGURE 8 – VARIATIONS WITH TEMPERATURE

EXPANDED BLOCK DIAGRAM

MOTOROLA *Semiconductor Products Inc.*

MC6800

MPU SIGNAL DESCRIPTION

Proper operation of the MPU requires that certain control and timing signals be provided to accomplish specific functions and that other signal lines be monitored to determine the state of the processor.

Clocks Phase One and Phase Two ($\phi1, \phi2$) — Two pins are used for a two-phase non-overlapping clock that runs at the V_{CC} voltage level.

Address Bus (A0-A15) — Sixteen pins are used for the address bus. The outputs are three-state bus drivers capable of driving one standard TTL load and 130 pF. When the output is turned off, it is essentially an open circuit. This permits the MPU to be used in DMA applications.

Data Bus (D0-D7) — Eight pins are used for the data bus. It is bi-directional, transferring data to and from the memory and peripheral devices. It also has three-state output buffers capable of driving one standard TTL load and 130 pF.

Halt — When this input is in the low state, all activity in the machine will be halted. This input is level sensitive. In the halt mode, the machine will stop at the end of an instruction, Bus Available will be at a one level, Valid Memory Address will be at a zero, and all other three-state lines will be in the three-state mode.

Transition of the Halt line must not occur during the last 250 ns of phase one. To insure single instruction operation, the Halt line must go high for one Clock cycle.

Three-State Control (TSC) — This input causes all of the address lines and the Read/Write line to go into the off or high impedance state. This state will occur 700 ns after TSC = 2.0 V. The Valid Memory Address and Bus Available signals will be forced low. The data bus is not affected by TSC and has its own enable (Data Bus Enable). In DMA applications, the Three-State Control line should be brought high on the leading edge of the Phase One Clock. The $\phi1$ clock must be held in the high state and the $\phi2$ in the low state for this function to operate properly. The address bus will then be available for other devices to directly address memory. Since the MPU is a dynamic device, it can be held in this state for only 4.5 μs or destruction of data will occur in the MPU.

Read/Write (R/W) — This TTL compatible output signals the peripherals and memory devices whether the MPU is in a Read (high) or Write (low) state. The normal standby state of this signal is Read (high). Three-State Control going high will turn Read/Write to the off (high impedance) state. Also, when the processor is halted, it will be in the off state. This output is capable of driving one standard TTL load and 90 pF.

Valid Memory Address (VMA) — This output indicates to peripheral devices that there is a valid address on the address bus. In normal operation, this signal should be utilized for enabling peripheral interfaces such as the PIA and ACIA. This signal is not three-state. One standard TTL load and 90 pF may be directly driven by this active high signal.

Data Bus Enable (DBE) — This input is the three-state control signal for the MPU data bus and will enable the bus drivers when in the high state. This input is TTL compatible; however in normal operation, it would be driven by the phase two clock. During an MPU read cycle, the data bus drivers will be disabled internally. When it is desired that another device control the data bus such as in Direct Memory Access (DMA) applications, DBE should be held low.

Bus Available (BA) — The Bus Available signal will normally be in the low state; when activated, it will go to the high state indicating that the microprocessor has stopped and that the address bus is available. This will occur if the Halt line is in the low state or the processor is in the WAIT state as a result of the execution of a WAIT instruction. At such time, all three-state output drivers will go to their off state and other outputs to their normally inactive level. The processor is removed from the WAIT state by the occurrence of a maskable (mask bit I = 0) or nonmaskable interrupt. This output is capable of driving one standard TTL load and 30 pF.

Interrupt Request (IRQ) — This level sensitive input requests that an interrupt sequence be generated within the machine. The processor will wait until it completes the current instruction that is being executed before it recognizes the request. At that time, if the interrupt mask bit in the Condition Code Register is not set, the machine will begin an interrupt sequence. The Index Register, Program Counter, Accumulators, and Condition Code Register are stored away on the stack. Next the MPU will respond to the interrupt request by setting the interrupt mask bit high so that no further interrupts may occur. At the end of the cycle, a 16-bit address will be loaded that points to a vectoring address which is located in memory locations FFF8 and FFF9. An address loaded at these locations causes the MPU to branch to an interrupt routine in memory.

The Halt line must be in the high state for interrupts to be serviced. Interrupts will be latched internally while Halt is low.

The IRQ has a high impedance pullup device internal to the chip; however a 3 kΩ external resistor to V_{CC} should be used for wire-OR and optimum control of interrupts.

Reset — This input is used to reset and start the MPU from a power down condition, resulting from a power failure or an initial start-up of the processor. If a high level is detected on the input, this will signal the MPU to begin the restart sequence. This will start execution of a routine to initialize the processor from its reset condition. All the higher order address lines will be forced high. For the restart, the last two (FFFE, FFFF) locations in memory will be used to load the program that is addressed by the program counter. During the restart routine, the interrupt mask bit is set and must be reset before the MPU can be interrupted by IRQ.

 MOTOROLA *Semiconductor Products Inc.*

MC6800

Figure 9 shows the initialization of the microprocessor after restart. Reset must be held low for at least eight clock periods after V_{CC} reaches 4.75 volts. If Reset goes high prior to the leading edge of φ2, on the next φ1 the first restart memory vector address (FFFE) will appear on the address lines. This location should contain the higher order eight bits to be stored into the program counter. Following, the next address FFFF should contain the lower order eight bits to be stored into the program counter.

Non-Maskable Interrupt (NMI) — A low-going edge on this input requests that a non-mask-interrupt sequence be generated within the processor. As with the Interrupt Request signal, the processor will complete the current instruction that is being executed before it recognizes the NMI signal. The interrupt mask bit in the Condition Code Register has no effect on NMI.

The Index Register, Program Counter, Accumulators, and Condition Code Register are stored away on the stack. At the end of the cycle, a 16-bit address will be loaded that points to a vectoring address which is located in memory locations FFFC and FFFD. An address loaded at these locations causes the MPU to branch to a non-maskable interrupt routine in memory.

NMI has a high impedance pullup resistor internal to the chip; however a 3 kΩ external resistor to V_{CC} should be used for wire-OR and optimum control of interrupts.

Inputs IRQ and NMI are hardware interrupt lines that are sampled during φ2 and will start the interrupt routine on the φ1 following the completion of an instruction.

Figure 10 is a flow chart describing the major decision paths and interrupt vectors of the microprocessor. Table 1 gives the memory map for interrupt vectors.

FIGURE 9 — INITIALIZATION OF MPU AFTER RESTART

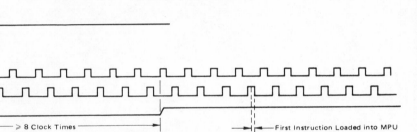

TABLE 1 — MEMORY MAP FOR INTERRUPT VECTORS

Vector MS	LS	Description
FFFE	FFFF	Restart
FFFC	FFFD	Non-maskable Interrupt
FFFA	FFFB	Software Interrupt
FFF8	FFF9	Interrupt Request

 MOTOROLA *Semiconductor Products Inc.*

MC6800

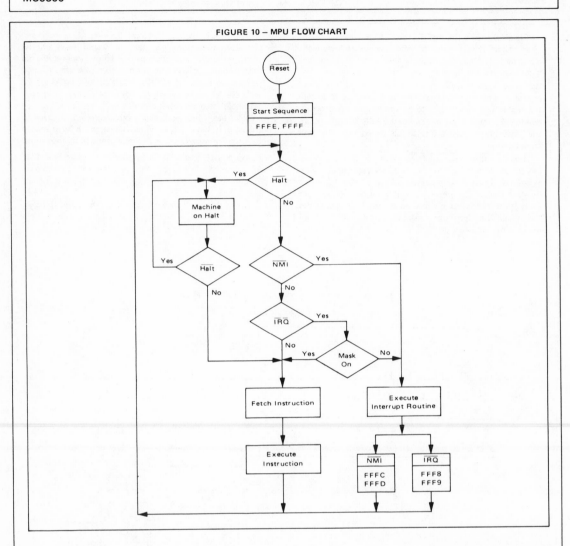

FIGURE 10 – MPU FLOW CHART

MPU REGISTERS

The MPU has three 16-bit registers and three 8-bit registers available for use by the programmer (Figure 11).

Program Counter — The program counter is a two byte (16-bits) register that points to the current program address.

Stack Pointer — The stack pointer is a two byte register that contains the address of the next available location in an external push-down/pop-up stack. This stack is normally a random access Read/Write memory that may have any location (address) that is convenient. In those applications that require storage of information in the stack when power is lost, the stack must be non-volatile.

Index Register — The index register is a two byte register that is used to store data or a sixteen bit memory address for the Indexed mode of memory addressing.

Accumulators — The MPU contains two 8-bit accumulators that are used to hold operands and results from an arithmetic logic unit (ALU).

 MOTOROLA *Semiconductor Products Inc.*

MC6800

FIGURE 11 – PROGRAMMING MODEL OF THE MICROPROCESSING UNIT

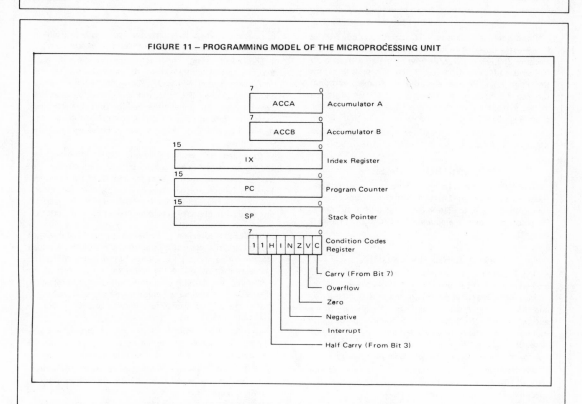

FIGURE 12 – SAVING THE STATUS OF THE MICROPROCESSOR IN THE STACK

SP = Stack Pointer
CC = Condition Codes (Also called the Processor Status Byte)
ACCB = Accumulator B
ACCA = Accumulator A
IXH = Index Register, Higher Order 8 Bits
IXL = Index Register, Lower Order 8 Bits
PCH = Program Counter, Higher Order 8 Bits
PCL = Program Counter, Lower Order 8 Bits

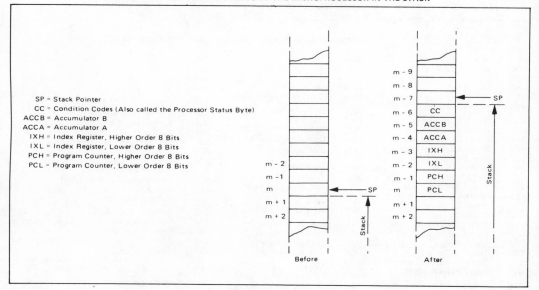

(M) MOTOROLA *Semiconductor Products Inc.*

MC6800

Condition Code Register — The condition code register indicates the results of an Arithmetic Logic Unit operation: Negative (N), Zero (Z), Overflow (V), Carry from bit 7 (C), and half carry from bit 3 (H). These bits of the Condition Code Register are used as testable conditions for the conditional branch instructions. Bit 4 is the interrupt mask bit (I). The unused bits of the Condition Code Register (b6 and b7) are ones.

Figure 12 shows the order of saving the microprocessor status within the stack.

MPU INSTRUCTION SET

The MC6800 has a set of 72 different instructions. Included are binary and decimal arithmetic, logical, shift, rotate, load, store, conditional or unconditional branch, interrupt and stack manipulation instructions (Tables 2 thru 6).

MPU ADDRESSING MODES

The MC6800 eight-bit microprocessing unit has seven address modes that can be used by a programmer, with the addressing mode a function of both the type of instruction and the coding within the instruction. A summary of the addressing modes for a particular instruction can be found in Table 7 along with the associated instruction execution time that is given in machine cycles. With a clock frequency of 1 MHz, these times would be microseconds.

Accumulator (ACCX) Addressing — In accumulator only addressing, either accumulator A or accumulator B is specified. These are one-byte instructions.

Immediate Addressing — In immediate addressing, the operand is contained in the second byte of the instruction except LDS and LDX which have the operand in the second and third bytes of the instruction. The MPU addresses this location when it fetches the immediate instruction for execution. These are two or three-byte instructions.

Direct Addressing — In direct addressing, the address of the operand is contained in the second byte of the instruction. Direct addressing allows the user to directly address the lowest 256 bytes in the machine i.e., locations zero through 255. Enhanced execution times are achieved by storing data in these locations. In most configurations, it should be a random access memory. These are two-byte instructions.

Extended Addressing — In extended addressing, the address contained in the second byte of the instruction is used as the higher eight-bits of the address of the operand. The third byte of the instruction is used as the lower eight-bits of the address for the operand. This is an absolute address in memory. These are three-byte instructions.

Indexed Addressing — In indexed addressing, the address contained in the second byte of the instruction is added to the index register's lowest eight bits in the MPU. The carry is then added to the higher order eight bits of the index register. This result is then used to address memory. The modified address is held in a temporary address register so there is no change to the index register. These are two-byte instructions.

Implied Addressing — In the implied addressing mode the instruction gives the address (i.e., stack pointer, index register, etc.). These are one-byte instructions.

Relative Addressing — In relative addressing, the address contained in the second byte of the instruction is added to the program counter's lowest eight bits plus two. The carry or borrow is then added to the high eight bits. This allows the user to address data within a range of –125 to +129 bytes of the present instruction. These are two-byte instructions.

TABLE 2 – MICROPROCESSOR INSTRUCTION SET – ALPHABETIC SEQUENCE

ABA	Add Accumulators	CLR	Clear	PUL	Pull Data
ADC	Add with Carry	CLV	Clear Overflow	ROL	Rotate Left
ADD	Add	CMP	Compare	ROR	Rotate Right
AND	Logical And	COM	Complement	RTI	Return from Interrupt
ASL	Arithmetic Shift Left	CPX	Compare Index Register	RTS	Return from Subroutine
ASR	Arithmetic Shift Right	DAA	Decimal Adjust	SBA	Subtract Accumulators
BCC	Branch if Carry Clear	DEC	Decrement	SBC	Subtract with Carry
BCS	Branch if Carry Set	DES	Decrement Stack Pointer	SEC	Set Carry
BEQ	Branch if Equal to Zero	DEX	Decrement Index Register	SEI	Set Interrupt Mask
BGE	Branch if Greater or Equal Zero	EOR	Exclusive OR	SEV	Set Overflow
BGT	Branch if Greater than Zero			STA	Store Accumulator
BHI	Branch if Higher	INC	Increment	STS	Store Stack Register
BIT	Bit Test	INS	Increment Stack Pointer	STX	Store Index Register
BLE	Branch if Less or Equal	INX	Increment Index Register	SUB	Subtract
BLS	Branch if Lower or Same	JMP	Jump	SWI	Software Interrupt
BLT	Branch if Less than Zero	JSR	Jump to Subroutine	TAB	Transfer Accumulators
BMI	Branch if Minus	LDA	Load Accumulator	TAP	Transfer Accumulators to Condition Code Reg.
BNE	Branch if Not Equal to Zero	LDS	Load Stack Pointer	TBA	Transfer Accumulators
BPL	Branch if Plus	LDX	Load Index Register	TPA	Transfer Condition Code Reg. to Accumulator
BRA	Branch Always	LSR	Logical Shift Right	TST	Test
BSR	Branch to Subroutine	NEG	Negate	TSX	Transfer Stack Pointer to Index Register
BVC	Branch if Overflow Clear	NOP	No Operation	TXS	Transfer Index Register to Stack Pointer
BVS	Branch if Overflow Set	ORA	Inclusive OR Accumulator	WAI	Wait for Interrupt
CBA	Compare Accumulators	PSH	Push Data		
CLC	Clear Carry				
CLI	Clear Interrupt Mask				

 MOTOROLA *Semiconductor Products Inc.*

MC6800

TABLE 3 – ACCUMULATOR AND MEMORY INSTRUCTIONS

OPERATIONS	MNEMONIC	IMMED OP ~ #	DIRECT OP ~ #	INDEX OP ~ #	EXTND OP ~ #	IMPLIED OP ~ #	BOOLEAN/ARITHMETIC OPERATION (All register labels refer to contents)	5 H	4 I	3 N	2 Z	1 V	0 C
Add	ADDA	8B 2 2	9B 3 2	AB 5 2	BB 4 3		A + M → A	:	●	:	:	:	:
	ADDB	CB 2 2	DB 3 2	EB 5 2	FB 4 3		B + M → B	:	●	:	:	:	:
Add Acmltrs	ABA					1B 2 1	A + B → A	:	●	:	:	:	:
Add with Carry	ADCA	89 2 2	99 3 2	A9 5 2	B9 4 3		A + M + C → A	:	●	:	:	:	:
	ADCB	C9 2 2	D9 3 2	E9 5 2	F9 4 3		B + M + C → B	:	●	:	:	:	:
And	ANDA	84 2 2	94 3 2	A4 5 2	B4 4 3		A · M → A	●	●	:	:	R	●
	ANDB	C4 2 2	D4 3 2	E4 5 2	F4 4 3		B · M → B	●	●	:	:	R	●
Bit Test	BITA	85 2 2	95 3 2	A5 5 2	B5 4 3		A · M	●	●	:	:	R	●
	BITB	C5 2 2	D5 3 2	E5 5 2	F5 4 3		B · M	●	●	:	:	R	●
Clear	CLR			6F 7 2	7F 6 3		00 → M	●	●	R	S	R	R
	CLRA					4F 2 1	00 → A	●	●	R	S	R	R
	CLRB					5F 2 1	00 → B	●	●	R	S	R	R
Compare	CMPA	81 2 2	91 3 2	A1 5 2	B1 4 3		A − M	●	●	:	:	:	:
	CMPB	C1 2 2	D1 3 2	E1 5 2	F1 4 3		B − M	●	●	:	:	:	:
Compare Acmltrs	CBA					11 2 1	A − B	●	●	:	:	:	:
Complement, 1's	COM			63 7 2	73 6 3		M̄ → M	●	●	:	:	R	S
	COMA					43 2 1	Ā → A	●	●	:	:	R	S
	COMB					53 2 1	B̄ → B	●	●	:	:	R	S
Complement, 2's	NEG			60 7 2	70 6 3		00 − M → M	●	●	:	:	①	②
(Negate)	NEGA					40 2 1	00 − A → A	●	●	:	:	①	②
	NEGB					50 2 1	00 − B → B	●	●	:	:	①	②
Decimal Adjust, A	DAA					19 2 1	Converts Binary Add. of BCD Characters into BCD Format	●	●	:	:	:	③
Decrement	DEC			6A 7 2	7A 6 3		M − 1 → M	●	●	:	:	④	●
	DECA					4A 2 1	A − 1 → A	●	●	:	:	④	●
	DECB					5A 2 1	B − 1 → B	●	●	:	:	④	●
Exclusive OR	EORA	88 2 2	98 3 2	A8 5 2	B8 4 3		A ⊕ M → A	●	●	:	:	R	●
	EORB	C8 2 2	D8 3 2	E8 5 2	F8 4 3		B ⊕ M → B	●	●	:	:	R	●
Increment	INC			6C 7 2	7C 6 3		M + 1 → M	●	●	:	:	⑤	●
	INCA					4C 2 1	A + 1 → A	●	●	:	:	⑤	●
	INCB					5C 2 1	B + 1 → B	●	●	:	:	⑤	●
Load Acmltr	LDAA	86 2 2	96 3 2	A6 5 2	B6 4 3		M → A	●	●	:	:	R	●
	LDAB	C6 2 2	D6 3 2	E6 5 2	F6 4 3		M → B	●	●	:	:	R	●
Or, Inclusive	ORAA	8A 2 2	9A 3 2	AA 5 2	BA 4 3		A + M → A	●	●	:	:	R	●
	ORAB	CA 2 2	DA 3 2	EA 5 2	FA 4 3		B + M → B	●	●	:	:	R	●
Push Data	PSHA					36 4 1	A → M$_{SP}$, SP − 1 → SP	●	●	●	●	●	●
	PSHB					37 4 1	B → M$_{SP}$, SP − 1 → SP	●	●	●	●	●	●
Pull Data	PULA					32 4 1	SP + 1 → SP, M$_{SP}$ → A	●	●	●	●	●	●
	PULB					33 4 1	SP + 1 → SP, M$_{SP}$ → B	●	●	●	●	●	●
Rotate Left	ROL			69 7 2	79 6 3		M	●	●	:	:	⑥	⑥
	ROLA					49 2 1	A	●	●	:	:	⑥	⑥
	ROLB					59 2 1	B	●	●	:	:	⑥	⑥
Rotate Right	ROR			66 7 2	76 6 3		M	●	●	:	:	⑥	⑥
	RORA					46 2 1	A	●	●	:	:	⑥	⑥
	RORB					56 2 1	B	●	●	:	:	⑥	⑥
Shift Left, Arithmetic	ASL			68 7 2	78 6 3		M	●	●	:	:	⑥	⑥
	ASLA					48 2 1	A	●	●	:	:	⑥	⑥
	ASLB					58 2 1	B	●	●	:	:	⑥	⑥
Shift Right, Arithmetic	ASR			67 7 2	77 6 3		M	●	●	:	:	⑥	⑥
	ASRA					47 2 1	A	●	●	:	:	⑥	⑥
	ASRB					57 2 1	B	●	●	:	:	⑥	⑥
Shift Right, Logic	LSR			64 7 2	74 6 3		M	●	●	R	:	⑥	⑥
	LSRA					44 2 1	A	●	●	R	:	⑥	⑥
	LSRB					54 2 1	B	●	●	R	:	⑥	⑥
Store Acmltr	STAA		97 4 2	A7 6 2	B7 5 3		A → M	●	●	:	:	R	●
	STAB		D7 4 2	E7 6 2	F7 5 3		B → M	●	●	:	:	R	●
Subtract	SUBA	80 2 2	90 3 2	A0 5 2	B0 4 3		A − M → A	●	●	:	:	:	:
	SUBB	C0 2 2	D0 3 2	E0 5 2	F0 4 3		B − M → B	●	●	:	:	:	:
Subtract Acmltrs	SBA					10 2 1	A − B → A	●	●	:	:	:	:
Subtr. with Carry	SBCA	82 2 2	92 3 2	A2 5 2	B2 4 3		A − M − C → A	●	●	:	:	:	:
	SBCB	C2 2 2	D2 3 2	E2 5 2	F2 4 3		B − M − C → B	●	●	:	:	:	:
Transfer Acmltrs	TAB					16 2 1	A → B	●	●	:	:	R	●
	TBA					17 2 1	B → A	●	●	:	:	R	●
Test, Zero or Minus	TST			6D 7 2	7D 6 3		M − 00	●	●	:	:	R	R
	TSTA					4D 2 1	A − 00	●	●	:	:	R	R
	TSTB					5D 2 1	B − 00	●	●	:	:	R	R
								H	I	N	Z	V	C

LEGEND:

OP   Operation Code (Hexadecimal).
~   Number of MPU Cycles.
#   Number of Program Bytes.
+   Arithmetic Plus.
−   Arithmetic Minus.
·   Boolean AND.
M$_{SP}$ Contents of memory location pointed to be Stack Pointer.

\+   Boolean Inclusive OR.
⊕   Boolean Exclusive OR.
M̄   Complement of M.
→   Transfer Into.
0   Bit = Zero.
00   Byte = Zero.

Note   Accumulator addressing mode instructions are included in the column for IMPLIED addressing

CONDITION CODE SYMBOLS

H   Half carry from bit 3.
I   Interrupt mask
N   Negative (sign bit)
Z   Zero (byte)
V   Overflow, 2's complement
C   Carry from bit 7
R   Reset Always
S   Set Always
:   Test and set if true, cleared otherwise
●   Not Affected

 MOTOROLA *Semiconductor Products Inc.*

MC6800

TABLE 4 — INDEX REGISTER AND STACK MANIPULATION INSTRUCTIONS

POINTER OPERATIONS	MNEMONIC	IMMED OP	~	#	DIRECT OP	~	#	INDEX OP	~	#	EXTND OP	~	#	IMPLIED OP	~	#	BOOLEAN/ARITHMETIC OPERATION	COND. CODE REG. 5 H	4 I	3 N	2 Z	1 V	0 C
Compare Index Reg	CPX	8C	3	3	9C	4	2	AC	6	2	BC	5	3				$X_H - M, X_L - (M+1)$	•	•	⑦	!	⑧	•
Decrement Index Reg	DEX													09	4	1	$X - 1 \cdot X$	•	•	•	!	•	•
Decrement Stack Pntr	DES													34	4	1	$SP - 1 \cdot SP$	•	•	•	•	•	•
Increment Index Reg	INX													08	4	1	$X + 1 \cdot X$	•	•	•	!	•	•
Increment Stack Pntr	INS													31	4	1	$SP + 1 \cdot SP$	•	•	•	•	•	•
Load Index Reg	LDX	CE	3	3	DE	4	2	EE	6	2	FE	5	3				$M \cdot X_H, (M+1) \cdot X_L$	•	•	⑨	!	R	•
Load Stack Pntr	LDS	8E	3	3	9E	4	2	AE	6	2	BE	5	3				$M \cdot SP_H, (M+1) \cdot SP_L$	•	•	⑨	!	R	•
Store Index Reg	STX				DF	5	2	EF	7	2	FF	6	3				$X_H \cdot M, X_L \cdot (M+1)$	•	•	⑨	!	R	•
Store Stack Pntr	STS				9F	5	2	AF	7	2	BF	6	3				$SP_H \cdot M, SP_L \cdot (M+1)$	•	•	⑨	!	R	•
Indx Reg · Stack Pntr	TXS													35	4	1	$X - 1 \cdot SP$	•	•	•	•	•	•
Stack Pntr · Indx Reg	TSX													30	4	1	$SP + 1 \cdot X$	•	•	•	•	•	•

TABLE 5 — JUMP AND BRANCH INSTRUCTIONS

OPERATIONS	MNEMONIC	RELATIVE OP	~	#	INDEX OP	~	#	EXTND OP	~	#	IMPLIED OP	~	#	BRANCH TEST	COND. CODE REG. 5 H	4 I	3 N	2 Z	1 V	0 C
Branch Always	BRA	20	4	2										None	•	•	•	•	•	•
Branch If Carry Clear	BCC	24	4	2										C = 0	•	•	•	•	•	•
Branch If Carry Set	BCS	25	4	2										C = 1	•	•	•	•	•	•
Branch If = Zero	BEQ	27	4	2										Z = 1	•	•	•	•	•	•
Branch If ≥ Zero	BGE	2C	4	2										N ⊕ V = 0	•	•	•	•	•	•
Branch If > Zero	BGT	2E	4	2										Z + (N ⊕ V) = 0	•	•	•	•	•	•
Branch If Higher	BHI	22	4	2										C + Z = 0	•	•	•	•	•	•
Branch If ≤ Zero	BLE	2F	4	2										Z + (N ⊕ V) = 1	•	•	•	•	•	•
Branch If Lower Or Same	BLS	23	4	2										C + Z = 1	•	•	•	•	•	•
Branch If < Zero	BLT	2D	4	2										N ⊕ V = 1	•	•	•	•	•	•
Branch If Minus	BMI	2B	4	2										N = 1	•	•	•	•	•	•
Branch If Not Equal Zero	BNE	26	4	2										Z = 0	•	•	•	•	•	•
Branch If Overflow Clear	BVC	28	4	2										V = 0	•	•	•	•	•	•
Branch If Overflow Set	BVS	29	4	2										V = 1	•	•	•	•	•	•
Branch If Plus	BPL	2A	4	2										N = 0	•	•	•	•	•	•
Branch To Subroutine	BSR	8D	8	2											•	•	•	•	•	•
Jump	JMP				6E	4	2	7E	3	3				} See Special Operations	•	•	•	•	•	•
Jump To Subroutine	JSR				AD	8	2	BD	9	3					•	•	•	•	•	•
No Operation	NOP										01	2	1	Advances Prog. Cntr. Only	•	•	•	•	•	•
Return From Interrupt	RTI										3B	10	1		—	—	— ⑩ —			
Return From Subroutine	RTS										39	5	1	} See Special Operations	•	•	•	•	•	•
Software Interrupt	SWI										3F	12	1		•	•	•	•	•	•
Wait for Interrupt *	WAI										3E	9	1	}	•	⑪	•	•	•	•

*WAI puts Address Bus, R/W, and Data Bus in the three-state mode while VMA is held low.

 MOTOROLA *Semiconductor Products Inc.*

MC6800

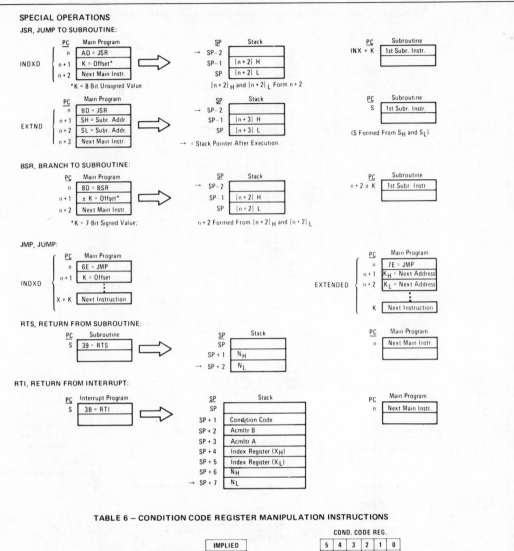

SPECIAL OPERATIONS

JSR, JUMP TO SUBROUTINE:

*K = 8-Bit Unsigned Value

$[n+2]_H$ and $[n+2]_L$ Form $n+2$

→ = Stack Pointer After Execution.

(S Formed From S_H and S_L)

BSR, BRANCH TO SUBROUTINE:

*K = 7-Bit Signed Value; $n+2$ Formed From $[n+2]_H$ and $[n+2]_L$

JMP, JUMP:

RTS, RETURN FROM SUBROUTINE:

RTI, RETURN FROM INTERRUPT:

TABLE 6 – CONDITION CODE REGISTER MANIPULATION INSTRUCTIONS

OPERATIONS	MNEMONIC	IMPLIED OP	~	=	BOOLEAN OPERATION	5 H	4 I	3 N	2 Z	1 V	0 C
Clear Carry	CLC	0C	2	1	0 → C	•	•	•	•	•	R
Clear Interrupt Mask	CLI	0E	2	1	0 → I	•	R	•	•	•	•
Clear Overflow	CLV	0A	2	1	0 → V	•	•	•	•	R	•
Set Carry	SEC	0D	2	1	1 → C	•	•	•	•	•	S
Set Interrupt Mask	SEI	0F	2	1	1 → I	•	S	•	•	•	•
Set Overflow	SEV	0B	2	1	1 → V	•	•	•	•	S	•
Acmltr A → CCR	TAP	06	2	1	A → CCR			⑫			
CCR → Acmltr A	TPA	07	2	1	CCR → A	•	•	•	•	•	•

(COND. CODE REG.)

CONDITION CODE REGISTER NOTES: (Bit set if test is true and cleared otherwise)

1 (Bit V) Test: Result = 10000000?
2 (Bit C) Test: Result = 00000000?
3 (Bit C) Test: Decimal value of most significant BCD Character greater than nine? (Not cleared if previously set.)
4 (Bit V) Test: Operand = 10000000 prior to execution?
5 (Bit V) Test: Operand = 01111111 prior to execution?
6 (Bit V) Test: Set equal to result of N⊕C after shift has occurred.

7 (Bit N) Test: Sign bit of most significant (MS) byte = 1?
8 (Bit V) Test: 2's complement overflow from subtraction of MS bytes?
9 (Bit N) Test: Result less than zero? (Bit 15 = 1)
10 (All) Load Condition Code Register from Stack. (See Special Operations)
11 (Bit I) Set when interrupt occurs. If previously set, a Non-Maskable Interrupt is required to exit the wait state.
12 (All) Set according to the contents of Accumulator A.

 MOTOROLA *Semiconductor Products Inc.*

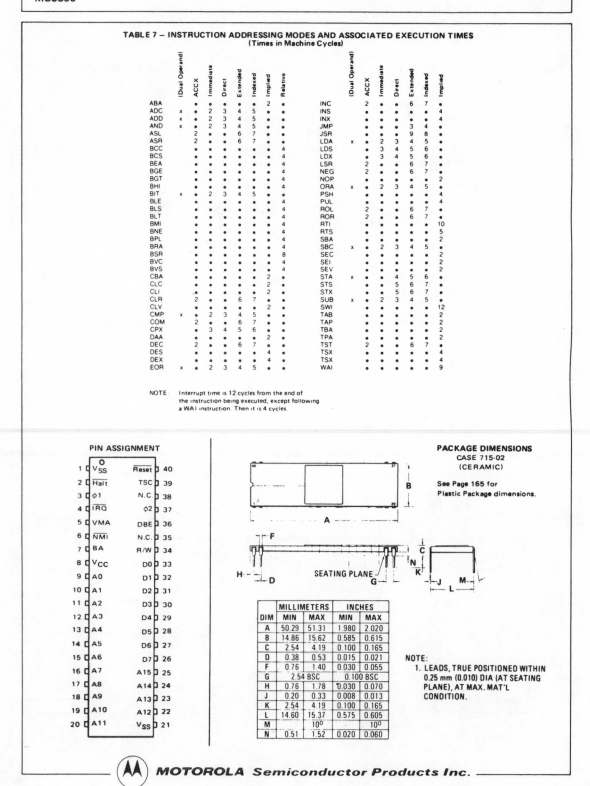

MC6800

TABLE 7 – INSTRUCTION ADDRESSING MODES AND ASSOCIATED EXECUTION TIMES
(Times in Machine Cycles)

	(Dual Operand)	ACCX	Immediate	Direct	Extended	Indexed	Implied	Relative
ABA	•	•	•	•	•	•	2	•
ADC	x	•	2	3	4	5	•	•
ADD	x	•	2	3	4	5	•	•
AND	x	•	2	3	4	5	•	•
ASL	•	2	•	•	6	7	•	•
ASR	•	2	•	•	6	7	•	•
BCC	•	•	•	•	•	•	•	4
BCS	•	•	•	•	•	•	•	4
BEA	•	•	•	•	•	•	•	4
BGE	•	•	•	•	•	•	•	4
BGT	•	•	•	•	•	•	•	4
BHI	•	•	•	•	•	•	•	4
BIT	x	•	2	3	4	5	•	•
BLE	•	•	•	•	•	•	•	4
BLS	•	•	•	•	•	•	•	4
BLT	•	•	•	•	•	•	•	4
BMI	•	•	•	•	•	•	•	4
BNE	•	•	•	•	•	•	•	4
BPL	•	•	•	•	•	•	•	4
BRA	•	•	•	•	•	•	•	4
BSR	•	•	•	•	•	•	•	8
BVC	•	•	•	•	•	•	•	4
BVS	•	•	•	•	•	•	•	4
CBA	•	•	•	•	•	•	2	•
CLC	•	•	•	•	•	•	2	•
CLI	•	•	•	•	•	•	2	•
CLR	•	2	•	•	6	7	•	•
CLV	•	•	•	•	•	•	2	•
CMP	x	•	2	3	4	5	•	•
COM	•	2	•	•	6	7	•	•
CPX	•	•	3	4	5	6	•	•
DAA	•	•	•	•	•	•	2	•
DEC	•	2	•	•	6	7	•	•
DES	•	•	•	•	•	•	4	•
DEX	•	•	•	•	•	•	4	•
EOR	x	•	2	3	4	5	•	•

	(Dual Operand)	ACCX	Immediate	Direct	Extended	Indexed	Implied
INC	•	2	•	•	6	7	•
INS	•	•	•	•	•	•	4
INX	•	•	•	•	•	•	4
JMP	•	•	•	•	3	4	•
JSR	•	•	•	•	9	8	•
LDA	x	•	2	3	4	5	•
LDS	•	•	3	4	5	6	•
LDX	•	•	3	4	5	6	•
LSR	•	2	•	•	6	7	•
NEG	•	2	•	•	6	7	•
NOP	•	•	•	•	•	•	2
ORA	x	•	2	3	4	5	•
PSH	•	•	•	•	•	•	4
PUL	•	•	•	•	•	•	4
ROL	•	2	•	•	6	7	•
ROR	•	2	•	•	6	7	•
RTI	•	•	•	•	•	•	10
RTS	•	•	•	•	•	•	5
SBA	•	•	•	•	•	•	2
SBC	x	•	2	3	4	5	•
SEC	•	•	•	•	•	•	2
SEI	•	•	•	•	•	•	2
SEV	•	•	•	•	•	•	2
STA	x	•	•	4	5	6	•
STS	•	•	•	5	6	7	•
STX	•	•	•	5	6	7	•
SUB	x	•	2	3	4	5	•
SWI	•	•	•	•	•	•	12
TAB	•	•	•	•	•	•	2
TAP	•	•	•	•	•	•	2
TBA	•	•	•	•	•	•	2
TPA	•	•	•	•	•	•	2
TST	•	2	•	•	6	7	•
TSX	•	•	•	•	•	•	4
TSX	•	•	•	•	•	•	4
WAI	•	•	•	•	•	•	9

NOTE: Interrupt time is 12 cycles from the end of the instruction being executed, except following a WAI instruction. Then it is 4 cycles.

PIN ASSIGNMENT

Pin	Signal	Signal	Pin
1	VSS	Reset	40
2	Halt	TSC	39
3	φ1	N.C.	38
4	IRQ	φ2	37
5	VMA	DBE	36
6	NMI	N.C.	35
7	BA	R/W	34
8	VCC	D0	33
9	A0	D1	32
10	A1	D2	31
11	A2	D3	30
12	A3	D4	29
13	A4	D5	28
14	A5	D6	27
15	A6	D7	26
16	A7	A15	25
17	A8	A14	24
18	A9	A13	23
19	A10	A12	22
20	A11	VSS	21

PACKAGE DIMENSIONS
CASE 715-02
(CERAMIC)

See Page 165 for Plastic Package dimensions.

SEATING PLANE

DIM	MILLIMETERS MIN	MAX	INCHES MIN	MAX
A	50.29	51.31	1.980	2.020
B	14.86	15.62	0.585	0.615
C	2.54	4.19	0.100	0.165
D	0.38	0.53	0.015	0.021
F	0.76	1.40	0.030	0.055
G	2.54 BSC		0.100 BSC	
H	0.76	1.78	0.030	0.070
J	0.20	0.33	0.008	0.013
K	2.54	4.19	0.100	0.165
L	14.60	15.37	0.575	0.605
M	10°		10°	
N	0.51	1.52	0.020	0.060

NOTE:
1. LEADS, TRUE POSITIONED WITHIN 0.25 mm (0.010) DIA (AT SEATING PLANE), AT MAX. MAT'L CONDITION.

MOTOROLA *Semiconductor Products Inc.*

MC6800

SUMMARY OF CYCLE BY CYCLE OPERATION

Table 8 provides a detailed description of the information present on the Address Bus, Data Bus, Valid Memory Address line (VMA), and the Read/Write line (R/W) during each cycle for each instruction.

This information is useful in comparing actual with expected results during debug of both software and hardware as the control program is executed. The information is categorized in groups according to Addressing Mode and Number of Cycles per instruction. (In general, instructions with the same Addressing Mode and Number of Cycles execute in the same manner; exceptions are indicated in the table.)

TABLE 8 – OPERATION SUMMARY

Address Mode and Instructions	Cycles	Cycle #	VMA Line	Address Bus	R/W Line	Data Bus
IMMEDIATE						
ADC EOR ADD LDA AND ORA BIT SBC CMP SUB	2	1	1	Op Code Address	1	Op Code
		2	1	Op Code Address + 1	1	Operand Data
CPX LDS LDX	3	1	1	Op Code Address	1	Op Code
		2	1	Op Code Address + 1	1	Operand Data (High Order Byte)
		3	1	Op Code Address + 2	1	Operand Data (Low Order Byte)
DIRECT						
ADC EOR ADD LDA AND ORA BIT SBC CMP SUB	3	1	1	Op Code Address	1	Op Code
		2	1	Op Code Address + 1	1	Address of Operand
		3	1	Address of Operand	1	Operand Data
CPX LDS LDX	4	1	1	Op Code Address	1	Op Code
		2	1	Op Code Address + 1	1	Address of Operand
		3	1	Address of Operand	1	Operand Data (High Order Byte)
		4	1	Operand Address + 1	1	Operand Data (Low Order Byte)
STA	4	1	1	Op Code Address	1	Op Code
		2	1	Op Code Address + 1	1	Destination Address
		3	0	Destination Address	1	Irrelevant Data (Note 1)
		4	1	Destination Address	0	Data from Accumulator
STS STX	5	1	1	Op Code Address	1	Op Code
		2	1	Op Code Address + 1	1	Address of Operand
		3	0	Address of Operand	1	Irrelevant Data (Note 1)
		4	1	Address of Operand	0	Register Data (High Order Byte)
		5	1	Address of Operand + 1	0	Register Data (Low Order Byte)
INDEXED						
JMP	4	1	1	Op Code Address	1	Op Code
		2	1	Op Code Address + 1	1	Offset
		3	0	Index Register	1	Irrelevant Data (Note 1)
		4	0	Index Register Plus Offset (w/o Carry)	1	Irrelevant Data (Note 1)
ADC EOR ADD LDA AND ORA BIT SBC CMP SUB	5	1	1	Op Code Address	1	Op Code
		2	1	Op Code Address + 1	1	Offset
		3	0	Index Register	1	Irrelevant Data (Note 1)
		4	0	Index Register Plus Offset (w/o Carry)	1	Irrelevant Data (Note 1)
		5	1	Index Register Plus Offset	1	Operand Data
CPX LDS LDX	6	1	1	Op Code Address	1	Up Code
		2	1	Op Code Address + 1	1	Offset
		3	0	Index Register	1	Irrelevant Data (Note 1)
		4	0	Index Register Plus Offset (w/o Carry)	1	Irrelevant Data (Note 1)
		5	1	Index Register Plus Offset	1	Operand Data (High Order Byte)
		6	1	Index Register Plus Offset + 1	1	Operand Data (Low Order Byte)

MC6800

TABLE 8 – OPERATION SUMMARY (Continued)

Address Mode and Instructions	Cycles	Cycle #	VMA Line	Address Bus	R/W Line	Data Bus
INDEXED (Continued)						
STA	6	1	1	Op Code Address	1	Op Code
		2	1	Op Code Address + 1	1	Offset
		3	0	Index Register	1	Irrelevant Data (Note 1)
		4	0	Index Register Plus Offset (w/o Carry)	1	Irrelevant Data (Note 1)
		5	0	Index Register Plus Offset	1	Irrelevant Data (Note 1)
		6	1	Index Register Plus Offset	0	Operand Data
ASL LSR ASR NEG CLR ROL COM ROR DEC TST INC	7	1	1	Op Code Address	1	Op Code
		2	1	Op Code Address + 1	1	Offset
		3	0	Index Register	1	Irrelevant Data (Note 1)
		4	0	Index Register Plus Offset (w/o Carry)	1	Irrelevant Data (Note 1)
		5	1	Index Register Plus Offset	1	Current Operand Data
		6	0	Index Register Plus Offset	1	Irrelevant Data (Note 1)
		7	1/0 (Note 3)	Index Register Plus Offset	0	New Operand Data (Note 3)
STS STX	7	1	1	Op Code Address	1	Op Code
		2	1	Op Code Address + 1	1	Offset
		3	0	Index Register	1	Irrelevant Data (Note 1)
		4	0	Index Register Plus Offset (w/o Carry)	1	Irrelevant Data (Note 1)
		5	0	Index Register Plus Offset	1	Irrelevant Data (Note 1)
		6	1	Index Register Plus Offset	0	Operand Data (High Order Byte)
		7	1	Index Register Plus Offset + 1	0	Operand Data (Low Order Byte)
JSR	8	1	1	Op Code Address	1	Op Code
		2	1	Op Code Address + 1	1	Offset
		3	0	Index Register	1	Irrelevant Data (Note 1)
		4	1	Stack Pointer	0	Return Address (Low Order Byte)
		5	1	Stack Pointer − 1	0	Return Address (High Order Byte)
		6	0	Stack Pointer − 2	1	Irrelevant Data (Note 1)
		7	0	Index Register	1	Irrelevant Data (Note 1)
		8	0	Index Register Plus Offset (w/o Carry)	1	Irrelevant Data (Note 1)
EXTENDED						
JMP	3	1	1	Op Code Address	1	Op Code
		2	1	Op Code Address + 1	1	Jump Address (High Order Byte)
		3	1	Op Code Address + 2	1	Jump Address (Low Order Byte)
ADC EOR ADD LDA AND ORA BIT SBC CMP SUB	4	1	1	Op Code Address	1	Op Code
		2	1	Op Code Address + 1	1	Address of Operand (High Order Byte)
		3	1	Op Code Address + 2	1	Address of Operand (Low Order Byte)
		4	1	Address of Operand	1	Operand Data
CPX LDS LDX	5	1	1	Op Code Address	1	Op Code
		2	1	Op Code Address + 1	1	Address of Operand (High Order Byte)
		3	1	Op Code Address + 2	1	Address of Operand (Low Order Byte)
		4	1	Address of Operand	1	Operand Data (High Order Byte)
		5	1	Address of Operand + 1	1	Operand Data (Low Order Byte)
STA A STA B	5	1	1	Op Code Address	1	Op Code
		2	1	Op Code Address + 1	1	Destination Address (High Order Byte)
		3	1	Op Code Address + 2	1	Destination Address (Low Order Byte)
		4	0	Operand Destination Address	1	Irrelevant Data (Note 1)
		5	1	Operand Destination Address	0	Data from Accumulator
ASL LSR ASR NEG CLR ROL COM ROR DEC TST INC	6	1	1	Op Code Address	1	Op Code
		2	1	Op Code Address + 1	1	Address of Operand (High Order Byte)
		3	1	Op Code Address + 2	1	Address of Operand (Low Order Byte)
		4	1	Address of Operand	1	Current Operand Data
		5	0	Address of Operand	1	Irrelevant Data (Note 1)
		6	1/0 (Note 3)	Address of Operand	0	New Operand Data (Note 3)

MC6800

TABLE 8 – OPERATION SUMMARY (Continued)

Address Mode and Instructions	Cycles	Cycle #	VMA Line	Address Bus	R/W Line	Data Bus
EXTENDED (Continued)						
STS STX	6	1	1	Op Code Address	1	Op Code
		2	1	Op Code Address + 1	1	Address of Operand (High Order Byte)
		3	1	Op Code Address + 2	1	Address of Operand (Low Order Byte)
		4	0	Address of Operand	1	Irrelevant Data (Note 1)
		5	1	Address of Operand	0	Operand Data (High Order Byte)
		6	1	Address of Operand + 1	0	Operand Data (Low Order Byte)
JSR	9	1	1	Op Code Address	1	Op Code
		2	1	Op Code Address + 1	1	Address of Subroutine (High Order Byte)
		3	1	Op Code Address + 2	1	Address of Subroutine (Low Order Byte)
		4	1	Subroutine Starting Address	1	Op Code of Next Instruction
		5	1	Stack Pointer	0	Return Address (Low Order Byte)
		6	1	Stack Pointer − 1	0	Return Address (High Order Byte)
		7	0	Stack Pointer − 2	1	Irrelevant Data (Note 1)
		8	0	Op Code Address + 2	1	Irrelevant Data (Note 1)
		9	1	Op Code Address + 2	1	Address of Subroutine (Low Order Byte)
INHERENT						
ABA DAA SEC ASL DEC SEI ASR INC SEV CBA LSR TAB CLC NEG TAP CLI NOP TBA CLR ROL TPA CLV ROR TST COM SBA	2	1	1	Op Code Address	1	Op Code
		2	1	Op Code Address + 1	1	Op Code of Next Instruction
DES DEX INS INX	4	1	1	Op Code Address	1	Op Code
		2	1	Op Code Address + 1	1	Op Code of Next Instruction
		3	0	Previous Register Contents	1	Irrelevant Data (Note 1)
		4	0	New Register Contents	1	Irrelevant Data (Note 1)
PSH	4	1	1	Op Code Address	1	Op Code
		2	1	Op Code Address + 1	1	Op Code of Next Instruction
		3	1	Stack Pointer	0	Accumulator Data
		4	0	Stack Pointer − 1	1	Accumulator Data
PUL	4	1	1	Op Code Address	1	Op Code
		2	1	Op Code Address + 1	1	Op Code of Next Instruction
		3	0	Stack Pointer	1	Irrelevant Data (Note 1)
		4	1	Stack Pointer + 1	1	Operand Data from Stack
TSX	4	1	1	Op Code Address	1	Op Code
		2	1	Op Code Address + 1	1	Op Code of Next Instruction
		3	0	Stack Pointer	1	Irrelevant Data (Note 1)
		4	0	New Index Register	1	Irrelevant Data (Note 1)
TXS	4	1	1	Op Code Address	1	Op Code
		2	1	Op Code Address + 1	1	Op Code of Next Instruction
		3	0	Index Register	1	Irrelevant Data
		4	0	New Stack Pointer	1	Irrelevant Data
RTS	5	1	1	Op Code Address	1	Op Code
		2	1	Op Code Address + 1	1	Irrelevant Data (Note 2)
		3	0	Stack Pointer	1	Irrelevant Data (Note 1)
		4	1	Stack Pointer + 1	1	Address of Next Instruction (High Order Byte)
		5	1	Stack Pointer + 2	1	Address of Next Instruction (Low Order Byte)

 MOTOROLA *Semiconductor Products Inc.*

MC6800

TABLE 8 – OPERATION SUMMARY (Continued)

Address Mode and Instructions	Cycles	Cycle #	VMA Line	Address Bus	R/W Line	Data Bus
INHERENT (Continued)						
WAI		1	1	Op Code Address	1	Op Code
		2	1	Op Code Address + 1	1	Op Code of Next Instruction
		3	1	Stack Pointer	0	Return Address (Low Order Byte)
		4	1	Stack Pointer − 1	0	Return Address (High Order Byte)
	9	5	1	Stack Pointer − 2	0	Index Register (Low Order Byte)
		6	1	Stack Pointer − 3	0	Index Register (High Order Byte)
		7	1	Stack Pointer − 4	0	Contents of Accumulator A
		8	1	Stack Pointer − 5	0	Contents of Accumulator B
		9	1	Stack Pointer − 6 (Note 4)	1	Contents of Cond. Code Register
RTI		1	1	Op Code Address	1	Op Code
		2	1	Op Code Address + 1	1	Irrelevant Data (Note 2)
		3	0	Stack Pointer	1	Irrelevant Data (Note 1)
		4	1	Stack Pointer + 1	1	Contents of Cond. Code Register from Stack
	10	5	1	Stack Pointer + 2	1	Contents of Accumulator B from Stack
		6	1	Stack Pointer + 3	1	Contents of Accumulator A from Stack
		7	1	Stack Pointer + 4	1	Index Register from Stack (High Order Byte)
		8	1	Stack Pointer + 5	1	Index Register from Stack (Low Order Byte)
		9	1	Stack Pointer + 6	1	Next Instruction Address from Stack (High Order Byte)
		10	1	Stack Pointer + 7	1	Next Instruction Address from Stack (Low Order Byte)
SWI		1	1	Op Code Address	1	Op Code
		2	1	Op Code Address + 1	1	Irrelevant Data (Note 1)
		3	1	Stack Pointer	0	Return Address (Low Order Byte)
		4	1	Stack Pointer − 1	0	Return Address (High Order Byte)
		5	1	Stack Pointer − 2	0	Index Register (Low Order Byte)
		6	1	Stack Pointer − 3	0	Index Register (High Order Byte)
	12	7	1	Stack Pointer − 4	0	Contents of Accumulator A
		8	1	Stack Pointer − 5	0	Contents of Accumulator B
		9	1	Stack Pointer − 6	0	Contents of Cond. Code Register
		10	0	Stack Pointer − 7	1	Irrelevant Data (Note 1)
		11	1	Vector Address FFFA (Hex)	1	Address of Subroutine (High Order Byte)
		12	1	Vector Address FFFB (Hex)	1	Address of Subroutine (Low Order Byte)
RELATIVE						
BCC BHI BNE BCS BLE BPL BEQ BLS BRA BGE BLT BVC BGT BMI BVS	4	1	1	Op Code Address	1	Op Code
		2	1	Op Code Address + 1	1	Branch Offset
		3	0	Op Code Address + 2	1	Irrelevant Data (Note 1)
		4	0	Branch Address	1	Irrelevant Data (Note 1)
BSR		1	1	Op Code Address	1	Op Code
		2	1	Op Code Address + 1	1	Branch Offset
		3	0	Return Address of Main Program	1	Irrelevant Data (Note 1)
	8	4	1	Stack Pointer	0	Return Address (Low Order Byte)
		5	1	Stack Pointer − 1	0	Return Address (High Order Byte)
		6	0	Stack Pointer − 2	1	Irrelevant Data (Note 1)
		7	0	Return Address of Main Program	1	Irrelevant Data (Note 1)
		8	0	Subroutine Address	1	Irrelevant Data (Note 1)

Note 1.   If device which is addressed during this cycle uses VMA, then the Data Bus will go to the high impedance three-state condition. Depending on bus capacitance, data from the previous cycle may be retained on the Data Bus.

Note 2.   Data is ignored by the MPU.

Note 3.   For TST, VMA = 0 and Operand data does not change.

Note 4.   While the MPU is waiting for the interrupt, Bus Available will go high indicating the following states of the control lines: VMA is low; Address Bus, R/W, and Data Bus are all in the high impedance state.

 MOTOROLA *Semiconductor Products Inc.*

MOTOROLA
Semiconductors

BOX 20912 • PHOENIX, ARIZONA 85036

MC6820
(0 to 70°C; L or P Suffix)

MC6820C
(−40 to 85°C; L Suffix only)

MOS
(N-CHANNEL, SILICON-GATE)

PERIPHERAL INTERFACE ADAPTER

PERIPHERAL INTERFACE ADAPTER (PIA)

The MC6820 Peripheral Interface Adapter provides the universal means of interfacing peripheral equipment to the MC6800 Micro-processing Unit (MPU). This device is capable of interfacing the MPU to peripherals through two 8-bit bidirectional peripheral data buses and four control lines. No external logic is required for interfacing to most peripheral devices.

The functional configuration of the PIA is programmed by the MPU during system initialization. Each of the peripheral data lines can be programmed to act as an input or output, and each of the four control/interrupt lines may be programmed for one of several control modes. This allows a high degree of flexibility in the over-all operation of the interface.

- 8-Bit Bidirectional Data Bus for Communication with the MPU
- Two Bidirectional 8-Bit Buses for Interface to Peripherals
- Two Programmable Control Registers
- Two Programmable Data Direction Registers
- Four Individually-Controlled Interrupt Input Lines; Two Usable as Peripheral Control Outputs
- Handshake Control Logic for Input and Output Peripheral Operation
- High-Impedance 3-State and Direct Transistor Drive Peripheral Lines
- Program Controlled Interrupt and Interrupt Disable Capability
- CMOS Drive Capability on Side A Peripheral Lines

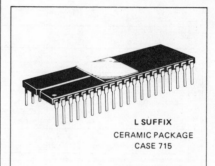

L SUFFIX
CERAMIC PACKAGE
CASE 715

NOT SHOWN: **P SUFFIX**
PLASTIC PACKAGE
CASE 711

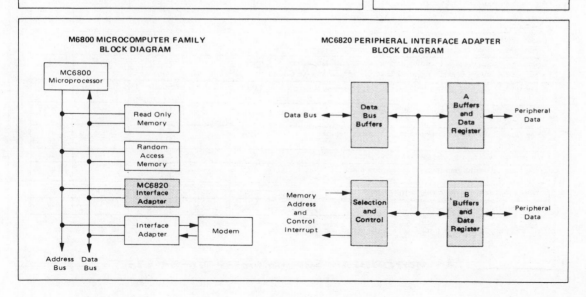

M6800 MICROCOMPUTER FAMILY BLOCK DIAGRAM

MC6820 PERIPHERAL INTERFACE ADAPTER BLOCK DIAGRAM

MC6820

ELECTRICAL CHARACTERISTICS (V_{CC} = 5.0 V ±5%, V_{SS} = 0, T_A = 0 to 70°C unless otherwise noted.)

Characteristic		Symbol	Min	Typ	Max	Unit
Input High Voltage	Enable	V_{IH}	V_{SS} + 2.4	–	V_{CC}	Vdc
	Other Inputs		V_{SS} + 2.0	–	V_{CC}	
Input Low Voltage	Enable	V_{IL}	V_{SS} –0.3	–	V_{SS} + 0.4	Vdc
	Other Inputs		V_{SS} –0.3	–	V_{SS} + 0.8	
Input Leakage Current R/W, $\overline{Reset}$, RS0, RS1, CS0, CS1, $\overline{CS2}$, CA1, CB1, Enable (V_{in} = 0 to 5.25 Vdc)		I_{in}	–	1.0	2.5	µAdc
Three-State (Off State) Input Current D0-D7, PB0-PB7, CB2 (V_{in} = 0.4 to 2.4 Vdc)		I_{TSI}	–	2.0	10	µAdc
Input High Current PA0-PA7, CA2 (V_{IH} = 2.4 Vdc)		I_{IH}	–100	–250	–	µAdc
Input Low Current PA0-PA7, CA2 (V_{IL} = 0.4 Vdc)		I_{IL}	–	–1.0	–1.6	mAdc
Output High Voltage		V_{OH}				Vdc
(I_{Load} = –205 µAdc, Enable Pulse Width < 25 µs) D0-D7			V_{SS} + 2.4	–	–	
(I_{Load} = –100 µAdc, Enable Pulse Width <25 µs) Other Outputs			V_{SS} + 2.4	–	–	
Output Low Voltage (I_{Load} = 1.6 mAdc, Enable Pulse Width < 25 µs)		V_{OL}	–	–	V_{SS} + 0.4	Vdc
Output High Current (Sourcing)		I_{OH}				
(V_{OH} = 2.4 Vdc) D0-D7			–205	–	–	µAdc
Other Outputs			–100	–	–	µAdc
(V_O = 1.5 Vdc, the current for driving other than TTL, e.g., Darlington Base) PB0-PB7, CB2			–1.0	–2.5	–10	mAdc
Output Low Current (Sinking) (V_{OL} = 0.4 Vdc)		I_{OL}	1.6	–	–	mAdc
Output Leakage Current (Off State) $\overline{IRQA}$, $\overline{IRQB}$ (V_{OH} = 2.4 Vdc)		I_{LOH}	–	1.0	10	µAdc
Power Dissipation		P_D	–	–	650	mW
Input Capacitance	Enable	C_{in}	–	–	20	pF
(V_{in} = 0, T_A = 25°C, f = 1.0 MHz) D0-D7			–	–	12.5	
PA0-PA7, PB0-PB7, CA2, CB2			–	–	10	
R/W, $\overline{Reset}$, RS0, RS1, CS0, CS1, $\overline{CS2}$, CA1, CB1			–	–	7.5	
Output Capacitance $\overline{IRQA}$, $\overline{IRQB}$		C_{out}	–	–	5.0	pF
(V_{in} = 0, T_A = 25°C, f = 1.0 MHz) PB0-PB7			–	–	10	
Peripheral Data Setup Time (Figure 1)		t_{PDSU}	200	–	–	ns
Delay Time, Enable negative transition to CA2 negative transition (Figure 2, 3)		t_{CA2}	–	–	1.0	µs
Delay Time, Enable negative transition to CA2 positive transition (Figure 2)		t_{RS1}	–	–	1.0	µs
Rise and Fall Times for CA1 and CA2 input signals (Figure 3)		t_r, t_f	–	–	1.0	µs
Delay Time from CA1 active transition to CA2 positive transition (Figure 3)		t_{RS2}	–	–	2.0	µs
Delay Time, Enable negative transition to Peripheral Data valid (Figures 4, 5)		t_{PDW}	–	–	1.0	µs
Delay Time, Enable negative transition to Peripheral CMOS Data Valid (V_{CC} – 30% V_{CC}, Figure 4; Figure 12 Load C) PA0-PA7, CA2		t_{CMOS}	–	–	2.0	µs
Delay Time, Enable positive transition to CB2 negative transition (Figure 6, 7)		t_{CB2}	–	–	1.0	µs
Delay Time, Peripheral Data valid to CB2 negative transition (Figure 5)		t_{DC}	20	–	–	ns
Delay Time, Enable positive transition to CB2 positive transition (Figure 6)		t_{RS1}	–	–	1.0	µs
Rise and Fall Time for CB1 and CB2 input signals (Figure 7)		t_r, t_f	–	–	1.0	µs
Delay Time, CB1 active transition to CB2 positive transition (Figure 7)		t_{RS2}	–	–	2.0	µs
Interrupt Release Time, $\overline{IRQA}$ and $\overline{IRQB}$ (Figure 8)		t_{IR}	–	–	1.6	µs
Reset Low Time* (Figure 9)		t_{RL}	2.0	–	–	µs

*The Reset line must be high a minimum of 1.0 µs before addressing the PIA.

 MOTOROLA *Semiconductor Products Inc.*

MC6820

MAXIMUM RATINGS

Rating	Symbol	Value	Unit
Supply Voltage	V_{CC}	−0.3 to +7.0	Vdc
Input Voltage	V_{in}	−0.3 to +7.0	Vdc
Operating Temperature Range	T_A	0 to +70	°C
Storage Temperature Range	T_{stg}	−55 to +150	°C
Thermal Resistance	θ_{JA}	82.5	°C/W

This device contains circuitry to protect the inputs against damage due to high static voltages or electric fields; however, it is advised that normal precautions be taken to avoid application of any voltage higher than maximum rated voltages to this high impedance circuit.

BUS TIMING CHARACTERISTICS

READ (Figures 10 and 12)

Characteristic	Symbol	Min	Typ	Max	Unit
Enable Cycle Time	t_{cycE}	1.0	–	–	µs
Enable Pulse Width, High	PW_{EH}	0.45	–	25	µs
Enable Pulse Width, Low	PW_{EL}	0.43	–	–	µs
Setup Time, Address and R/W valid to Enable positive transition	t_{AS}	160	–	–	ns
Data Delay Time	t_{DDR}	–	–	320	ns
Data Hold Time	t_H	10	–	–	ns
Address Hold Time	t_{AH}	10	–	–	ns
Rise and Fall Time for Enable input	t_{Er}, t_{Ef}	–	–	25	ns

WRITE (Figures 11 and 12)

Characteristic	Symbol	Min	Typ	Max	Unit
Enable Cycle Time	t_{cycE}	1.0	–	–	µs
Enable Pulse Width, High	PW_{EH}	0.45	–	25	µs
Enable Pulse Width, Low	PW_{EL}	0.43	–	–	µs
Setup Time, Address and R/W valid to Enable positive transition	t_{AS}	160	–	–	ns
Data Setup Time	t_{DSW}	195	–	–	ns
Data Hold Time	t_H	10	–	–	ns
Address Hold Time	t_{AH}	10	–	–	ns
Rise and Fall Time for Enable input	t_{Er}, t_{Ef}	–	–	25	ns

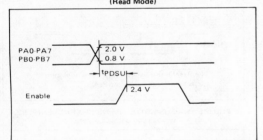

FIGURE 1 – PERIPHERAL DATA SETUP TIME
(Read Mode)

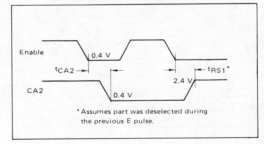

FIGURE 2 – CA2 DELAY TIME
(Read Mode; CRA-5 = CRA-3 = 1, CRA-4 = 0)

*Assumes part was deselected during the previous E pulse.

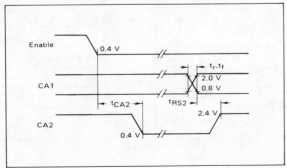

FIGURE 3 – CA2 DELAY TIME
(Read Mode; CRA-5 = 1, CRA-3 = CRA-4 = 0)

Ⓜ **MOTOROLA** *Semiconductor Products Inc.*

MC6820

FIGURE 4 – PERIPHERAL CMOS DATA DELAY TIMES
(Write Mode; CRA-5 = CRA-3 = 1, CRA-4 = 0)

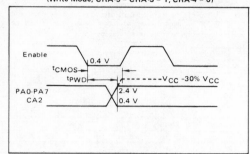

FIGURE 5 – PERIPHERAL DATA AND CB2 DELAY TIMES
(Write Mode; CRB-5 = CRB-3 = 1, CRB-4 = 0)

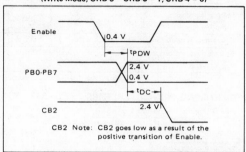

CB2 Note: CB2 goes low as a result of the positive transition of Enable.

FIGURE 6 – CB2 DELAY TIME
(Write Mode; CRB-5 = CRB-3 = 1, CRB-4 = 0)

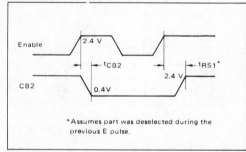

*Assumes part was deselected during the previous E pulse.

FIGURE 7 – CB2 DELAY TIME
(Write Mode; CRB-5 = 1, CRB-3 = CRB-4 = 0)

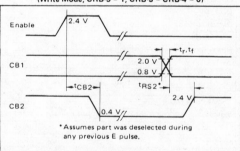

*Assumes part was deselected during any previous E pulse.

FIGURE 8 – IRQ RELEASE TIME

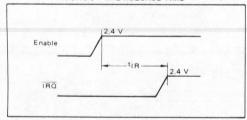

FIGURE 9 – RESET LOW TIME

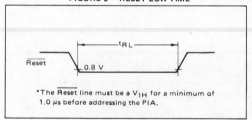

*The Reset line must be a V_{IH} for a minimum of 1.0 μs before addressing the PIA.

FIGURE 10 – BUS READ TIMING CHARACTERISTICS
(Read Information from PIA)

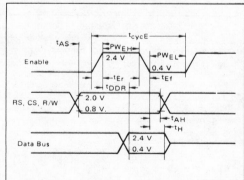

FIGURE 11 – BUS WRITE TIMING CHARACTERISTICS
(Write Information into PIA)

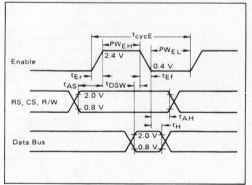

MOTOROLA Semiconductor Products Inc.

MC6820

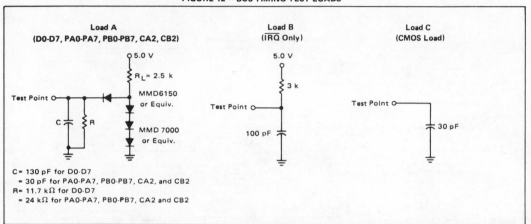

FIGURE 12 — BUS TIMING TEST LOADS

Load A
(D0-D7, PA0-PA7, PB0-PB7, CA2, CB2)

Load B
($\overline{IRQ}$ Only)

Load C
(CMOS Load)

C = 130 pF for D0-D7
  = 30 pF for PA0-PA7, PB0-PB7, CA2, and CB2
R = 11.7 kΩ for D0-D7
  = 24 kΩ for PA0-PB7, PB0-PB7, CA2 and CB2

PIA INTERFACE SIGNALS FOR MPU

The PIA interfaces to the MC6800 MPU with an eight-bit bi-directional data bus, three chip select lines, two register select lines, two interrupt request lines, read/write line, enable line and reset line. These signals, in conjunction with the MC6800 VMA output, permit the MPU to have complete control over the PIA. VMA should be utilized in conjunction with an MPU address line into a chip select of the PIA.

PIA Bi-Directional Data (D0-D7) — The bi-directional data lines (D0-D7) allow the transfer of data between the MPU and the PIA. The data bus output drivers are three-state devices that remain in the high-impedance (off) state except when the MPU performs a PIA read operation. The Read/Write line is in the Read (high) state when the PIA is selected for a Read operation.

PIA Enable (E) — The enable pulse, E, is the only timing signal that is supplied to the PIA. Timing of all other signals is referenced to the leading and trailing edges of the E pulse. This signal will normally be a derivative of the MC6800 φ2 Clock.

PIA Read/Write (R/W) — This signal is generated by the MPU to control the direction of data transfers on the Data Bus. A low state on the PIA Read/Write line enables the input buffers and data is transferred from the MPU to the PIA on the E signal if the device has been selected. A high on the Read/Write line sets up the PIA for a transfer of data to the bus. The PIA output buffers are enabled when the proper address and the enable pulse E are present.

Reset — The active low Reset line is used to reset all register bits in the PIA to a logical zero (low). This line can be used as a power-on reset and as a master reset during system operation.

PIA Chip Select (CS0, CS1 and $\overline{CS2}$) — These three input signals are used to select the PIA. CS0 and CS1 must be high and $\overline{CS2}$ must be low for selection of the device. Data transfers are then performed under the control of the Enable and Read/Write signals. The chip select lines must be stable for the duration of the E pulse. The device is deselected when any of the chip selects are in the inactive state.

PIA Register Select (RS0 and RS1) — The two register select lines are used to select the various registers inside the PIA. These two lines are used in conjunction with internal Control Registers to select a particular register that is to be written or read.

The register and chip select lines should be stable for the duration of the E pulse while in the read or write cycle.

Interrupt Request ($\overline{IRQA}$ and $\overline{IRQB}$) — The active low Interrupt Request lines ($\overline{IRQA}$ and $\overline{IRQB}$) act to interrupt the MPU either directly or through interrupt priority circuitry. These lines are "open drain" (no load device on the chip). This permits all interrupt request lines to be tied together in a wire-OR configuration.

Each Interrupt Request line has two internal interrupt flag bits that can cause the Interrupt Request line to go low. Each flag bit is associated with a particular peripheral interrupt line. Also four interrupt enable bits are provided in the PIA which may be used to inhibit a particular interrupt from a peripheral device.

Servicing an interrupt by the MPU may be accomplished by a software routine that, on a prioritized basis, sequentially reads and tests the two control registers in each PIA for interrupt flag bits that are set.

The interrupt flags are cleared (zeroed) as a result of an

 MOTOROLA *Semiconductor Products Inc.*

MC6820

EXPANDED BLOCK DIAGRAM

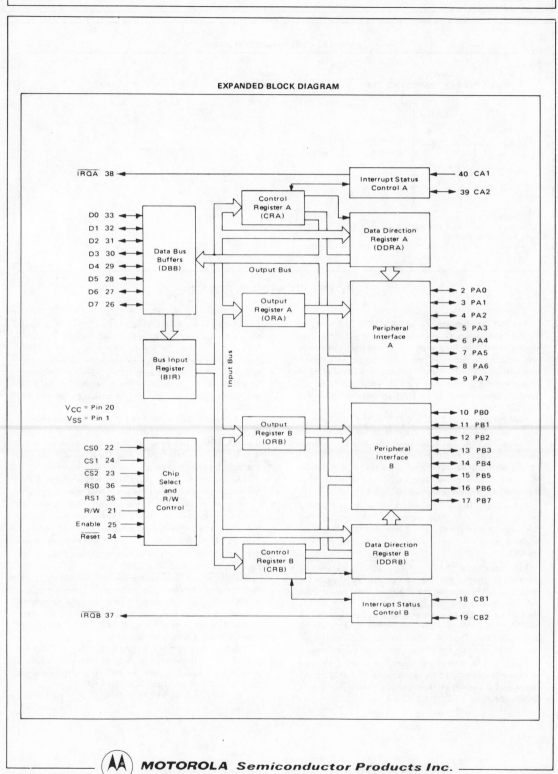

MC6820

MPU Read Peripheral Data Operation of the corresponding data register. After being cleared, the interrupt flag bit cannot be enabled to be set until the PIA is deselected during an E pulse. The E pulse is used to condition the interrupt control lines (CA1, CA2, CB1, CB2). When these lines are used as interrupt inputs at least one E pulse must occur from the inactive edge to the active edge of the interrupt input signal to condition the edge sense network. If the interrupt flag has been enabled and the edge sense circuit has been properly conditioned, the interrupt flag will be set on the next active transition of the interrupt input pin.

PIA PERIPHERAL INTERFACE LINES

The PIA provides two 8-bit bi-directional data buses and four interrupt/control lines for interfacing to peripheral devices.

Section A Peripheral Data (PA0-PA7) — Each of the peripheral data lines can be programmed to act as an input or output. This is accomplished by setting a "1" in the corresponding Data Direction Register bit for those lines which are to be outputs. A "0" in a bit of the Data Direction Register causes the corresponding peripheral data line to act as an input. During an MPU Read Peripheral Data Operation, the data on peripheral lines programmed to act as inputs appears directly on the corresponding MPU Data Bus lines. In the input mode the internal pullup resistor on these lines represents a maximum of one standard TTL load.

The data in Output Register A will appear on the data lines that are programmed to be outputs. A logical "1" written into the register will cause a "high" on the corresponding data line while a "0" results in a "low". Data in Output Register A may be read by an MPU "Read Peripheral Data A" operation when the corresponding lines are programmed as outputs. This data will be read properly if the voltage on the peripheral data lines is greater than 2.0 volts for a logic "1" output and less than 0.8 volt for a logic "0" output. Loading the output lines such that the voltage on these lines does not reach full voltage causes the data transferred into the MPU on a Read operation to differ from that contained in the respective bit of Output Register A.

Section B Peripheral Data (PB0-PB7) — The peripheral data lines in the B Section of the PIA can be programmed to act as either inputs or outputs in a similar manner to PA0-PA7. However, the output buffers driving these lines differ from those driving lines PA0-PA7. They have three-state capability, allowing them to enter a high impedance state when the peripheral data line is used as an input. In addition, data on the peripheral data lines PB0-PB7 will be read properly from those lines programmed as outputs even if the voltages are below 2.0 volts for a "high". As outputs, these lines are compatible with standard TTL and may also be used as a source of up to 1 milliampere at 1.5 volts to directly drive the base of a transistor switch.

Interrupt Input (CA1 and CB1) — Peripheral Input lines CA1 and CB1 are input only lines that set the interrupt flags of the control registers. The active transition for these signals is also programmed by the two control registers.

Peripheral Control (CA2) — The peripheral control line CA2 can be programmed to act as an interrupt input or as a peripheral control output. As an output, this line is compatible with standard TTL; as an input the internal pullup resistor on this line represents one standard TTL load. The function of this signal line is programmed with Control Register A.

Peripheral Control (CB2) — Peripheral Control line CB2 may also be programmed to act as an interrupt input or peripheral control output. As an input, this line has high input impedance and is compatible with standard TTL. As an output it is compatible with standard TTL and may also be used as a source of up to 1 milliampere at 1.5 volts to directly drive the base of a transistor switch. This line is programmed by Control Register B.

NOTE: It is recommended that the control lines (CA1, CA2, CB1, CB2) should be held in a logic 1 state when Reset is active to prevent setting of corresponding interrupt flags in the control register when Reset goes to an inactive state. Subsequent to Reset going inactive, a read of the data registers may be used to clear any undesired interrupt flags.

 MOTOROLA *Semiconductor Products Inc.*

MC6820

INTERNAL CONTROLS

There are six locations within the PIA accessible to the MPU data bus: two Peripheral Registers, two Data Direction Registers, and two Control Registers. Selection of these locations is controlled by the RS0 and RS1 inputs together with bit 2 in the Control Register, as shown in Table 1.

TABLE 1 – INTERNAL ADDRESSING

		Control Register Bit		
RS1	RS0	CRA-2	CRB-2	Location Selected
0	0	1	X	Peripheral Register A
0	0	0	X	Data Direction Register A
0	1	X	X	Control Register A
1	0	X	1	Peripheral Register B
1	0	X	0	Data Direction Register B
1	1	X	X	Control Register B

X = Don't Care

INITIALIZATION

A low reset line has the effect of zeroing all PIA registers. This will set PA0-PA7, PB0-PB7, CA2 and CB2 as inputs, and all interrupts disabled. The PIA must be configured during the restart program which follows the reset.

Details of possible configurations of the Data Direction and Control Register are as follows.

DATA DIRECTION REGISTERS (DDRA and DDRB)

The two Data Direction Registers allow the MPU to control the direction of data through each corresponding peripheral data line. A Data Direction Register bit set at "0" configures the corresponding peripheral data line as an input; a "1" results in an output.

CONTROL REGISTERS (CRA and CRB)

The two Control Registers (CRA and CRB) allow the MPU to control the operation of the four peripheral control lines CA1, CA2, CB1 and CB2. In addition they allow the MPU to enable the interrupt lines and monitor the status of the interrupt flags. Bits 0 through 5 of the two registers may be written or read by the MPU when the proper chip select and register select signals are applied. Bits 6 and 7 of the two registers are read only and are modified by external interrupts occurring on control lines CA1, CA2, CB1 or CB2. The format of the control words is shown in Table 2.

TABLE 2 – CONTROL WORD FORMAT

	7	6	5	4	3	2	1	0
CRA	IRQA1	IRQA2	CA2 Control			DDRA Access	CA1 Control	

	7	6	5	4	3	2	1	0
CRB	IRQB1	IRQB2	CB2 Control			DDRB Access	CB1 Control	

Data Direction Access Control Bit (CRA-2 and CRB-2) – Bit 2 in each Control register (CRA and CRB) allows selection of either a Peripheral Interface Register or the Data Direction Register when the proper register select signals are applied to RS0 and RS1.

Interrupt Flags (CRA-6, CRA-7, CRB-6, and CRB-7) – The four interrupt flag bits are set by active transitions of signals on the four Interrupt and Peripheral Control lines when those lines are programmed to be inputs. These bits cannot be set directly from the MPU Data Bus and are reset indirectly by a Read Peripheral Data Operation on the appropriate section.

TABLE 3 – CONTROL OF INTERRUPT INPUTS CA1 AND CB1

CRA-1 (CRB-1)	CRA-0 (CRB-0)	Interrupt Input CA1 (CB1)	Interrupt Flag CRA-7 (CRB-7)	MPU Interrupt Request IRQA (IRQB)
0	0	↓ Active	Set high on ↓ of CA1 (CB1)	Disabled — IRQ remains high
0	1	↓ Active	Set high on ↓ of CA1 (CB1)	Goes low when the interrupt flag bit CRA-7 (CRB-7) goes high
1	0	↑ Active	Set high on ↑ of CA1 (CB1)	Disabled — IRQ remains high
1	1	↑ Active	Set high on ↑ of CA1 (CB1)	Goes low when the interrupt flag bit CRA-7 (CRB-7) goes high

Notes:
1. ↑ indicates positive transition (low to high)
2. ↓ indicates negative transition (high to low)
3. The Interrupt flag bit CRA-7 is cleared by an MPU Read of the A Data Register and CRB-7 is cleared by an MPU Read of the B Data Register.
4. If CRA-0 (CRB-0) is low when an interrupt occurs (Interrupt disabled) and is later brought high, IRQA (IRQB) occurs after CRA-0 (CRB-0) is written to a "one".

 MOTOROLA *Semiconductor Products Inc.*

MC6820

Control of CA1 and CB1 Interrupt Input Lines (CRA-0, CRB-0, CRA-1, and CRB-1) — The two lowest order bits of the control registers are used to control the interrupt input lines CA1 and CB1. Bits CRA-0 and CRB-0 are used to enable the MPU interrupt signals $\overline{IRQA}$ and $\overline{IRQB}$, respectively. Bits CRA-1 and CRB-1 determine the active transition of the interrupt input signals CA1 and CB1 (Table 3).

TABLE 4 — CONTROL OF CA2 AND CB2 AS INTERRUPT INPUTS
CRA5 (CRB5) is low

CRA-5 (CRB-5)	CRA-4 (CRB-4)	CRA-3 (CRB-3)	Interrupt Input CA2 (CB2)	Interrupt Flag CRA-6 (CRB-6)	MPU Interrupt Request $\overline{IRQA}$ $(\overline{IRQB})$
0	0	0	↓ Active	Set high on ↓ of CA2 (CB2)	Disabled — $\overline{IRQ}$ remains high
0	0	1	↓ Active	Set high on ↓ of CA2 (CB2)	Goes low when the interrupt flag bit CRA-6 (CRB-6) goes high
0	1	0	↑ Active	Set high on ↑ of CA2 (CB2)	Disabled — $\overline{IRQ}$ remains high
0	1	1	↑ Active	Set high on ↑ of CA2 (CB2)	Goes low when the interrupt flag bit CRA-6 (CRB-6) goes high

Notes: 1. ↑ indicates positive transition (low to high)

2. ↓ indicates negative transition (high to low)

3. The Interrupt flag bit CRA-6 is cleared by an MPU Read of the A Data Register and CRB-6 is cleared by an MPU Read of the B Data Register.

4. If CRA-3 (CRB-3) is low when an interrupt occurs (Interrupt disabled) and is later brought high, $\overline{IRQA}$ ($\overline{IRQB}$) occurs after CRA-3 (CRB-3) is written to a "one".

TABLE 5 — CONTROL OF CB2 AS AN OUTPUT
CRB-5 is high

CRB-5	CRB-4	CRB-3	CB2 Cleared	CB2 Set
1	0	0	Low on the positive transition of the first E pulse following an MPU Write "B" Data Register operation.	High when the interrupt flag bit CRB-7 is set by an active transition of the CB1 signal.
1	0	1	Low on the positive transition of the first E pulse after an MPU Write "B" Data Register operation.	High on the positive edge of the first "E" pulse following an "E" pulse which occurred while the part was deselected.
1	1	0	Low when CRB-3 goes low as a result of an MPU Write in Control Register "B".	Always low as long as CRB-3 is low. Will go high on an MPU Write in Control Register "B" that changes CRB-3 to "one".
1	1	1	Always high as long as CRB-3 is high. Will be cleared when an MPU Write Control Register "B" results in clearing CRB-3 to "zero".	High when CRB-3 goes high as a result of an MPU Write into Control Register "B".

 MOTOROLA *Semiconductor Products Inc.*

MC6820

Control of CA2 and CB2 Peripheral Control Lines (CRA-3, CRA-4, CRA-5, CRB-3, CRB-4, and CRB-5) — Bits 3, 4, and 5 of the two control registers are used to control the CA2 and CB2 Peripheral Control lines. These bits determine if the control lines will be an interrupt input or an output control signal. If bit CRA-5 (CRB-5) is low, CA2 (CB2) is an interrupt input line similar to CA1 (CB1) (Table 4). When CRA-5 (CRB-5) is high, CA2 (CB2) becomes an output signal that may be used to control peripheral data transfers. When in the output mode, CA2 and CB2 have slightly different characteristics (Tables 5 and 6).

TABLE 6 — CONTROL OF CA-2 AS AN OUTPUT
CRA-5 is high

CRA-5	CRA-4	CRA-3	CA2 Cleared	CA2 Set
1	0	0	Low on negative transition of E after an MPU Read "A" Data operation.	High when the interrupt flag bit CRA-7 is set by an active transition of the CA1 signal.
1	0	1	Low on negative transition of E after an MPU Read "A" Data operation.	High on the negative edge of the first "E" pulse which occurs during a deselect.
1	1	0	Low when CRA-3 goes low as a result of an MPU Write to Control Register "A".	Always low as long as CRA-3 is low. Will go high on an MPU Write to Control Register "A" that changes CRA-3 to "one".
1	1	1	Always high as long as CRA-3 is high. Will be cleared on an MPU Write to Control Register "A" that clears CRA-3 to a "zero".	High when CRA-3 goes high as a result of an MPU Write to Control Register "A".

PIN ASSIGNMENT

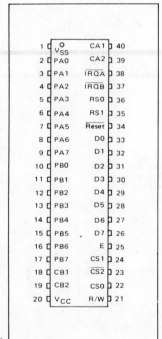

PACKAGE DIMENSIONS

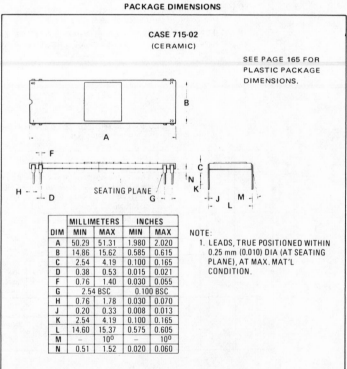

CASE 715-02
(CERAMIC)

SEE PAGE 165 FOR PLASTIC PACKAGE DIMENSIONS.

DIM	MILLIMETERS MIN	MILLIMETERS MAX	INCHES MIN	INCHES MAX
A	50.29	51.31	1.980	2.020
B	14.86	15.62	0.585	0.615
C	2.54	4.19	0.100	0.165
D	0.38	0.53	0.015	0.021
F	0.76	1.40	0.030	0.055
G	2.54 BSC		0.100 BSC	
H	0.76	1.78	0.030	0.070
J	0.20	0.33	0.008	0.013
K	2.54	4.19	0.100	0.165
L	14.60	15.37	0.575	0.605
M	–	10°	–	10°
N	0.51	1.52	0.020	0.060

NOTE:
1. LEADS, TRUE POSITIONED WITHIN 0.25 mm (0.010) DIA (AT SEATING PLANE), AT MAX. MAT'L CONDITION.

Ⓜ MOTOROLA *Semiconductor Products Inc.*

MOTOROLA Semiconductors
BOX 20912 • PHOENIX, ARIZONA 85036

MC6850
(0 to 70°C; L or P Suffix)

MC6850C
(−40 to 85°C; L Suffix only)

ASYNCHRONOUS COMMUNICATIONS INTERFACE ADAPTER (ACIA)

The MC6850 Asynchronous Communications Interface Adapter provides the data formatting and control to interface serial asynchronous data communications information to bus organized systems such as the MC6800 Microprocessing Unit.

The bus interface of the MC6850 includes select, enable, read/write, interrupt and bus interface logic to allow data transfer over an 8-bit bi-directional data bus. The parallel data of the bus system is serially transmitted and received by the asynchronous data interface, with proper formatting and error checking. The functional configuration of the ACIA is programmed via the data bus during system initialization. A programmable Control Register provides variable word lengths, clock division ratios, transmit control, receive control, and interrupt control. For peripheral or modem operation three control lines are provided. These lines allow the ACIA to interface directly with the MC6860L 0-600 bps digital modem.

- Eight and Nine-Bit Transmission
- Optional Even and Odd Parity
- Parity, Overrun and Framing Error Checking
- Programmable Control Register
- Optional ÷1, ÷16, and ÷64 Clock Modes
- Up to 500 kbps Transmission
- False Start Bit Deletion
- Peripheral/Modem Control Functions
- Double Buffered
- One or Two Stop Bit Operation

MOS

(N-CHANNEL, SILICON-GATE)

ASYNCHRONOUS COMMUNICATIONS INTERFACE ADAPTER

L SUFFIX
CERAMIC PACKAGE
CASE 716

NOT SHOWN: **P SUFFIX**

PLASTIC PACKAGE
CASE 709

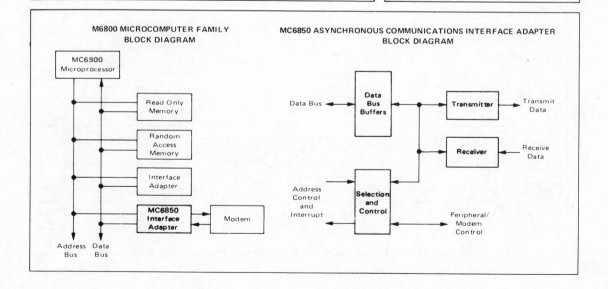

M6800 MICROCOMPUTER FAMILY BLOCK DIAGRAM

MC6850 ASYNCHRONOUS COMMUNICATIONS INTERFACE ADAPTER BLOCK DIAGRAM

MAXIMUM RATINGS

Rating	Symbol	Value	Unit
Supply Voltage	V_{CC}	-0.3 to +7.0	Vdc
Input Voltage	V_{in}	-0.3 to +7.0	Vdc
Operating Temperature Range	T_A	0 to +70	°C
Storage Temperature Range	T_{stg}	-55 to +150	°C
Thermal Resistance	θ_{JA}	82.5	°C/W

This device contains circuitry to protect the inputs against damage due to high static voltages or electric fields; however, it is advised that normal precautions be taken to avoid application of any voltage higher than maximum rated voltages to this high-impedance circuit.

ELECTRICAL CHARACTERISTICS (V_{CC} = 5.0 V ±5%, V_{SS} = 0, T_A = 0 to 70°C unless otherwise noted.)

Characteristic		Symbol	Min	Typ	Max	Unit
Input High Voltage		V_{IH}	V_{SS} + 2.0	–	V_{CC}	Vdc
Input Low Voltage		V_{IL}	V_{SS} -0.3	–	V_{SS} + 0.8	Vdc
Input Leakage Current (V_{in} = 0 to 5.25 Vdc)	R/W,CS0,CS1,$\overline{CS2}$,Enable	I_{in}	–	1.0	2.5	µAdc
Three-State (Off State) Input Current (V_{in} = 0.4 to 2.4 Vdc)	D0-D7	I_{TSI}	–	2.0	10	µAdc
Output High Voltage	D0-D7	V_{OH}				Vdc
(I_{Load} = -205 µAdc, Enable Pulse Width <25 µs)			V_{SS} + 2.4	–	–	
(I_{Load} = -100 µAdc, Enable Pulse Width <25 µs)	Tx Data, $\overline{RTS}$		V_{SS} + 2.4	–	–	
Output Low Voltage (I_{Load} = 1.6 mAdc, Enable Pulse Width <25 µs)		V_{OL}	–	–	V_{SS} + 0.4	Vdc
Output Leakage Current (Off State) (V_{OH} = 2.4 Vdc)	$\overline{IRQ}$	I_{LOH}	–	1.0	10	µAdc
Power Dissipation		P_D	–	300	525	mW
Input Capacitance		C_{in}				pF
(V_{in} = 0, T_A = 25°C, f = 1.0 MHz)	D0-D7		–	10	12.5	
	E, Tx Clk, Rx Clk, R/W, RS, Rx Data, CS0, CS1, $\overline{CS2}$, $\overline{CTS}$, $\overline{DCD}$		–	7.0	7.5	
Output Capacitance	$\overline{RTS}$, Tx Data	C_{out}	–	–	10	pF
(V_{in} = 0, T_A = 25°C, f = 1.0 MHz)	$\overline{IRQ}$		–	–	5.0	
Minimum Clock Pulse Width, Low (Figure 1)	÷16, ÷64 Modes	PW_{CL}	600	–	–	ns
Minimum Clock Pulse Width, High (Figure 2)	÷16, ÷64 Modes	PW_{CH}	600	–	–	ns
Clock Frequency	÷1 Mode	f_C	–	–	500	kHz
	÷16, ÷64 Modes		–	–	800	
Clock-to-Data Delay for Transmitter (Figure 3)		t_{TDD}	–	–	1.0	µs
Receive Data Setup Time (Figure 4)	÷1 Mode	t_{RDSU}	500	–	–	ns
Receive Data Hold Time (Figure 5)	÷1 Mode	t_{RDH}	500	–	–	ns
Interrupt Request Release Time (Figure 6)		t_{IR}	–	–	1.2	µs
Request-to-Send Delay Time (Figure 6)		t_{RTS}	–	–	1.0	µs
Input Transition Times (Except Enable)		t_r, t_f	–	–	1.0*	µs

*1.0 µs or 10% of the pulse width, whichever is smaller.

BUS TIMING CHARACTERISTICS

READ (Figures 7 and 9)

Characteristic	Symbol	Min	Typ	Max	Unit
Enable Cycle Time	t_{cycE}	1.0	–	–	µs
Enable Pulse Width, High	PW_{EH}	0.45	–	25	µs
Enable Pulse Width, Low	PW_{EL}	0.43	–	–	µs
Setup Time, Address and R/W valid to Enable positive transition	t_{AS}	160	–	–	ns
Data Delay Time	t_{DDR}	–	–	320	ns
Data Hold Time	t_H	10	–	–	ns
Address Hold Time	t_{AH}	10	–	–	ns
Rise and Fall Time for Enable input	t_{Er}, t_{Ef}	–	–	25	ns

WRITE (Figure 8 and 9)

Characteristic	Symbol	Min	Typ	Max	Unit
Enable Cycle Time	t_{cycE}	1.0	–	–	µs
Enable Pulse Width, High	PW_{EH}	0.45	–	25	µs
Enable Pulse Width, Low	PW_{EL}	0.43	–	–	µs
Setup Time, Address and R/W valid to Enable positive transition	t_{AS}	160	–	–	ns
Data Setup Time	t_{DSW}	195	–	–	ns
Data Hold Time	t_H	10	–	–	ns
Address Hold Time	t_{AH}	10	–	–	ns
Rise and Fall Time for Enable input	t_{Er}, t_{Ef}	–	–	25	ns

 MOTOROLA *Semiconductor Products Inc.*

MC6850

FIGURE 1 — CLOCK PULSE WIDTH, LOW-STATE

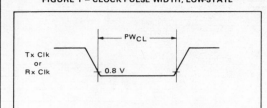

FIGURE 2 — CLOCK PULSE WIDTH, HIGH-STATE

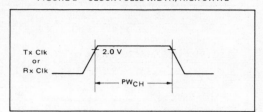

FIGURE 3 — TRANSMIT DATA OUTPUT DELAY

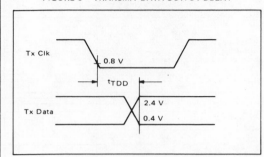

FIGURE 4 — RECEIVE DATA SETUP TIME
(÷1 Mode)

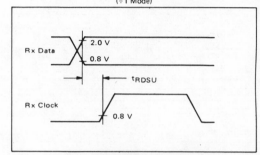

FIGURE 5 — RECEIVE DATA HOLD TIME
(÷1 Mode)

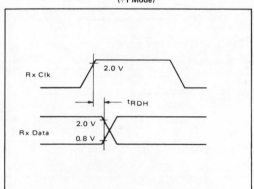

FIGURE 6 — REQUEST-TO-SEND DELAY AND
INTERRUPT-REQUEST RELEASE TIMES

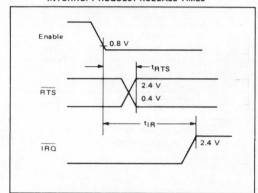

FIGURE 7 — BUS READ TIMING CHARACTERISTICS
(Read information from ACIA)

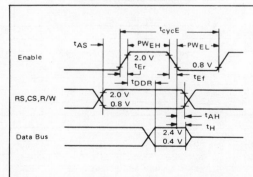

FIGURE 8 — BUS WRITE TIMING CHARACTERISTICS
(Write information into ACIA)

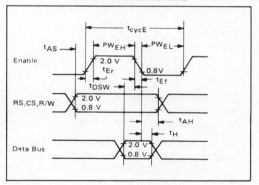

Ⓜ **MOTOROLA** *Semiconductor Products Inc.*

MC6850

FIGURE 9 – BUS TIMING TEST LOADS

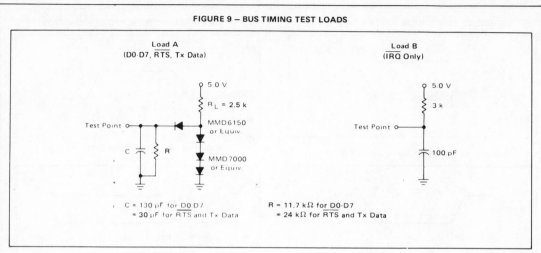

Load A
(D0-D7, RTS, Tx Data)

Load B
(IRQ Only)

C = 130 pF for D0-D7
= 30 pF for RTS and Tx Data

R = 11.7 kΩ for D0-D7
= 24 kΩ for RTS and Tx Data

EXPANDED BLOCK DIAGRAM

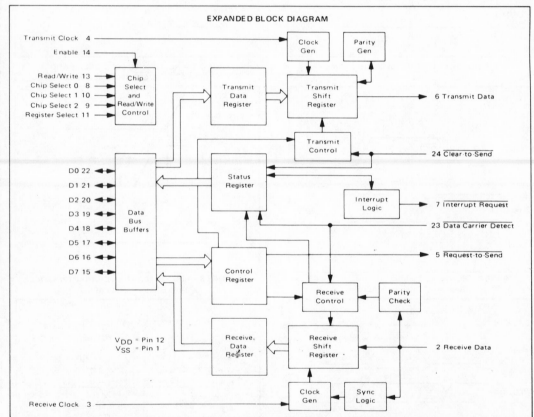

DEVICE OPERATION

At the bus interface, the ACIA appears as two address-able memory locations. Internally, there are four registers: two read-only and two write-only registers. The read-only registers are Status and Receive Data; the write-only registers are Control and Transmit Data. The serial inter-face consists of serial input and output lines with inde-pendent clocks, and three peripheral/modem control lines.

 MOTOROLA *Semiconductor Products Inc.*

MC6850

POWER ON/MASTER RESET

The master reset (CR0, CR1) should be set during system initialization to insure the reset condition and prepare for programming the ACIA functional configuration when the communications channel is required. Control bits CR5 and CR6 should also be programmed to define the state of $\overline{RTS}$ whenever master reset is utilized. The ACIA also contains internal power-on reset logic to detect the power line turn-on transition and hold the chip in a reset state to prevent erroneous output transitions prior to initialization. This circuitry depends on clean power turn-on transitions. The power-on reset is released by means of the bus-programmed master reset which must be applied prior to operating the ACIA. After master resetting the ACIA, the programmable Control Register can be set for a number of options such as variable clock divider ratios, variable word length, one or two stop bits, parity (even, odd, or none), etc.

TRANSMIT

A typical transmitting sequence consists of reading the ACIA Status Register either as a result of an interrupt or in the ACIA's turn in a polling sequence. A character may be written into the Transmit Data Register if the status read operation has indicated that the Transmit Data Register is empty. This character is transferred to a Shift Register where it is serialized and transmitted from the Transmit Data output preceded by a start bit and followed by one or two stop bits. Internal parity (odd or even) can be optionally added to the character and will occur between the last data bit and the first stop bit. After the first character is written in the Data Register, the Status Register can be read again to check for a Transmit Data Register Empty condition and current peripheral status. If the register is empty, another character can be loaded for transmission even though the first character is in the process of being transmitted (because of double buffering). The second character will be automatically transferred into the Shift Register when the first character transmission is completed. This sequence continues until all the characters have been transmitted.

RECEIVE

Data is received from a peripheral by means of the Receive Data input. A divide-by-one clock ratio is provided for an externally synchronized clock (to its data) while the divide-by-16 and 64 ratios are provided for internal synchronization. Bit synchronization in the divide-by-16 and 64 modes is initiated by the detection of the leading mark-to-space transition of the start bit. False start bit deletion capability insures that a full half bit of a start bit has been received before the internal clock is synchronized to the bit time. As a character is being received, parity (odd or even) will be checked and the error indication will be available in the Status Register along with framing error, overrun error, and Receive Data Register full. In a typical receiving sequence, the Status Register is read to determine if a character has been re-

ceived from a peripheral. If the Receiver Data Register is full, the character is placed on the 8-bit ACIA bus when a Read Data command is received from the MPU. When parity has been selected for an 8-bit word (7 bits plus parity), the receiver strips the parity bit (D7 = 0) so that data alone is transferred to the MPU. This feature reduces MPU programming. The Status Register can continue to be read again to determine when another character is available in the Receive Data Register. The receiver is also double buffered so that a character can be read from the data register as another character is being received in the shift register. The above sequence continues until all characters have been received.

INPUT/OUTPUT FUNCTIONS

ACIA INTERFACE SIGNALS FOR MPU

The ACIA interfaces to the MC6800 MPU with an 8-bit bi-directional data bus, three chip select lines, a register select line, an interrupt request line, read/write line, and enable line. These signals, in conjunction with the MC6800 VMA output, permit the MPU to have complete control over the ACIA.

ACIA Bi-Directional Data (D0-D7) — The bi-directional data lines (D0-D7) allow for data transfer between the ACIA and the MPU. The data bus output drivers are three-state devices that remain in the high-impedance (off) state except when the MPU performs an ACIA read operation.

ACIA Enable (E) — The Enable signal, E, is a high impedance TTL compatible input that enables the bus input/output data buffers and clocks data to and from the ACIA. This signal will normally be a derivative of the MC6800 φ2 Clock.

Read/Write (R/W) — The Read/Write line is a high impedance input that is TTL compatible and is used to control the direction of data flow through the ACIA's input/output data bus interface. When Read/Write is high (MPU Read cycle), ACIA output drivers are turned on and a selected register is read. When it is low, the ACIA output drivers are turned off and the MPU writes into a selected register. Therefore, the Read/Write signal is used to select read-only or write-only registers within the ACIA.

Chip Select (CS0, CS1, $\overline{CS2}$) — These three high impedance TTL compatible input lines are used to address the ACIA. The ACIA is selected when CS0 and CS1 are high and $\overline{CS2}$ is low. Transfers of data to and from the ACIA are then performed under the control of the Enable signal, Read/Write, and Register Select.

Register Select (RS) — The Register Select line is a high impedance input that is TTL compatible. A high level is used to select the Transmit/Receive Data Registers and a low level the Control/Status Registers. The Read/Write signal line is used in conjunction with Register Select to select the read-only or write-only register in each register pair.

Interrupt Request ($\overline{IRQ}$) — Interrupt Request is a TTL compatible, open-drain (no internal pullup), active low

MC6850

output that is used to interrupt the MPU. The $\overline{IRQ}$ output remains low as long as the cause of the interrupt is present and the appropriate interrupt enable within the ACIA is set. The IRQ status bit, when high, indicates the $\overline{IRQ}$ output is in the active state.

Interrupts result from conditions in both the transmitter and receiver sections of the ACIA. The transmitter section causes an interrupt when the Transmitter Interrupt Enabled condition is selected (CR5 · $\overline{CR6}$), and the Transmit Data Register Empty (TDRE) status bit is high. The TDRE status bit indicates the current status of the Transmitter Data Register except when inhibited by $\overline{\text{Clear-to-Send}}$ ($\overline{CTS}$) being high or the ACIA being maintained in the Reset condition. The interrupt is cleared by writing data into the Transmit Data Register. The interrupt is masked by disabling the Transmitter Interrupt via CR5 or CR6 or by the loss of $\overline{CTS}$ which inhibits the TDRE status bit. The Receiver section causes an interrupt when the Receiver Interrupt Enable is set and the Receive Data Register Full (RDRF) status bit is high, an Overrun has occurred, or $\overline{\text{Data Carrier Detect}}$ ($\overline{DCD}$) has gone high. An interrupt resulting from the RDRF status bit can be cleared by reading data or resetting the ACIA. Interrupts caused by Overrun or loss of $\overline{DCD}$ are cleared by reading the status register after the error condition has occurred and then reading the Receive Data Register or resetting the ACIA. The receiver interrupt is masked by resetting the Receiver Interrupt Enable.

CLOCK INPUTS

Separate high impedance TTL compatible inputs are provided for clocking of transmitted and received data. Clock frequencies of 1, 16 or 64 times the data rate may be selected.

Transmit Clock (Tx Clk) — The Transmit Clock input is used for the clocking of transmitted data. The transmitter initiates data on the negative transition of the clock.

Receive Clock (Rx Clk) — The Receive Clock input is used for synchronization of received data. (In the ÷ 1 mode, the clock and data must be synchronized externally.) The receiver samples the data on the positive transiton of the clock.

SERIAL INPUT/OUTPUT LINES

Receive Data (Rx Data) — The Receive Data line is a high impedance TTL compatible input through which data is received in a serial format. Synchronization with a clock for detection of data is accomplished internally when clock rates of 16 or 64 times the bit rate are used. Data rates are in the range of 0 to 500 kbps when external synchronization is utilized.

Transmit Data (Tx Data) — The Transmit Data output line transfers serial data to a modem or other peripheral. Data rates are in the range of 0 to 500 kbps when external synchronization is utilized.

PERIPHERAL/MODEM CONTROL

The ACIA includes several functions that permit limited control of a peripheral or modem. The functions included are $\overline{\text{Clear-to-Send}}$, $\overline{\text{Request-to-Send}}$ and $\overline{\text{Data Carrier Detect}}$.

Clear-to-Send ($\overline{CTS}$) — This high impedance TTL compatible input provides automatic control of the transmitting end of a communications link via the modem $\overline{\text{Clear-to-Send}}$ active low output by inhibiting the Transmit Data Register Empty (TDRE) status bit.

Request-to-Send ($\overline{RTS}$) — The $\overline{\text{Request-to-Send}}$ output enables the MPU to control a peripheral or modem via the data bus. The $\overline{RTS}$ output corresponds to the state of the Control Register bits CR5 and CR6. When CR6 = 0 or both CR5 and CR6 = 1, the $\overline{RTS}$ output is low (the active state). This output can also be used for $\overline{\text{Data Terminal Ready}}$ ($\overline{DTR}$).

Data Carrier Detect ($\overline{DCD}$) — This high impedance TTL compatible input provides automatic control, such as in the receiving end of a communications link by means of a modem $\overline{\text{Data Carrier Detect}}$ output. The $\overline{DCD}$ input inhibits and initializes the receiver section of the ACIA when high. A low to high transition of the $\overline{\text{Data Carrier Detect}}$ initiates an interrupt to the MPU to indicate the occurrence of a loss of carrier when the Receive Interrupt Enable bit is set.

ACIA REGISTERS

The expanded block diagram for the ACIA indicates the internal registers on the chip that are used for the status, control, receiving, and transmitting of data. The content of each of the registers is summarized in Table 1.

TRANSMIT DATA REGISTER (TDR)

Data is written in the Transmit Data Register during the negative transition of the enable (E) when the ACIA has been addressed and RS · $\overline{R/W}$ is selected. Writing data into the register causes the Transmit Data Register Empty bit in the Status Register to go low. Data can then be transmitted. If the transmitter is idling and no character is being transmitted, then the transfer will take place within one bit time of the trailing edge of the Write command. If a character is being transmitted, the new data character will commence as soon as the previous character is complete. The transfer of data causes the Transmit Data Register Empty (TDRE) bit to indicate empty.

RECEIVE DATA REGISTER (RDR)

Data is automatically transferred to the empty Receive Data Register (RDR) from the receiver deserializer (a shift register) upon receiving a complete character. This event causes the Receive Data Register Full bit (RDRF) in the status buffer to go high (full). Data may then be read through the bus by addressing the ACIA and selecting the Receive Data Register with RS and R/W high when the ACIA is enabled. The non-destructive read cycle causes the RDRF bit to be cleared to empty although

 MOTOROLA *Semiconductor Products Inc.*

MC6850

TABLE 1 – DEFINITION OF ACIA REGISTER CONTENTS

Data Bus Line Number	Buffer Address			
	RS • R̄/W̄	RS • R/W	R̄S̄ • R̄/W̄	R̄S̄ • R/W
	Transmit Data Register	Receive Data Register	Control Register	Status Register
	(Write Only)	(Read Only)	(Write Only)	(Read Only)
0	Data Bit 0*	Data Bit 0	Counter Divide Select 1 (CR0)	Receive Data Register Full (RDRF)
1	Data Bit 1	Data Bit 1	Counter Divide Select 2 (CR1)	Transmit Data Register Empty (TDRE)
2	Data Bit 2	Data Bit 2	Word Select 1 (CR2)	Data Carrier Detect (D̄C̄D̄)
3	Data Bit 3	Data Bit 3	Word Select 2 (CR3)	Clear to Send (C̄T̄S̄)
4	Data Bit 4	Data Bit 4	Word Select 3 (CR4)	Framing Error (FE)
5	Data Bit 5	Data Bit 5	Transmit Control 1 (CR5)	Receiver Overrun (OVRN)
6	Data Bit 6	Data Bit 6	Transmit Control 2 (CR6)	Parity Error (PE)
7	Data Bit 7***	Data Bit 7**	Receive Interrupt Enable (CR7)	Interrupt Request (IRQ)

* Leading bit = LSB = Bit 0
** Data bit will be zero in 7 bit plus parity modes.
*** Data bit is "don't care" in 7 bit plus parity modes.

the data is retained in the RDR. The status is maintained by RDRF as to whether or not the data is current. When the Receive Data Register is full, the automatic transfer of data from the Receiver Shift Register to the Data Register is inhibited and the RDR contents remain valid with its current status stored in the Status Register.

CONTROL REGISTER

The ACIA Control Register consists of eight bits of write-only buffer that are selected when RS and R/W are low. This register controls the function of the receiver, transmitter, interrupt enables, and the Request-to-Send peripheral/modem control output.

Counter Divide Select Bits (CR0 and CR1) — The Counter Divide Select Bits (CR0 and CR1) determine the divide ratios utilized in both the transmitter and receiver sections of the ACIA. Additionally, these bits are used to provide a master reset for the ACIA which clears the Status Register (except for external conditions on C̄T̄S̄ and D̄C̄D̄) and initializes both the receiver and transmitter. Master reset does not affect other Control Register bits. Note that after power-on or a power fail/restart, these bits must be set high to reset the ACIA. After reseting, the clock divide ratio may be selected. These counter select bits provide for the following clock divide ratios:

CR1	CR0	Function
0	0	÷ 1
0	1	÷ 16
1	0	÷ 64
1	1	Master Reset

Word Select Bits (CR2, CR3, and CR4) — The Word

Select bits are used to select word length, parity, and the number of stop bits. The encoding format is as follows:

CR4	CR3	CR2	Function
0	0	0	7 Bits + Even Parity + 2 Stop Bits
0	0	1	7 Bits + Odd Parity + 2 Stop Bits
0	1	0	7 Bits + Even Parity + 1 Stop Bit
0	1	1	7 Bits + Odd Parity + 1 Stop Bit
1	0	0	8 Bits + 2 Stop Bits
1	0	1	8 Bits + 1 Stop Bit
1	1	0	8 Bits + Even Parity + 1 Stop Bit
1	1	1	8 Bits + Odd Parity + 1 Stop Bit

Word length, Parity Select, and Stop Bit changes are not buffered and therefore become effective immediately.

Transmitter Control Bits (CR5 and CR6) — Two Transmitter Control bits provide for the control of the interrupt from the Transmit Data Register Empty condition, the Request-to-Send (R̄T̄S̄) output, and the transmission of a Break level (space). The following encoding format is used:

CR6	CR5	Function
0	0	R̄T̄S̄ = low, Transmitting Interrupt Disabled.
0	1	R̄T̄S̄ = low, Transmitting Interrupt Enabled.
1	0	R̄T̄S̄ = high, Transmitting Interrupt Disabled.
1	1	R̄T̄S̄ = low, Transmits a Break level on the Transmit Data Output. Transmitting Interrupt Disabled.

Receive Interrupt Enable Bit (CR7) — The following interrupts will be enabled by a high level in bit position 7 of the Control Register (CR7): Receive Data Register Full, Overrun, or a low to high transistion on the Data Carrier Detect (D̄C̄D̄) signal line.

 MOTOROLA *Semiconductor Products Inc.*

MC6850

STATUS REGISTER

Information on the status of the ACIA is available to the MPU by reading the ACIA Status Register. This read-only register is selected when RS is low and R/W is high. Information stored in this register indicates the status of the Transmit Data Register, the Receive Data Register and error logic, and the peripheral/modem status inputs of the ACIA.

Receive Data Register Full (RDRF), Bit 0 — Receive Data Register Full indicates that received data has been transferred to the Receive Data Register. RDRF is cleared after an MPU read of the Receive Data Register or by a master reset. The cleared or empty state indicates that the contents of the Receive Data Register are not current. Data Carrier Detect being high also causes RDRF to indicate empty.

Transmit Data Register Empty (TDRE), Bit 1 — The Transmit Data Register Empty bit being set high indicates that the Transmit Data Register contents have been transferred and that new data may be entered. The low state indicates that the register is full and that transmission of a new character has not begun since the last write data command.

Data Carrier Detect (DCD), Bit 2 — The Data Carrier Detect bit will be high when the DCD input from a modem has gone high to indicate that a carrier is not present. This bit going high causes an Interrupt Request to be generated when the Receive Interrupt Enable is set. It remains high after the DCD input is returned low until cleared by first reading the Status Register and then the Data Register or until a master reset occurs. If the DCD input remains high after read status and read data or master reset has occurred, the interrupt is cleared, the DCD status bit remains high and will follow the DCD input.

Clear-to-Send (CTS), Bit 3 — The Clear-to-Send bit indicates the state of the Clear-to-Send input from a modem. A low CTS indicates that there is a Clear-to-Send from the modem. In the high state, the Transmit Data Register Empty bit is inhibited and the Clear-to-Send status bit will be high. Master reset does not affect the Clear-to-Send Status bit.

Framing Error (FE), Bit 4 — Framing error indicates that the received character is improperly framed by a start and a stop bit and is detected by the absence of the 1st stop bit. This error indicates a synchronization error, faulty transmission, or a break condition. The framing error flag is set or reset during the receive data transfer time. Therefore, this error indicator is present throughout the time that the associated character is available.

Receiver Overrun (OVRN), Bit 5 — Overrun is an error flag that indicates that one or more characters in the data stream were lost. That is, a character or a number of characters were received but not read from the Receive Data Register (RDR) prior to subsequent characters being received. The overrun condition begins at the midpoint of the last bit of the second character received in succession without a read of the RDR having occurred. The Overrun does not occur in the Status Register until the valid character prior to Overrun has been read. The RDRF bit remains set until the Overrun is reset. Character synchronization is maintained during the Overrun condition. The Overrun indication is reset after the reading of data from the Receive Data Register or by a Master Reset.

Parity Error (PE), Bit 6 — The parity error flag indicates that the number of highs (ones) in the character does not agree with the preselected odd or even parity. Odd parity is defined to be when the total number of ones is odd. The parity error indication will be present as long as the data character is in the RDR. If no parity is selected, then both the transmitter parity generator output and the receiver parity check results are inhibited.

Interrupt Request (IRQ), Bit 7 — The IRQ bit indicates the state of the IRQ output. Any interrupt condition with its applicable enable will be indicated in this status bit. Anytime the IRQ output is low the IRQ bit will be high to indicate the interrupt or service request status. IRQ is cleared by a read operation to the Receive Data Register or a write operation to the Transmit Data Register.

PIN ASSIGNMENT

1	V_SS	CTS	24
2	Rx Data	DCD	23
3	Rx Clk	D0	22
4	Tx Clk	D1	21
5	RTS	D2	20
6	Tx Data	D3	19
7	IRQ	D4	18
8	CS0	D5	17
9	CS2	D6	16
10	CS1	D7	15
11	RS	E	14
12	V_DD	R/W	13

PACKAGE DIMENSIONS

CASE 716-02
(CERAMIC)

SEE PAGE 165 FOR PLASTIC PACKAGE DIMENSIONS

DIM	MILLIMETERS MIN	MILLIMETERS MAX	INCHES MIN	INCHES MAX
A	29.97	30.99	1.180	1.220
B	14.88	15.62	0.585	0.615
C	3.05	4.19	0.120	0.165
D	0.38	0.53	0.015	0.021
F	0.76	1.40	0.030	0.055
G	2.54 BSC		0.100 BSC	
H	0.76	1.78	0.030	0.070
J	0.20	0.30	0.008	0.012
K	2.54	4.19	0.100	0.165
L	14.88	15.37	0.585	0.605
M	—	10°	—	10°
N	0.51	1.52	0.020	0.060

SEATING PLANE

NOTE:
1. LEADS TRUE POSITIONED WITHIN 0.25mm (0.010) DIA (AT SEATING PLANE) AT MAXIMUM MATERIAL CONDITION.

Ⓜ **MOTOROLA** *Semiconductor Products Inc.*

MOTOROLA
Semiconductors

BOX 20912 • PHOENIX, ARIZONA 85036

MCM6810A

(0 to 70°C; L or P Suffix)

MCM6810AC

(–40 to 85°C; L Suffix only)

MOS

(N-CHANNEL, SILICON-GATE)

128 X 8-BIT STATIC RANDOM ACCESS MEMORY

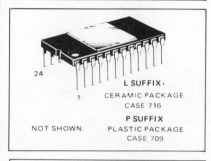

24

L SUFFIX
CERAMIC PACKAGE
CASE 716

NOT SHOWN:

P SUFFIX
PLASTIC PACKAGE
CASE 709

128 X 8-BIT STATIC RANDOM ACCESS MEMORY

The MCM6810 is a byte-organized memory designed for use in bus-organized systems. It is fabricated with N-channel silicon-gate technology. For ease of use, the device operates from a single power supply, has compatibility with TTL and DTL, and needs no clocks or refreshing because of static operation.

The memory is compatible with the M6800 Microcomputer Family, providing random storage in byte increments. Memory expansion is provided through multiple Chip Select inputs.

- Organized as 128 Bytes of 8 Bits
- Static Operation
- Bi-Directional Three-State Data Input/Output
- Six Chip Select Inputs (Four Active Low, Two Active High)
- Single 5-Volt Power Supply
- TTL Compatible
- Maximum Access Time = 350 ns – MCM6810AL1
  450 ns – MCM6810AL

PIN ASSIGNMENT

1	Gnd O	V_{CC}	24
2	D0	A0	23
3	D1	A1	22
4	D2	A2	21
5	D3	A3	20
6	D4	A4	19
7	D5	A5	18
8	D6	A6	17
9	D7	R/W	16
10	CS0	$\overline{CS5}$	15
11	$\overline{CS1}$	$\overline{CS4}$	14
12	$\overline{CS2}$	CS3	13

ABSOLUTE MAXIMUM RATINGS (See Note 1)

Rating	Symbol	Value	Unit
Supply Voltage	V_{CC}	–0.3 to +7.0	Vdc
Input Voltage	V_{in}	–0.3 to +7.0	Vdc
Operating Temperature Range	T_A	0 to +70	°C
Storage Temperature Range	T_{stg}	–65 to +150	°C

NOTE 1: Permanent device damage may occur if ABSOLUTE MAXIMUM RATINGS are exceeded. Functional operation should be restricted to RECOMMENDED OPERATING CONDITIONS. Exposure to higher than recommended voltages for extended periods of time could affect device reliability.

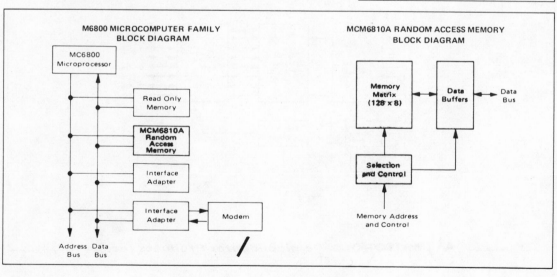

M6800 MICROCOMPUTER FAMILY BLOCK DIAGRAM

MC6800 Microprocessor

Read Only Memory

MCM6810A Random Access Memory

Interface Adapter

Interface Adapter — Modem

Address Bus   Data Bus

MCM6810A RANDOM ACCESS MEMORY BLOCK DIAGRAM

Memory Matrix (128 x 8) — Data Buffers — Data Bus

Selection and Control

Memory Address and Control

MCM6810A

DC OPERATING CONDITIONS AND CHARACTERISTICS
(Full operating voltage and temperature range unless otherwise noted.)

RECOMMENDED DC OPERATING CONDITIONS

Parameter	Symbol	Min	Nom	Max	Unit
Supply Voltage	V_{CC}	4.75	5.0	5.25	Vdc
Input High Voltage	V_{IH}	2.0	–	5.25	Vdc
Input Low Voltage	V_{IL}	-0.3	–	0.8	Vdc

DC CHARACTERISTICS

Characteristic	Symbol	Min	Typ	Max	Unit
Input Current (A_n, R/W, CS_n, $\overline{CS_n}$) (V_{in} = 0 to 5.25 V)	I_{in}	–	–	2.5	μAdc
Output High Voltage (I_{OH} = –205 μA)	V_{OH}	2.4	–	–	Vdc
Output Low Voltage (I_{OL} = 1.6 mA)	V_{OL}	–	–	0.4	Vdc
Output Leakage Current (Three-State) (CS = 0.8 V or $\overline{CS}$ = 2.0 V, V_{out} = 0.4 V to 2.4 V)	I_{LO}	–	–	10	μAdc
Supply Current (V_{CC} = 5.25 V, all other pins grounded, T_A = 0°C) MCM6810AL	I_{CC}	–	–	70	mAdc
MCM6810AL1		–	–	80	

CAPACITANCE (f = 1.0 MHz, T_A = 25°C, periodically sampled rather than 100% tested.)

Characteristic	Symbol	Max	Unit
Input Capacitance	C_{in}	7.5	pF
Output Capacitance	C_{out}	12.5	pF

This device contains circuitry to protect the inputs against damage due to high static voltages or electric fields; however, it is advised that normal precautions be taken to avoid application of any voltage higher than maximum rated voltages to this high-impedance circuit.

BLOCK DIAGRAM

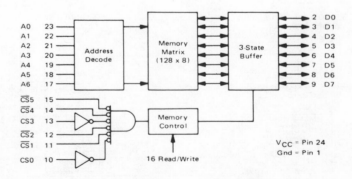

 MOTOROLA *Semiconductor Products Inc.*

MCM6810A

AC OPERATING CONDITIONS AND CHARACTERISTICS
(Full operating voltage and temperature unless otherwise noted.)

FIGURE 1 – AC TEST LOAD

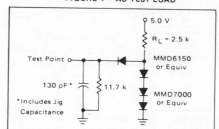

AC TEST CONDITIONS

Condition	Value
Input Pulse Levels	0.8 V to 2.0 V
Input Rise and Fall Times	20 ns
Output Load	See Figure 1

READ CYCLE

Characteristic	Symbol	MCM6810AL		MCM6810AL1		Unit
		Min	Max	Min	Max	
Read Cycle Time	$t_{cyc(R)}$	450	–	350	–	ns
Access Time	t_{acc}	–	450	–	350	ns
Address Setup Time	t_{AS}	20	–	20	–	ns
Address Hold Time	t_{AH}	0	–	0	–	ns
Data Delay Time (Read)	t_{DDR}	–	230	–	180	ns
Read to Select Delay Time	t_{RCS}	0	–	0	–	ns
Data Hold from Address	t_{DHA}	10	–	10	–	ns
Output Hold Time	t_H	10	–	10	–	ns
Data Hold from Write	t_{DHW}	10	80	10	60	ns

READ CYCLE TIMING

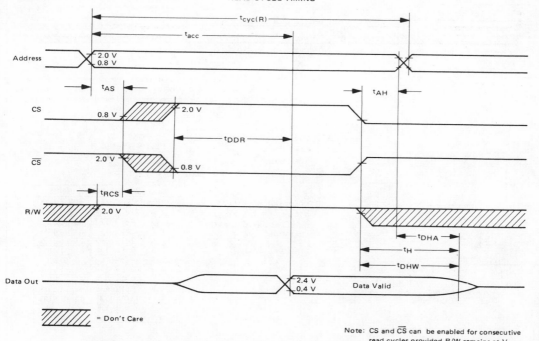

////// = Don't Care

Note: CS and $\overline{CS}$ can be enabled for consecutive read cycles provided R/W remains at V_{IH}.

 MOTOROLA *Semiconductor Products Inc.*

MCM6810A

WRITE CYCLE

Characteristic	Symbol	MCM6810AL		MCM6810AL1		Unit
		Min	Max	Min	Max	
Write Cycle Time	$t_{cyc(W)}$	450	–	350	–	ns
Address Setup Time	t_{AS}	20	–	20	–	ns
Address Hold Time	t_{AH}	0	–	0	–	ns
Chip Select Pulse Width	t_{CS}	300	–	250	–	ns
Write to Chip Select Delay Time	t_{WCS}	0	–	0	–	ns
Data Setup Time (Write)	t_{DSW}	190	–	150	–	ns
Input Hold Time	t_H	10	–	10	–	ns

WRITE CYCLE TIMING

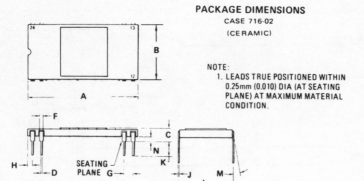

 = Don't Care

Note: CS and $\overline{CS}$ can be enabled for consecutive write cycles provided R/W is strobed to V_{IH} before or coincident with the Address change, and remains high for time t_{AS}.

PACKAGE DIMENSIONS
CASE 716-02
(CERAMIC)

See Page 165 for
Plastic Package dimensions.

NOTE:
1. LEADS TRUE POSITIONED WITHIN 0.25mm (0.010) DIA (AT SEATING PLANE) AT MAXIMUM MATERIAL CONDITION.

DIM	MILLIMETERS		INCHES	
	MIN	MAX	MIN	MAX
A	29.97	30.99	1.180	1.220
B	14.88	15.62	0.585	0.615
C	3.05	4.19	0.120	0.165
D	0.38	0.53	0.015	0.021
F	0.76	1.40	0.030	0.055
G	2.54 BSC		0.100 BSC	
H	0.76	1.78	0.030	0.070
J	0.20	0.30	0.008	0.012
K	2.54	4.19	0.100	0.165
L	14.88	15.37	0.585	0.605
M	–	10°	–	10°
N	0.51	1.52	0.020	0.060

 MOTOROLA *Semiconductor Products Inc.*

Advance Information

1024 X 8-BIT READ ONLY MEMORY

The MCM6830A is a mask-programmable byte-organized memory designed for use in bus-organized systems. It is fabricated with N-channel silicon-gate technology. For ease of use, the device operates from a single power supply, has compatibility with TTL and DTL, and needs no clocks or refreshing because of static operation.

The memory is compatible with the M6800 Microcomputer Family, providing read only storage in byte increments. Memory expansion is provided through multiple Chip Select inputs. The active level of the Chip Select inputs and the memory content are defined by the customer.

- Organized as 1024 Bytes of 8 Bits
- Static Operation
- Three-State Data Output
- Four Chip Select Inputs (Programmable)
- Single 5-Volt Power Supply
- TTL Compatible
- Maximum Access Time = 500 ns

MCM6830A

MOS
(N-CHANNEL, SILICON-GATE)

1024 X 8-BIT
READ ONLY MEMORY

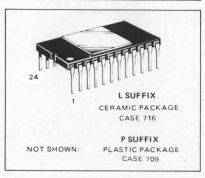

L SUFFIX
CERAMIC PACKAGE
CASE 716

P SUFFIX
NOT SHOWN: PLASTIC PACKAGE
CASE 709

PIN ASSIGNMENT

1	Gnd	A0	24
2	D0	A1	23
3	D1	A2	22
4	D2	A3	21
5	D3	A4	20
6	D4	A5	19
7	D5	A6	18
8	D6	A7	17
9	D7	A8	16
10	CS0	A9	15
11	CS1	CS3	14
12	VCC	CS2	13

ABSOLUTE MAXIMUM RATINGS (See Note 1)

Rating	Symbol	Value	Unit
Supply Voltage	V_{CC}	–0.3 to +7.0	Vdc
Input Voltage	V_{in}	–0.3 to +7.0	Vdc
Operating Temperature Range	T_A	0 to +70	°C
Storage Temperature Range	T_{stg}	–65 to +150	°C

NOTE 1: Permanent device damage may occur if ABSOLUTE MAXIMUM RATINGS are exceeded. Functional operation should be restricted to RECOMMENDED OPERATING CONDITIONS. Exposure to higher than recommended voltages for extended periods of time could affect device reliability.

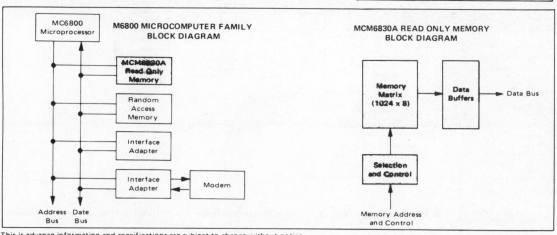

This is advance information and specifications are subject to change without notice.

MCM6830A

DC OPERATING CONDITIONS AND CHARACTERISTICS
(Full operating voltage and temperature range unless otherwise noted.)

RECOMMENDED DC OPERATING CONDITIONS

Parameter	Symbol	Min	Nom	Max	Unit
Supply Voltage	V_{CC}	4.75	5.0	5.25	Vdc
Input High Voltage	V_{IH}	2.0	–	5.25	Vdc
Input Low Voltage	V_{IL}	-0.3	–	0.8	Vdc

DC CHARACTERISTICS

Characteristic	Symbol	Min	Typ	Max	Unit
Input Current (V_{in} = 0 to 5.25 V)	I_{in}	–	–	2.5	μAdc
Output High Voltage (I_{OH} = −205μA)	V_{OH}	2.4	–	–	Vdc
Output Low Voltage (I_{OL} = 1.6 mA)	V_{OL}	–	–	0.4	Vdc
Output Leakage Current (Three-State) (CS = 0.8 V or $\overline{CS}$ = 2.0 V, V_{out} = 0.4 V to 2.4 V)	I_{LO}	–	–	10	μAdc
Supply Current (V_{CC} = 5.25 V, T_A = 0°C)	I_{CC}	–	–	130	mAdc

CAPACITANCE (f = 1.0 MHz, T_A = 25°C, periodically sampled rather than 100% tested.)

Characteristic	Symbol	Max	Unit
Input Capacitance	C_{in}	7.5	pF
Output Capacitance	C_{out}	12.5	pF

This device contains circuitry to protect the inputs against damage due to high static voltages or electric fields; however, it is advised that normal precautions be taken to avoid application of any voltage higher than maximum rated voltages to this high-impedance circuit.

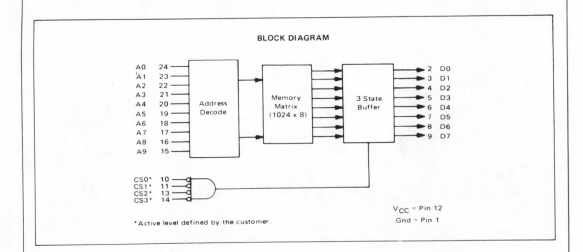

BLOCK DIAGRAM

*Active level defined by the customer.

V_{CC} = Pin 12
Gnd = Pin 1

 MOTOROLA *Semiconductor Products Inc.*

MCM6830A

AC OPERATING CONDITIONS AND CHARACTERISTICS

(Full operating voltage and temperature unless otherwise noted.)

(All timing with $t_r = t_f = 20$ ns, Load of Figure 1)

Characteristic	Symbol	Min	Max	Unit
Cycle Time	t_{cyc}	500	—	ns
Access Time	t_{acc}	—	500	ns
Data Delay Time (Read)	t_{DDR}	—	300	ns
Data Hold from Address	t_{DHA}	10	—	ns
Data Hold from Deselection	t_H	10	150	ns

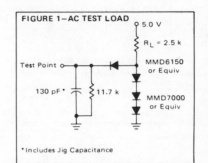

FIGURE 1 — AC TEST LOAD

* Includes Jig Capacitance

TIMING DIAGRAM

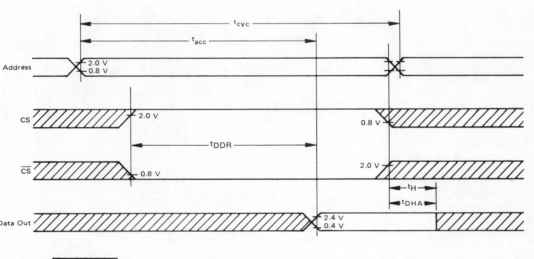

///// = Don't care

PACKAGE DIMENSIONS
CASE 716-02
(CERAMIC)

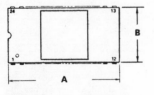

NOTE:
1. LEADS TRUE POSITIONED WITHIN 0.25mm (0.010) DIA (AT SEATING PLANE) AT MAXIMUM MATERIAL CONDITION.

See Page 165 for Plastic Package dimensions.

DIM	MILLIMETERS		INCHES	
	MIN	MAX	MIN	MAX
A	29.97	30.99	1.180	1.220
B	14.88	15.62	0.585	0.615
C	3.05	4.19	0.120	0.165
D	0.38	0.53	0.015	0.021
F	0.76	1.40	0.030	0.055
G	2.54 BSC		0.100 BSC	
H	0.76	1.78	0.030	0.070
J	0.20	0.30	0.008	0.012
K	2.54	4.19	0.100	0.165
L	14.88	15.37	0.585	0.605
M	—	10°	—	10°
N	0.51	1.52	0.020	0.060

MOTOROLA *Semiconductor Products Inc.*

MCM6830A

CUSTOM PROGRAMMING

By the programming of a single photomask for the MCM6830A, the customer may specify the content of the memory and the method of enabling the outputs.

Information on the general options of the MCM6830A should be submitted on an Organizational Data form such as that shown in Figure 3.

Information for custom memory content may be sent to Motorola in one of two forms (shown in order of preference):

1. Paper tape output of the Motorola M6800 Software.
2. Hexadecimal coding using IBM Punch Cards.

PAPER TAPE

Included in the software packages developed for the M6800 Micromputer Family is the ability to produce a paper tape output for computerized mask generation. The assembler directives are used to control allocation of memory, to assign values for stored data, and for controlling the assembly process. The paper tape must specify the full 1024 bytes.

Note: Motorola can accept magnetic tape and truth table table formats. For further information, contact your local Motorola sales representative.

FIGURE 2 – BINARY TO HEXADECIMAL CONVERSION

Binary Data				Hexadecimal Character
0	0	0	0	0
0	0	0	1	1
0	0	1	0	2
0	0	1	1	3
0	1	0	0	4
0	1	0	1	5
0	1	1	0	6
0	1	1	1	7
1	0	0	0	8
1	0	0	1	9
1	0	1	0	A
1	0	1	1	B
1	1	0	0	C
1	1	0	1	D
1	1	1	0	E
1	1	1	1	F

IBM PUNCH CARDS

The hexadecimal equivalent (from Figure 2) may be placed on 80 column IBM punch cards as follows:

Step	Column	
1	12	Byte "0" Hexadecimal equivalent for outputs D7 thru D4 (D7 = M.S.B.)
2	13	Byte "0" Hexadecimal equivalent for outputs D3 thru D0 (D3 = M.S.B.)
3	14-75	Alternate steps 1 and 2 for consecutive bytes.
4	77-78	Card number (starting 01)
5	79-80	Total number of cards (32)

FIGURE 3 – FORMAT FOR PROGRAMMING GENERAL OPTIONS

ORGANIZATIONAL DATA
MCM6830A MOS READ ONLY MEMORY

Customer:

Company _____

Part No. _____

Originator _____

Phone No. _____

Motorola Use Only:

Quote: _____

Part No.: _____

Specif. No.: _____

Enable Options:

	1	0	
			1 is most positive
			0 is most negative
CS0	☐	☐	
CS1	☐	☐	
CS2	☐	☐	
CS3	☐	☐	

 MOTOROLA *Semiconductor Products Inc.*

MOTOROLA
Semiconductors
BOX 20912 • PHOENIX, ARIZONA 85036

MCM6832

Advance Information

MOS

(N-CHANNEL, LOW THRESHOLD)

2048 x 8-BIT
READ ONLY MEMORY

2048 x 8-BIT READ ONLY MEMORY

The MCM6832 is a mask-programmable byte-organized memory designed for use in bus-organized systems. It is fabricated with N-channel metal-gate technology. For ease of use, the device is compatible with TTL and DTL, and needs no clocks or refreshing because of static operation.

The memory is compatible with the M6800 Microcomputer Family, providing read only storage in byte increments. Memory expansion is provided through a Chip Select input. The active level of the Chip Select input and the memory content are defined by the customer.

- Organized as 2048 Bytes of 8 Bits
- Static Operation
- Three-State Data Output
- Programmable Chip Select
- TTL Compatible
- Maximum Access Time = 500 ns

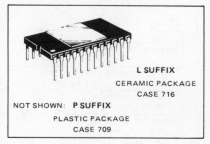

L SUFFIX
CERAMIC PACKAGE
CASE 716

NOT SHOWN: **P SUFFIX**

PLASTIC PACKAGE
CASE 709

PIN ASSIGNMENT

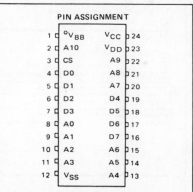

1	V_{BB}	V_{CC}	24
2	A10	V_{DD}	23
3	CS	A9	22
4	D0	A8	21
5	D1	A7	20
6	D2	D4	19
7	D3	D5	18
8	A0	D6	17
9	A1	D7	16
10	A2	A6	15
11	A3	A5	14
12	V_{SS}	A4	13

ABSOLUTE MAXIMUM RATINGS[1] (Referenced to V_{SS})

Rating	Symbol	Value	Unit
Supply Voltages	V_{DD}	–0.3 to +15	Vdc
	V_{CC}	–0.3 to +6.0	
	V_{BB}	–10 to +0.3	
Address/Control Input Voltage	V_{in}	–0.3 to +15	Vdc
Operating Temperature Range	T_A	0 to +70	°C
Storage Temperature Range	T_{stg}	–55 to +125	°C

Note 1: Permanent device damage may occur if ABSOLUTE MAXIMUM RATINGS are exceeded. Functional operation should be restricted to RECOMMENDED OPERATING CONDITIONS. Exposure to higher than recommended voltages for extended periods of time could affect device reliability.

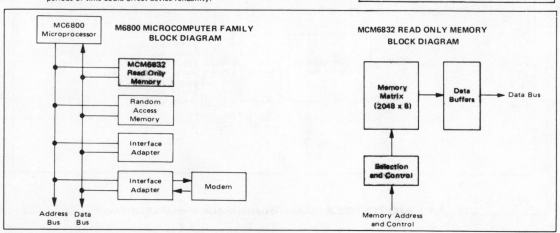

M6800 MICROCOMPUTER FAMILY BLOCK DIAGRAM

MCM6832 READ ONLY MEMORY BLOCK DIAGRAM

This is advance information and specifications are subject to change without notice.

MCM6832

DC OPERATING CONDITIONS AND CHARACTERISTICS
(Full operating voltage and temperature range unless otherwise noted.)

RECOMMENDED DC OPERATING CONDITIONS (Referenced to V_{SS} = Ground)

Parameter	Symbol	Min	Typ	Max	Unit
Supply Voltage	V_{DD}	11.4	12	12.6	Vdc
	V_{CC}	4.75	5.0	5.25	Vdc
	V_{BB}	-5.25	-5.0	-4.75	Vdc
Input High Voltage (A_n, CS)	V_{IH}	3.0		V_{CC}	Vdc
Input Low Voltage (A_n, CS)	V_{IL}	-0.3		0.8	Vdc

DC CHARACTERISTICS

Characteristic	Symbol	Min	Typ	Max	Unit
Input Leakage Current (A_n, CS) (V_{in} = 0 to 5.25 V)	I_{in}			10	μAdc
Output Leakage Current (Three-State) (V_O = 0.4 V to -2.4 V, CS = 0.4 V or CS = 2.4 V)	I_{LO}			10	μAdc
Output High Voltage (I_{OH} = -100 μA)	V_{OH}	3.7		V_{CC}	Vdc
Output Low Voltage (I_{OL} = 1.6 mA)	V_{OL}	0		0.4	Vdc
Supply Current	I_{DD}			25	mAdc
(Chip Deselected or Selected)	I_{CC}			45	mAdc
	I_{BB}			500	μAdc

CAPACITANCE (Periodically Sampled Rather Than 100% Tested.)

Characteristic	Symbol	Min	Typ	Max	Unit
Input Capacitance (f = 1 MHz)	C_{in}		5.0	7.5	pF
Output Capacitance (f = 1 MHz)	C_{out}	--	5.0	10	pF

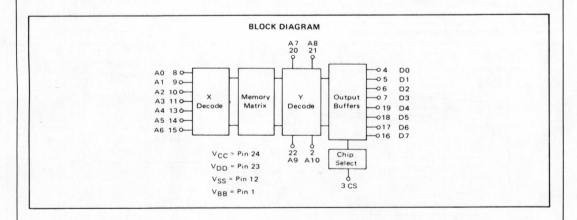

BLOCK DIAGRAM

MOTOROLA *Semiconductor Products Inc.*

MCM6832

AC CHARACTERISTICS

(Full operating voltage and temperature unless otherwise noted. All timing with $t_r = t_f \leqslant 20$ ns;
Load = 1 TTL Gate (MC7400 Series) biased to draw 1.6 mA; $C_L = 130$ pF.)

Characteristic	Symbol	Min	Typ*	Max	Unit
Address Access Time	t_{acc}		320*	500	ns
Output Select Time	t_{OS}		175*	300	ns
Output Deselect Time	t_{OD}	30	100*	150	ns

*Typical values measured at 25°C and nominal supply voltages.

FIGURE 1 – AC TEST LOAD

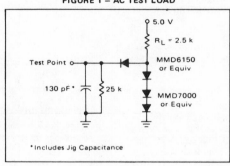

FIGURE 2 – TIMING DIAGRAM

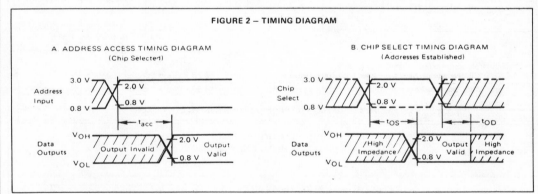

A. ADDRESS ACCESS TIMING DIAGRAM
(Chip Selected)

B. CHIP SELECT TIMING DIAGRAM
(Addresses Established)

PACKAGE DIMENSIONS

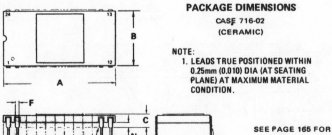

CASE 716-02
(CERAMIC)

NOTE:
1. LEADS TRUE POSITIONED WITHIN
0.25mm (0.010) DIA (AT SEATING
PLANE) AT MAXIMUM MATERIAL
CONDITION.

SEE PAGE 165 FOR
PLASTIC PACKAGE
DIMENSIONS.

DIM	MILLIMETERS		INCHES	
	MIN	MAX	MIN	MAX
A	29.97	30.99	1.180	1.220
B	14.88	15.62	0.585	0.615
C	3.05	4.19	0.120	0.165
D	0.38	0.53	0.015	0.021
F	0.76	1.40	0.030	0.055
G	2.54 BSC		0.100 BSC	
H	0.76	1.78	0.030	0.070
J	0.20	0.30	0.008	0.012
K	2.54	4.19	0.100	0.165
L	14.88	15.37	0.585	0.605
M	–	10°	–	10°
N	0.51	1.52	0.020	0.060

 MOTOROLA *Semiconductor Products Inc.*

MCM6832

CUSTOM PROGRAMMING

By the programming of a single photomask for the MCM6832, the customer may specify the content of the memory and the method of enabling the outputs.

Information on the general options of the MCM6832 should be submitted on an Organizational Data form such as that shown in Figure 4.

Information for custom memory content may be sent to Motorola in one of two forms (shown in order of preference):

1. Paper tape output of the Motorola M6800 Software.
2. Hexadecimal coding using IBM Punch Cards.

PAPER TAPE

Included in the software packages developed for the M6800 Microcomputer Family is the ability to produce a paper tape output for computerized mask generation. The assembler directives are used to control allocation of memory, to assign values for stored data, and for controlling the assembly process. The paper tape must specify the full 2048 bytes.

Note: Motorola can accept magnetic tape and truth table table formats. For further information, contact your local Motorola sales representative.

FIGURE 3 — BINARY TO HEXADECIMAL CONVERSION

MSB D7 D3	D6 D2	D5 D1	LSB D4 D0	Hexadecimal Character
0	0	0	0	0
0	0	0	1	1
0	0	1	0	2
0	0	1	1	3
0	1	0	0	4
0	1	0	1	5
0	1	1	0	6
0	1	1	1	7
1	0	0	0	8
1	0	0	1	9
1	0	1	0	A
1	0	1	1	B
1	1	0	0	C
1	1	0	1	D
1	1	1	0	E
1	1	1	1	F

$0 = V_{OL}$
$1 = V_{OH}$

IBM PUNCH CARDS

The hexadecimal equivalent (from Figure 3) may be placed on 80 column IBM punch cards as follows:

Step	Column	
1	12	Byte "0" Hexadecimal equivalent for outputs D7 thru D4 (D7 = M.S.B.)
2	13	Byte "0" Hexadecimal equivalent for outputs D3 thru D0 (D3 = M.S.B.)
3	14-75	Alternate steps 1 and 2 for consecutive bytes.
4	77-78	Card number (starting 01)
5	79-80	Total number of cards (64)

FIGURE 4 — FORMAT FOR PROGRAMMING GENERAL OPTIONS

ORGANIZATIONAL DATA
MCM6832 MOS READ ONLY MEMORY

Customer:

Company _____

Part No. _____

Originator _____

Phone No. _____

Motorola Use Only:

Quote _____

Part No. _____

Specif. No. _____

True Chip Select Options:

I. 1 ☐

II. 0 ☐

1 is most positive
0 is most negative

 MOTOROLA *Semiconductor Products Inc.*

POSITIVE POWERS OF 2

n	2^n	
0	1	
1	2	
2	4	
3	8	
4	16	
5	32	
6	64	
7	128	
8	256	
9	512	
10	1024	
11	2048	
12	4096	
13	8192	
14	16384	
15	32768	
16	65536	
17	13107	2
18	26214	4
19	52428	8
20	10485	76
21	20971	52
22	41943	04
23	83886	08
24	16777	216
25	33554	432
26	67108	864
27	13421	7728
28	26843	5456
29	53687	0912
30	10737	41824
31	21474	83648
32	42949	67296

NEGATIVE POWERS OF 2

n	2^{-n}					
0	1.0					
1	0.5					
2	0.25					
3	0.125					
4	0.0625					
5	0.03125					
6	0.01562	5				
7	0.00781	25				
8	0.00390	625				
9	0.00195	3125				
10	0.00097	65625				
11	0.00048	82812	5			
12	0.00024	41406	25			
13	0.00012	20703	125			
14	0.00006	10351	5625			
15	0.00003	05175	78125			
16	0.00001	52587	89062	5		
17	0.00000	76293	94531	25		
18	0.00000	38146	97265	625		
19	0.00000	19073	48632	8125		
20	0.00000	09536	74316	40625		
21	0.00000	04768	37158	20312	5	
22	0.00000	02384	18579	10156	25	
23	0.00000	01192	09289	55078	125	
24	0.00000	00596	04644	77539	0625	
25	0.00000	00298	02322	38769	53125	
26	0.00000	00149	01161	19384	76562	5
27	0.00000	00074	50580	59692	38281	25
28	0.00000	00037	25290	29846	19140	625
29	0.00000	00018	62645	14923	09570	3125
30	0.00000	00009	31322	57461	54785	15625
31	0.00000	00004	65661	28730	77392	57812 5
32	0.00000	00002	32830	64365	38696	28906 25

POSITIVE POWERS OF 8

n	8^n		
0	1		
1	8		
2	64		
3	512		
4	409	6	
5	327	68	
6	262	144	
7	209	715	2
8	167	772	16

POSITIVE POWERS OF 16

n	16^n		
0	1		
1	16		
2	256		
3	409	6	
4	655	36	
5	104	857	6
6	167	772	16
7	268	435	456
8	429	496	729	6

NEGATIVE POWERS OF 16

n	16^{-n}					
0	1.0					
1	0.062	5				
2	0.003	906	25			
3	0.000	244	140	625		
4	0.000	015	258	789	062	5